introduction to STATISTICS

introduction to STATISTICS

Herbert Robbins

Higgins Professor of Mathematical Statistics
Columbia University

John Van Ryzin

Professor of Statistics
University of Wisconsin, Madison

SCIENCE RESEARCH ASSOCIATES, INC.
Chicago, Palo Alto, Toronto, Henley-on-Thames, Sydney, Paris
A Subsidiary of IBM

Library of Congress Cataloging in Publication Data

Robbins, Herbert.
  Introduction to statistics.

  Includes index.
  1. Mathematical statistics. I. Van Ryzin, John,
joint author. II. Title.
QA76.R58   519.5   75-1005
ISBN 0-574-18132-6

PREFACE

This book is designed as a text for a survey course in statistics for students with a knowledge of high school algebra. Such a course will usually include students from a great variety of disciplines. With this in mind we have illustrated the basic general theory by many applications to the physical, biological, and social sciences as well as to education and business. We have aimed at brevity rather than discursiveness in our discussion of the general theory, hoping to provide a useful framework of methods and exercises around which the instructor can organize lectures and discussions to communicate his or her personal approach to statistical thinking. The topics presented are characteristic of current statistical practice. We have tried to provide interesting examples to convey the broad applicability of statistical methods, but our principal emphasis is on the logic of statistical inference from experimental data, which forms the real subject matter of statistics. This is presented as early and clearly as possible, so that the student will quickly begin to develop the power of thinking statistically about the meaning of data.

Chapters 1 to 7 form the core of the text, and are arranged in logical sequence, while chapters 8 to 11 may be taken up in any order. After the brief introductory chapter 1 we introduce the probabilistic concepts needed for statistical inference in chapters 2 and 3. We then present in chapter 4 the basic notions of inference by applying them to the binomial distribution; sections 4.1–4.4, in particular, should be covered slowly and carefully. Chapter 5 on the sample mean and variance, chapter 6 on large-sample inference, and chapter 7 on small-sample inference complete the core material. Chapter 8 on the analysis of variance, chapter 9 on linear regression, chapter 10 on categorical data, and chapter 11 on distribution-free methods are self-contained, and may be covered as time permits after chapter 7. The book contains more material than can be covered in a three-hour one-semester course, but the arrangement of material will allow the instructor to select those topics that are most suitable to the needs of the students. If two semesters are available the whole text can be covered, and at many points the instructor may wish to introduce additional problems from applied fields or provide proofs that have been omitted; for example, the proof that for independent random variables the variance of a sum is the sum of the variances.

To facilitate use in a one-semester course we give below a table showing which sections of chapters 1 to 7 are essential and which can be omitted without impairment to the understanding of chapters 8 to 11.

Chapter	Essential sections	Optional sections
1	1.1–1.3	
2	2.1–2.7	2.8–2.9
3	3.1–3.8	3.9 (necessary for 4.7), 3.10
4	4.1–4.4	4.5 (useful for chapter 11), 4.6, 4.7
5	5.1, 5.2, 5.4, 5.5 (up to example 11)	5.3, example 11 of 5.5
6	6.1, 6.2, 6.4–6.8	6.3, 6.9
7	7.1–7.6	7.7, 7.8 (necessary for chapter 8)

The problems at the end of each section are mostly in pairs that are similar in content, with short answers to the odd-numbered problems listed at the end of the book. The exceptions to this rule allow for at least one review problem of each type. A solutions manual, available to the instructor, gives complete answers to both odd- and even-numbered problems.

That one can use quantitative methods to describe and analyze the phenomenon of random variation in the real world represents a revolution in human thought. We hope that the reader of this book will acquire some sense of the excitement that comes with the ability to do things previously undreamed of.

Herbert Robbins
John Van Ryzin

CONTENTS

WHAT IS STATISTICS?

1 What Is Statistics?

The word *statistics* has two meanings. The first and most familiar is that of numerical data—batting averages, populations of cities, cost of living indices, unemployment rates, and so on. The various techniques for summarizing and presenting numerical data form the subject called *descriptive statistics*. A second and less familiar aspect involves the use of numerical data obtained from samples to make reliable inferences about the true nature of the populations under study. This is called *statistical inference*.

The object of this text is to present some of the most basic and useful methods of statistical inference, methods that have been found to be of value in a great variety of disciplines, ranging from the physical, biological, and social sciences to the applied fields of engineering, education, business, and government. The power and generality of the techniques involved in statistical inference will become apparent as we proceed.

Taking into account both aspects of statistics, we may say that *statistics is the science of collecting, summarizing, and analyzing experimental data to provide the basis for inferences or decisions concerning the true nature of the populations under study.*

The words *experiment* and *population* have special meanings in statistical theory. Roughly speaking, an experiment is a planned operation that produces outcomes in the form of counts or numerical data, and a population is the entire collection of possible outcomes of such an experiment together with the probabilities with which the various outcomes will occur. Consider as an example the following report taken from the New York *Times* of August 26, 1974.

Watergate Issue Found Still Alive
Survey of Michigan District Indicates Scandal
Remains a Factor in Election

A limited but scientific survey taken last week suggests that pronouncements that Watergate is behind us may be a bit premature. The survey consisted of interviews with a sample of 411 persons of voting age chosen by a random dialing of telephone numbers in Michigan's Eighth Congressional District. This number was large enough to establish with 95 percent certainty that the results erred by no more than 5 percent in either direction. The survey suffered from certain methodological imperfections that may have somewhat further diminished its reliability; for example, the poll had no way of gauging the extent to which Mr. Traxler's new strength stems from his assiduous personal and mail campaigning. Among independents (42 percent of the sample) nearly 7 of every 10 said they would now vote for Mr. Traxler, and those in the Traxler camp were much more likely to be "outraged" or "very disturbed" about the Watergate abuses. Another startling finding was that this rather conservative area was taking a relatively lenient attitude toward war resisters, with 52 percent favoring a conditional amnesty.

Two of the methodological imperfections referred to were (a) the sample was only one of telephone subscribers in Mr. Traxler's congressional district, and (b) the effect of Mr. Traxler's personal post-campaign activity could not be separated from the political issues involved. For our purposes, however, the most salient point is contained in the third sentence of the story, which relates the sample size (411) to the probability (95%) of making an error of no more than a given amount (5%) in estimating an unknown population proportion from the data of a random sample from that population. The reader will see later on that this assessment of reliability is quite correct, if the sample was indeed random.

1.1 The Nature of Statistical Inference
Why Study Statistics?

As the example of the Watergate story shows, statisticians are usually concerned with making inferences about certain numerical characteristics, called *parameters*, of the entire population from which a random sample has been drawn. A parameter might be, for example, the proportion of voters favoring amnesty for war resisters. The data from which such inferences are drawn is obtained by *sampling*. A sample from any population in question should be drawn in such a way that it has a high probability of accurately representing its parent population. Information obtained from the sample is used to compute an appropriate *statistic* that estimates the unknown population parameter. For this process to be valid the sample must be "random" (as defined in chapter 3).

Example 1

The Bureau of Labor Statistics wants to estimate the average income of all full-time workers in Michigan, based on a random sample of 1200 workers. Procedures for doing this, and for assessing the degree of reliability of the estimate, are given in chapters 6 and 7.

Example 2

A bacteriologist wants to estimate the probability p that a mouse will be protected against an injection of pathogenic bacteria by a preliminary dose of a certain drug. Suppose that of 200 such mice it is observed that 112 are protected. In chapter 4 we shall use the sample proportion of mice protected, $\hat{p} = 112/200 = .56$, as an estimate of p, and we shall find a value ϵ such that the interval $\hat{p} - \epsilon$ to $\hat{p} + \epsilon$ has a 95 percent chance of containing the unknown parameter p.

Example 3

A nutrition study of a high-protein diet is made to determine whether two forms (solid and liquid) afford the same mean protein uptake for children. In a random sample of 30 children, 15 are randomly assigned to the solid diet and 15 to the liquid diet for one week; the protein uptake is then measured for each child. These measurements may or may not provide evidence to reject convincingly the hypothesis that the mean protein uptakes of the two forms are the same. Methods for such problems of *hypothesis testing* are given in chapters 6, 7, 8, and 11.

Example 4

A college admissions official draws a sample of College Qualification Test (CQT) scores and first-year grade point averages (GPA) for 50 freshmen. Assuming these 50 pairs of scores to be a random sample of all scores made by currently enrolled freshmen, how well can the GPA be predicted from the CQT for subsequent entering freshmen? A model relating pairs of measurements so that one can make such predictions and assess their reliability is discussed in chapter 9.

These basic problems of estimation, hypothesis testing, and prediction, based on random samples from a population, will be illustrated by many examples in the chapters that follow.

This book was written to give an understanding of some fundamental ideas that underlie statistical theory and that are necessary for the proper use and critical evaluation of any method of analyzing data. Even though a professional statistician may be consulted in the course of an investigation, the nonprofessional should have some knowledge of how a particular problem should be treated, and some appreciation of what statistical analysis can and cannot be expected to do. We hope to give the reader a basis for such an understanding in this book, whether he is concerned with trying to understand and to evaluate someone else's use (or misuse) of statistics or with designing and analyzing a study of his own.

1.2 Subscript and Summation Notation for Numerical Data

To indicate a succession of numbers obtained in some experiment without reference to their specific values, we often denote the first number obtained by x_1, the second by x_2, and so on.

Example 5

In Chicago, the minimum temperatures for one week in January were

Day	Sun.	Mon.	Tues.	Wed.	Thurs.	Fri.	Sat.
Temp. (F.)	9°	5°	2°	0°	−6°	14°	18°

In subscript notation, if x denotes temperature and its subscript denotes the day of the week, then $x_1 = 9$, $x_2 = 5$, . . . , $x_7 = 18$.

Example 6

A coin is tossed five times and

$$x_i = \begin{cases} 1 \text{ if the } i\text{th toss is a head} \\ 0 \text{ if the } i\text{th toss is a tail} \end{cases}$$

where $i = 1, 2, \ldots, 5$. The values obtained by the authors were $x_1 = 1$, $x_2 = 1$, $x_3 = 0$, $x_4 = 0$, $x_5 = 1$.

The subscript notation is also used when there are two variables under study, say x and y. Thus, if we are measuring the height x and weight y of several persons, we can denote the results by (x_1, y_1) for the first person, (x_2, y_2) for the second, and so on.

Example 7

A group of 10 persons had the following heights (in inches) and weights (in pounds), measured to the nearest integer.

Person	1	2	3	4	5	6	7	8	9	10
Height	70	66	63	71	69	73	70	68	60	68
Weight	160	142	118	167	136	190	203	150	108	147

In this example the height and weight of the ith person would be denoted by the pair (x_i, y_i). For the eighth person $(x_8, y_8) = (68, 150)$.

We frequently wish to form the *sum* of a given set of numbers. If these numbers are denoted by $x_1, x_2, \ldots, x_n$ then this sum is represented by the symbol

$$\sum_{i=1}^{n} x_i = x_1 + x_2 + \ldots + x_n$$

The letter Σ, a capital Greek sigma, means "sum of," and the subscript values $i = 1$ to n tell us what x values the summation includes. Thus $i = 1$ (on the bottom) indicates the first value in the series to be summed, and n (on the top) indicates the last.

For the data in example 1, the sum of all seven daily temperatures is

$$\sum_{i=1}^{7} x_i = 9 + 5 + 2 + 0 + (-6) + 14 + 18 = 42$$

while the *average* daily temperature is

$$\frac{1}{7} \sum_{i=1}^{7} x_i = \frac{42}{7} = 6$$

The summation notation obeys certain simple formal rules.

Rule 1 If $x_i = c$, a constant (that is, a value that does not change with i), then

$$\sum_{i=1}^{n} x_i = \sum_{i=1}^{n} c = c + c + \ldots + c = nc$$

Rule 2 If c is a constant, then

$$\sum_{i=1}^{n} (cx_i) = cx_1 + cx_2 + \ldots + cx_n = c(x_1 + \ldots + x_n) = c \sum_{i=1}^{n} x_i$$

Rule 3

$$\sum_{i=1}^{n} (x_i + y_i) = (x_1 + y_1) + (x_2 + y_2) + \ldots + (x_n + y_n)$$

$$= (x_1 + \ldots + x_n) + (y_1 + \ldots + y_n) = \sum_{i=1}^{n} x_i + \sum_{i=1}^{n} y_i$$

In practice, these rules are often combined in various ways.

Example 8

$$\sum_{i=1}^{n} (x_i + c)^2 = \sum_{i=1}^{n} (x_i^2 + 2cx_i + c^2)$$

$$= \sum_{i=1}^{n} x_i^2 + \sum_{i=1}^{n} (2cx_i) + \sum_{i=1}^{n} c^2 \text{ by rule 3}$$

$$= \sum_{i=1}^{n} x_i^2 + 2c \sum_{i=1}^{n} x_i + nc^2 \text{ by rules 2 and 1}$$

Example 9

$$\sum_{i=1}^{n} (x_i + y_i)^2 = \sum_{i=1}^{n} (x_i^2 + 2x_iy_i + y_i^2)$$

$$= \sum_{i=1}^{n} x_i^2 + 2 \sum_{i=1}^{n} x_iy_i + \sum_{i=1}^{n} y_i^2 \text{ by rules 3 and 2}$$

In subsequent chapters we shall frequently use this subscript and summation notation, and extend it to the use of double subscripts and double summation. Thus, suppose that there are four sections of a class, with n_1, n_2, n_3, n_4, students, respectively, and that the students in each section are numbered in alphabetical order. We then use x_{ij} to denote the examination grade of the jth student in the ith section. Here x takes on the value of the examination grade, the subscript i takes on the values 1, 2, 3, 4, (for each section), and the subscript j takes on the values 1, 2, . . . , n_i (for the numbers of the students in the ith section). The average grade of the students in section 2 would be denoted by

$$\frac{1}{n_2} \sum_{j=1}^{n_2} x_{2j}$$

The average grade of all the students in the class would be denoted by

$$\frac{1}{n} \sum_{i=1}^{4} \sum_{j=1}^{n_i} x_{ij}$$

where $n = n_1 + n_2 + n_3 + n_4$.

Note how the operations involved in this double summation are carried out. Working from right to left, we first sum the x values for each fixed i. Next we add these sums for each $i = 1, 2, 3, 4$, and finally divide by n (the total number of students in all sections).

PROBLEMS 1.2

1. Ten graduating seniors at the University of Michigan had the following grade point averages (GPA).

Student	1	2	3	4	5	6	7	8	9	10
GPA	3.07	2.62	2.40	3.26	3.74	2.31	2.57	2.16	2.85	3.12

a. Write down the values of x_1, x_3, x_6, x_8, and x_{10}.

b. Compute $\sum_{i=1}^{10} x_i$

c. Compute $\sum_{i=1}^{7} x_i$

d. Compute $\bar{x} = (1/10) \sum_{i=1}^{10} x_i$ (the average GPA of the ten students)

e. Compute $\sum_{i=1}^{10} (3x_i)$

f. Compute $\sum_{i=1}^{10} (x_i + 5)$

g. Compute $\sum_{i=1}^{10} (x_i - 2)^2$

2. Eight persons on a high protein diet showed the following weight gains (in ounces) for one week.

Person	1	2	3	4	5	6	7	8
Gain	30	−4	21	12	0	−10	17	14

a. Write down the values of x_1, x_6, x_7 and x_8.

b. Compute $\sum_{i=1}^{8} x_i$

c. Compute $\sum_{i=1}^{5} x_i$

d. Compute $\bar{x}_8 = 1/8 \sum_{i=1}^{8} x_i$ (the average weight gain)

e. Compute $\sum_{i=1}^{8} (1/16) x_i$ (the total weight gain in pounds)

f. Compute $\sum_{i=1}^{8} (x_i - 16)$

g. Compute $\sum_{i=1}^{8} (x_i - 16)^2$

3. The following data represent the ages of couples applying for

marriage licenses in Dane County, Wisconsin, on a given day.

Couple (i)	1	2	3	4	5	6	7
Man's age (x_i)	23	32	20	26	47	29	19
Woman's age (y_i)	19	38	23	26	35	32	16

a. Write down the ages (x_i, y_i) for $i = 1$, 5, and 6.

b. Compute $\sum_{i=1}^{7} x_i$ and $\sum_{i=1}^{7} y_i$

c. Compute $\sum_{i=1}^{7} (x_i + y_i)$

d. Compute $\sum_{i=1}^{7} (x_i + y_i)^2$

e. Compute $\sum_{i=1}^{7} (2x_i - 3y_i)^2$

4. The following data show the annual income and years in school for five persons.

Person (i)	1	2	3	4	5
School years (x_i)	10	12	13	16	20
Income (y_i)	7500	9700	9200	12,400	17,700

a. Write down the pair (x_i, y_i) for $i = 1$, 3, and 4.

b. Compute the averages $(1/5) \sum_{i=1}^{5} x_i$, $(1/5) \sum_{i=1}^{5} y_i$

c. Compute $\sum_{i=1}^{5} 1/5 \, (x_i + y_i)$

d. Compute $\sum_{i=1}^{5} (x_i + y_i)^2$

e. Compute $\sum_{i=1}^{5} (y_i - 800x_i)^2$

5. Using rules 1, 2, and 3 verify each of the following statements.

a. $\sum_{i=1}^{n} (ax_i + b) = a \sum_{i=1}^{n} x_i + nb$

b. $\sum_{i=1}^{n} (cx_i - 1)^2 = c^2 \sum_{i=1}^{n} x_i^2 - 2c \sum_{i=1}^{n} x_i + n$

c. $\sum_{i=1}^{n} (x_i - y_i)^2 = \sum_{i=1}^{n} x_i^2 - 2 \sum_{i=1}^{n} x_i y_i + \sum_{i=1}^{n} y_i^2$

6. Using rules 1, 2, and 3 verify each of the following statements.

a. $\displaystyle\sum_{i=1}^{n} (x_i - c)^2 = \sum_{i=1}^{n} x_i^2 - 2c \sum_{i=1}^{n} x_i + nc^2$

b. $\displaystyle\sum_{i=1}^{n} (x_i + y_i + z_i) = \sum_{i=1}^{n} x_i + \sum_{i=1}^{n} y_i + \sum_{i=1}^{n} z_i$

c. $\displaystyle\sum_{i=1}^{n} (x_i + y_i)^3 = \sum_{i=1}^{n} x_i^3 + 3 \sum_{i=1}^{n} x_i^2 y_i + 3 \sum_{i=1}^{n} x_i y_i^2 + \sum_{i=1}^{n} y_i^3$

7. The following data are the grade point averages for students at the University of Nebraska for each of four years.

Year (i)	1 (Freshmen)	2 (Sophomores)	3 (Juniors)	4 (Seniors)
Number (n)	$n_1 = 3$	$n_2 = 4$	$n_3 = 5$	$n_4 = 2$
GPA	2.18	3.21	2.17	3.28
	3.42	2.47	3.26	2.44
	2.74	2.60	2.49	
		3.04	2.33	
			2.65	

a. Write down the values of x_{13}, x_{22}, x_{34}, and x_{41}.
b. Compute the average GPA for each year.
c. Compute the average GPA for all these students.

8. The following is a record of running times for five athletes for the 440-yard run (to the nearest second).

Athlete (i)	1	2	3	4	5
Running times	50	49	52	43	48
	47	46	48	47	54
	48	44	47	48	51
	51	47	51	46	47

a. Write down the values of x_{11}, x_{23}, x_{34}, x_{42} and x_{53}.
b. Compute the average running time for each athlete.
c. Compute the average running time for all the above data.

Probability

2 Probability

Many things in life are uncertain. It is useful, therefore, to have a numerical measure of the degree of uncertainty involved in the occurrence of some future event. This degree of uncertainty is called *probability*; it is measured by a number between 0 and 1.

Suppose, for example, that one has a bothersome hearing defect. The defect can possibly be cured by an operation, but if the operation fails, total deafness will result. Should the operation be risked? It is not easy to answer such a question. If the probability of success is only 50 percent, surely one will forgo the operation and live with the defect. But suppose the probability of success is 95, or 99, or 99.99 percent? Clearly, one's choice of an action—in this case, whether to risk the operation—should depend on its probability of success. Without such knowledge, one is much more likely to make a wrong decision. This somewhat extreme example suggests the value of having numerical probability estimates before taking an action.

In this chapter we shall study the concept of probability. An understanding of probability is crucial to rational decision making under conditions of uncertainty.

We begin by introducing some ideas and terms—*experiment, outcome space*, and *event*—that provide a convenient language for discussing probabilities.

2.1 Experiments, Outcome Spaces, and Events

The basis of investigation in the physical, biological, or social sciences is experimental observation. For example: a biologist measures bacterial growth in various media, an anthropologist records the dimensions of skulls, an industrial engineer counts the defective items in batches of parts produced, and an economist tabulates wage changes over a period of time. These activities are all "experiments" in our sense of the word. They involve observing outcomes—bacteria counts, skull dimensions, numbers of defective items, and monthly wages—in the form of counts or measurements which are then analyzed to discover the laws that govern the phenomena in question. If similar experimental conditions always resulted in the same outcome, these laws would be called *deterministic*. When, as is almost always the case, *different outcomes are found to occur in repeated trials under similar experimental conditions,* the laws are called *probabilistic*. It is with the latter situation that we are concerned.

Definition 1

An *experiment* is an operation producing outcomes that can be categorized or measured. Examples are:

	Experiment	*Outcome*
1.	Measuring a skull	Cranial capacity
2.	Tossing a coin once	Heads or tails
3.	Interviewing a potential voter	Preferred candidate is named, or lack of preference indicated
4.	Observing a student's academic record	Cumulative grade point average
5.	Inspecting a batch of manufactured items	Number of defective items in the batch

Often we are interested not in which individual outcome will occur but only in whether the outcome will belong to a certain set or *collection* of outcomes. For example, in experiment 5 above, if a batch of n items is taken from a large lot, and if the lot is to be accepted only if no more than m (some preassigned number) defective items are found in the batch, then the lot will be accepted only if the number of defective items in the batch belongs to the set $\{0, 1, 2, \ldots, m\}$.

Definition 2

The totality I of all possible individual outcomes of an experiment is called the *outcome space* of the experiment. An *event A* is any specified collection of the individual outcomes of the experiment; that is, any well-defined *subset* of I. If, when the experiment is performed, the observed outcome belongs to the given subset A of I, the event A is said to *occur* on that trial of the experiment.

Events will be denoted by capital letters. When we wish to display an outcome space I with some finite number N of possible individual outcomes we write $I = \{a_1, a_2, \ldots, a_N\}$, where $a_1, a_2, \ldots$ denote all the possible individual outcomes of the experiment. We display events in a similar manner; thus $A = \{a_2, a_4\}$ denotes the event consisting of a_2 and a_4 only.

Example 1

  Experiment: Rolling a single die.

  Outcomes: Outcome i means that the number i appears on the top face. The values of i are 1,2,3,4,5,6.

Outcome space: $I = \{1,2,3,4,5,6\}$.

  Some events: $A = \{1,3,5\} =$ an odd number appears; $B = \{1\} =$ the 1 appears; $C = \{2,4,6\} =$ an even number appears.

Example 2

  Experiment: Tossing a coin twice.

  Outcomes: A typical outcome is HT, where the H in the first position means that a head appears on the first toss, while the T in the second position means that a tail appears on the second toss.

Outcome space: $I = \{HH, HT, TH, TT\}$.

  Some events: $A = \{HH, HT, TH\} =$ at least one head; $B = \{HH, TT\} =$ both tosses are the same; $C = \{HT, TH\} =$ one head and one tail.

Example 3

  Experiment: Choosing a student at random* from a given group of students and recording the student's grade point average (GPA) on a 4.0 scale.

---

*The concept of "random" selection is hard to define without using terms that are equally in need of definition. Operationally, we may suppose that the names of all the individuals are written on identical chips. These are placed in a bowl and thoroughly mixed, and then a blindfolded and disinterested agent draws one chip from the bowl.

Outcomes: A number x between 0 and 4.

Outcome space: $I = \{0 \leq x \leq 4\}$ (that is, the set of all real numbers x between and including 0 and 4).

Some events: $A = \{3 < x \leq 4\} = $ GPA above 3; $B = \{0 \leq x < 2\}$ = GPA below 2; $C = \{1.5 \leq x \leq 3\} = $ GPA between and including 1.5 and 3.0.

Example 4

Experiment: Rolling a pair of dice, one red and one blue.

Outcomes: A typical outcome is listed as (i, j), where $i = $ the number on the red die and $j = $ the number on the blue die.

Outcome space: $I = $ all $36 = 6 \cdot 6$ ordered pairs (i, j), where $i = 1$, ..., 6 and $j = 1, \ldots, 6$. (The outcome space of this experiment is shown in figure 2.1.)

Some events: $A = $ the sum is $7 = \{(1.6), (2.5), (3,4), (4,3), (5,2), (6,1)\}$;
$B = $ a pair $= \{(1,1), (2,2), (3,3), (4,4), (5,5), (6,6)\}$;
$C = $ the sum is even $= \{(1,1), (3,1), (2,2), (1,3), (5,1), (4,2), (3,3), (2,4), (1,5), (6,2), (5,3), (4,4), (3,5), (2,6), (6,4), (5,5), (4,6), (6,6)\}$.

Example 5

Experiment: Four patients are treated for two weeks. The success or failure of the treatment for each patient is recorded.

Outcome: A typical outcome is listed as SSSF, where the S's

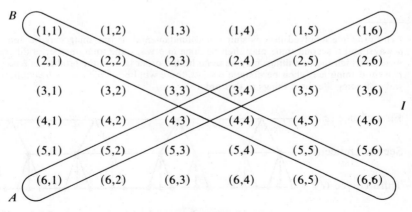

FIGURE 2.1
The outcome space for rolling a pair of dice

represent cures for patients 1, 2, 3, while the F means noncure for patient 4.

Outcome space: The outcome space has $2 \cdot 2 \cdot 2 \cdot 2 = 2^4 = 16$ elements,* a complete listing of which is

$$I = \left\{ \begin{array}{l} \text{SSSS, SSSF, SSFS, SFSS, FSSS,} \\ \text{SSFF, SFSF, SFFS, FSSF, FSFS, FFSS} \\ \text{SFFF, FSFF, FFSF, FFFS, FFFF} \end{array} \right\}$$

Some events: A = all patients are cured = {SSSS};
B = more than half the patients are cured = {SSSS, SSSF, SSFS, SFSS, FSSS};
C = exactly three patients are cured {SSSF, SSFS, SFSS, FSSS}.

PROBLEMS 2.1

For each of the following, list the outcome space for the experiment described.

1. Tossing a coin once.

2. Tossing a coin three times.

3. Recording the number of automobile accidents in a certain city on a given day.

4. Injecting a drug into five diseased mice and observing each of them for one week to see if the disease is cured or not.

5. Measuring the height to the nearest inch of a person chosen at random from a group of persons.

---

*The principle involved here is simple and fundamental. If one thing may be done in a ways, and a second thing may then be done in b ways, the total number of different ways in which the two things may be done in that order is $a \cdot b$, the product of a and b. If a third thing may then be done in c ways, there will be $(a \cdot b) \cdot c = a \cdot b \cdot c$ different ways of doing the three things in that order.

First choice (a)

Second choice (b)

Third choice (c)

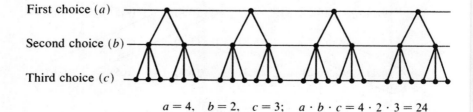

$$a = 4, \quad b = 2, \quad c = 3; \quad a \cdot b \cdot c = 4 \cdot 2 \cdot 3 = 24$$

6. Recording the annual salary of a full-time worker chosen at random from full-time workers in New York City.

7. Drawing one card from a standard deck of 52 cards and recording the face value, but not the suit.

8. As in problem 7, but recording only the suit of the card drawn.

9. Choosing at random six graduating seniors from Michigan State University and recording whether or not they intend to go to graduate school.

10. A jar contains four balls, numbered 1, 2, 3, and 4. The experiment consists of drawing one ball from the jar, recording the number drawn, replacing the ball, shaking the jar, and recording the number of a second drawn ball.

11. In the experiments described in problems 1, 7, and 9, give the number of outcomes in the outcome space. Can this be done for problems 3 and 5? Why or why not?

12. In problems 2, 4, 8, and 10, give the number of outcomes in the outcome space. Can this be done for problem 6? Why or why not?

13. How many outcomes in an experiment consisting of one toss of a coin? Two tosses of a coin? Three tosses of a coin? Four tosses of a coin? Can you write a general formula for the number of outcomes in n tosses of a coin?

14. Do problem 13 with a die in place of a coin.

15. In problem 2, write the following events as lists of outcomes:
    A = all coins show the same face.
    B = at least one coin is heads.

16. In problem 5, write the following events as lists of outcomes:
    A = the person is less than 6 feet tall.
    B = the person is between 5 and 6-1/2 feet tall.
    C = the person is taller than you.

17. In problem 3, write the following events as lists of outcomes:
    A = no accidents.
    B = no more than 10 accidents.
    C = at least five accidents.

18. In problem 4, write the following events as lists of outcomes:
    A = all mice are cured.
    B = more than half the mice are cured.
    C = an even number of mice are cured.

19. In problem 7, write the following events as lists of outcomes:

A = the card is a face card.

B = the face value is a number less than 8 (ace counts as 1).

C = the card is a face card or shows an even number.

20. In problem 3, list all events you can think of in the outcome space.

21. In problem 9, give an outcome space different from the one you gave originally. (Hint: Consider only the *number* of graduating seniors who plan to attend graduate school.) For both the outcome space given here and the original one, write as lists of outcomes the events:

A = more than half the seniors intend to go to graduate school.

B = less than three of the seniors intend to go to graduate school.

22. In problem 10, write the following events as lists of outcomes.

A = sum of the two numbers drawn is even.

B = sum of the two numbers drawn is at least 5.

C = the number on the first ball is even.

23. In problem 10, give an outcome space which involves only the *sum* of the two numbers on the drawn balls. Describe events *A* and *B* of problem 22 in this new outcome space. Can event *C* of problem 22 be described in this new outcome space?

2.2 Operations on Events

All events to be considered are assumed to be subsets of the outcome space *I* of some given experiment. It is convenient to consider as events both the *entire outcome space I* and the *empty set* ∅, which by definition contains no outcomes at all. *I* is the "certain" event, since it always occurs; ∅ is the "impossible" event, since it can never occur.

New events are constructed from given events by three basic operations. These operations, called *union, intersection,* and *complementation,* arise naturally out of the use of the words "or," "and," and "not."

Definition 3

The union of two events A, B, *denoted by* (A *or* B), *is the set of all outcomes either in* A *or in* B *(including those in both, if any).*

The intersection of two events A, B, *denoted by* (A *and* B), *is the set of all outcomes both in* A *and in* B.

The complement of an event A, *denoted by* A', *is the set of all outcomes not in* A.

These operations can be represented geometrically by the following Venn diagrams.

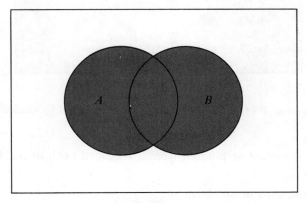

FIGURE 2.2
Union (*A* or *B*) of two events (set of outcomes indicated by shaded area)

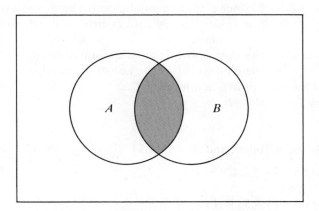

FIGURE 2.3
Intersection (*A* and *B*) of two events
(set of outcomes indicated by shaded area)

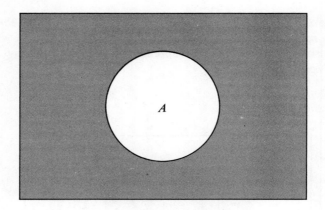

FIGURE 2.4
Complement A' of an event (set of outcomes indicated by shaded area)

Example 6
One card is picked at random from a standard deck of 52. Consider the events:

A = the card drawn is an ace;
H = the card drawn is a heart;
D = the card drawn is a diamond;
R = the card drawn is red;
B = the card drawn is black.

Then

$(H$ or $D)$ = the card drawn is a heart or a diamond = R.
$(H$ and $D)$ = $\emptyset$, since a card cannot be both a heart and a diamond.
$(H$ or D or $B)$ = I, since every card is either a heart, a diamond, or black.
$(A$ and $D)$ = the card drawn is an ace and a diamond
$\qquad$ = the card drawn is the ace of diamonds.
R' = the card drawn is not red = B.
$(H$ or $D)' = R' = B$.

Example 7
If a single die is rolled, and $A = \{1,3,5\}$, $B = \{1\}$; $C = \{2,4,6\}$, then

$(A$ or $C) = \{1,2,3,4,5,6\} = I$
$A' = \{2,4,6\} = C$
$(A$ or $B) = \{1,3,5\} = A$
$(B$ or $C) = \{1,2,4,6\}$
$(A$ and $C) = \emptyset$
$(A$ and $B) = \{1\} = B$
$B' = \{2,3,4,5,6\}$
$(B'$ and $A) = \{3,5\}$

Example 8

If x is a student's GPA, and $A = \{3 < x \leq 4\}$, $B = \{0 \leq x < 2\}$, $C = \{1.5 \leq x \leq 3\}$, then

$\quad$ $(A \text{ or } C) = \{1.5 \leq x \leq 4\}$
$\quad$ $(A \text{ and } C) = \emptyset$
$\quad$ $(B \text{ and } C) = \{1.5 \leq x < 2\}$
$\quad$ $(A \text{ or } B \text{ or } C) = \{0 \leq x \leq 4\} = I$
$\quad$ $A' = \{0 \leq x \leq 3\}$
$\quad$ $(A' \text{ and } C) = \{1.5 \leq x \leq 3\} = C$
$\quad$ $(A' \text{ or } C) = \{0 \leq x \leq 3\} = A'$

Two important general rules of the "algebra of events" are known as De Morgan's laws:

$\quad$ $(A \text{ or } B)' = (A' \text{ and } B')$; that is, *the complement of a union is the intersection of the complements,*
$\quad$ $(A \text{ and } B)' = (A' \text{ or } B')$; that is, *the complement of an intersection is the union of the complements.*

These facts may be verified by drawing Venn diagrams.

PROBLEMS 2.2

1. A coin is tossed three times. Events A, B, C, and D are defined as

   A = at least one head appears.
   B = all three tosses are heads.
   C = an odd number of heads appears.
   D = an even number of heads appears.

   Describe in words and list the outcomes for each of the following events:

a. $(A \text{ or } B)$	**d.** C'	**g.** $(C \text{ and } D)$
b. $(A \text{ and } B)$	**e.** B'	**h.** $(A \text{ and } B')$
c. A'	**f.** $(C \text{ or } D)$	

2. A die is rolled twice. Events A, B, C, and D are defined as

   A = first roll shows an even number.
   B = second roll shows an odd number.
   C = second roll shows a 1.
   D = first roll shows a 6.

   Describe in words and list the outcomes for each of the following events:

a. A'	**d.** $(D' \text{ and } B)$	**g.** $(A \text{ and } B)$
b. $(A \text{ or } B)$	**e.** $(C \text{ and } B)$	**h.** $(C' \text{ and } A)$
c. $(D \text{ or } A)$	**f.** $(C \text{ and } D')$	

3. A single card is drawn from a deck of 52 cards, and

F = the card drawn is a face card (king, queen, or jack).
C = the card drawn is a club.
B = the card drawn is black.
H = the card drawn is a heart.

Describe the following events in words:

a. C'
b. $(F$ and $C)$
c. $(B$ or $H)$
d. $(B$ and $H)$
e. $(C$ and $B)$
f. $(C$ or $B)$
g. $(F$ or $C)$
h. $(H$ and $F)$

4. A college class consists of nine males and eight females. Of the nine males, three are undergraduates and six graduate students. Of the eight females, four are undergraduates and four are graduate students. One student is chosen at random from the class. Consider the events: M = chosen student is male, F = chosen student is female, G = chosen student is a graduate student, and U = chosen student is an undergraduate. Describe in words each of the following events:

a. $(M$ or $G)$
b. $(M$ and $G)$
c. $(F$ or $M)$
d. $(F$ and $M)$
e. U'
f. $(G'$ and $M')$
g. $(M$ or $G)'$
h. $(F$ or $U')$

5. Let x be the age of a person to the nearest year, and consider the events

$A = (x > 21)$
$B = (13 \le x \le 18)$
$C = (x \le 65)$
$D = (x \ge 50)$

Describe in terms of x each of the events

a. $(A$ and $C)$
b. $(A$ or $C)$
c. D'
d. $(C'$ and $D)$
e. $(C$ or $D)$
f. $(C$ and $D)$
g. $(B$ or $A')$
h. $(B'$ and $C)$

6. Let x be the height of a person to the nearest inch, and consider the events

$A = (x < 60)$
$B = (x \ge 48)$
$C = (x \le 66)$
$D = (50 \le x \le 55)$

Describe in terms of x each of the events

a. A'
b. $(A$ and $B)$
c. $(C$ or $D)$
d. $(B$ or $D)$
e. D'
f. $(A$ or $B)$
g. $(A'$ and $D)$
h. $(D$ and $C)$

7. Five babies are born on a given day. Describe each of the following events in terms of its outcomes: A = all the babies born are girls, B = the number of baby girls is even, and C = more boys than girls

born. Give each of the following events as a list of outcomes:

a. B'

b. $(C \text{ or } A)$

c. $(C \text{ and } A)$

d. $(B \text{ or } A)'$

e. $(A' \text{ and } B)$

f. $(C' \text{ or } B)'$

g. $(B \text{ and } C)'$

h. $[A \text{ and } (B \text{ or } C)]$

i. $[A' \text{ and } (B \text{ and } C)]$

j. $[B \text{ or } (A \text{ and } C)]$

8. A carton of 10 light bulbs contains four of 60 watts and six of 100 watts. Four bulbs are taken at random from the carton. Consider the events: A = all the bulbs selected are 100 watts, B = all the bulbs selected are 60 watts, and C = at least half the bulbs selected are 100 watts. Give each of the following events as a list of outcomes.

a. $(A \text{ or } B')$

b. $(A \text{ or } B)'$

c. $(A \text{ and } B)'$

d. $(A' \text{ or } C)$

e. $(A \text{ or } C)'$

f. $[B \text{ or } (A \text{ and } C)]$

g. $[C \text{ and } (A \text{ or } B)]$

h. $[C \text{ and } (A \text{ or } B)']$

i. $[A' \text{ or } (C \text{ and } B)']$

j. $(A' \text{ and } B' \text{ and } C')$

9. Suppose two voters are interviewed; each is either a Democrat (D), a Republican (R), or an Independent (In). Describe in terms of outcomes the events

A = at least one voter is a Republican.
B = both voters are Independents.
C = at least one voter is a Democrat.
E = one voter is an Independent and the other is not.

Verify each of the following rules for operations on events by finding each side separately

a. $(A')' = A$

b. $(A \text{ or } E)' = (A' \text{ and } E')$

c. $(A \text{ and } E)' = (A' \text{ or } E')$

d. $(A \text{ and } C)' = (A' \text{ or } C')$

e. $[(A \text{ and } C) \text{ or } B] = [(A \text{ or } B) \text{ and } (C \text{ or } B)]$

f. $[(E \text{ or } B) \text{ and } C] = [(E \text{ and } C) \text{ or } (B \text{ and } C)]$

Observe that (a)–(f) hold for *any* events A, B, C, E.

10. A jar contains three balls labeled 1, 2, 3. If two balls are chosen one after the other without replacing the first, list all the outcomes in the sample space. Describe in terms of outcomes the events

A = sum of the numbers on the two balls is even.
B = first ball drawn is even.
C = second ball drawn is odd.
D = sum of the numbers on the two balls is 5.

Verify each of the following rules for operation on events by finding each side separately:

    a. $(B')' = B$
    b. $(A \text{ or } B)' = (A' \text{ and } B')$
    c. $(A \text{ and } C)' = (A' \text{ or } C')$
    d. $[A \text{ and } (B \text{ or } C)] = [(A \text{ and } B) \text{ or } (A \text{ and } C)]$
    e. $[D \text{ or } (A \text{ or } B)] = [(D \text{ or } A) \text{ or } B)]$
    f. $[(A \text{ and } B) \text{ or } D] = [(A \text{ or } D) \text{ and } (B \text{ or } D)]$

    Observe that (a)–(f) hold for *any* events A, B, C, D.

11. Draw Venn diagrams for
    a. $(A \text{ or } B)'$ **c.** $(A \text{ and } B)'$
    b. $(A' \text{ and } B')$ **d.** $(A' \text{ or } B')$

Examine (a) and (b) as a pair and (c) and (d) as a pair to verify De Morgan's laws.

2.3 The Concept of Probability in the Case of Equal Likelihood

In the experiment of rolling two fair dice, let A be the event that the sum is 7. There are $6 \cdot 6 = 36$ elements in the outcome space I, as shown in figure 2.1, and each element is assumed to be equally likely to occur. Of these, exactly six belong to the event A in question. An important numerical characteristic of the event A is the *ratio of the number of outcomes in* A *to the total number of outcomes in* I; that is,

$$\frac{\text{Number of outcomes in } A}{\text{Total number of outcomes in } I} = \frac{6}{36} = \frac{1}{6}$$

This ratio is called the probability of the event A.

Definition 4
Assume that an outcome space I consists of a *finite number of equally likely individual outcomes*, and let A be any event (that is, subset of I). *The probability* P *that event* A *will occur* when the experiment is performed is defined as the ratio

$$P(A) = \frac{\#(A)}{\#(I)} \tag{1}$$

where the symbol $\#(\cdot \cdot \cdot)$ denotes the number of individual outcomes in any event $(\cdot \cdot \cdot)$.

Example 9
If A is the event "an odd number appears" in one roll of a fair die, then $\#(A) = 3$ and $\#(I) = 6$. Hence $P(\text{odd}) = 3/6 = 1/2$. Similarly, $P(1) = 1/6$, and $P(\text{even}) = 1/2$.

Example 10

In rolling two fair dice, the event "a pair" comprises six individual outcomes (B in figure 2.1). Since there are 36 equally likely outcomes in I, $P(\text{a pair}) = 6/36 = 1/6$. Similarly, $P(\text{sum is even}) = 18/36 = 1/2$.

A standard way of illustrating the definition (formula 1) of numerical probability is as follows. A bowl contains N chips, of which a are white and the remaining $N - a$ are black. The chips are thoroughly mixed and one chip is selected blindly. Let the event A consist of drawing a white chip. Then the probability $P(A)$ is the ratio

$$P(A) = \frac{\#(A)}{\#(I)} = \frac{a}{N} = \frac{\text{number of white chips in the bowl}}{\text{total number of chips in the bowl}}$$

When we assert of some event A (for example, "rain tomorrow") that it has, say, probability .35 of occurring, we mean that is as likely to rain as it is that we will draw a white chip from a bowl containing 100 chips, 35 of which are white and the rest black.

We shall analyze the concept of probability by supposing that the outcome space I of the experiment in question consists of a finite number of equally likely individual outcomes, and taking (1) as the definition of the probability of any event A. On this basis we shall list a few simple but extremely useful properties of probability that always hold, no matter what the particular details of the experiment in question.

For any event A

$$0 \le P(A) \le 1 \qquad (2)$$

Since $0 \le \#(A) \le \#(I)$, (2) follows by dividing each term of this inequality by $\#(I)$ and applying (1).

$$P(\emptyset) = 0, \; P(I) = 1 \qquad (3)$$

This is immediate, since by (1)

$$P(\emptyset) = \frac{\#(\emptyset)}{\#(I)} = \frac{0}{\#(I)} = 0, \; P(I) = \frac{\#(I)}{\#(I)} = 1$$

Definition 5

Two events A, B with no outcomes in common—in other words, such that $(A \text{ and } B) = \emptyset$—are said to be *mutually exclusive*.

For any two mutually exclusive events A, B

$$P(A \text{ or } B) = P(A) + P(B) \qquad (4)$$

To verify this we observe that for any two events A, B, mutually exclusive or not,

$$\#(A \text{ or } B) = \#(A) + \#(B) - \#(A \text{ and } B) \qquad (5)$$

since in the sum $\#(A) + \#(B)$, the outcomes in the intersection (A and B) are counted twice. Dividing (5) by $\#(I)$ gives the general law, valid for any two events A, B,

$$P(A \text{ or } B) = P(A) + P(B) - P(A \text{ and } B) \qquad (6)$$

Now, if A, B are mutually exclusive then (A and B) $= \emptyset$, so (4) follows from the fact that $P(\emptyset) = 0$.

Three or more events $A, B, C, \ldots$ are said to be mutually exclusive if *no two* of them have any outcome in common, so that at most one of the events $A, B, C, \ldots$ can occur on any single trial of the experiment in question. If three events A, B, C are mutually exclusive; that is, if (A and B) = (A and C) = (B and C) $= \emptyset$, then by applying (4) twice we obtain the formula

$$P(A \text{ or } B \text{ or } C) = P[(A \text{ or } B) \text{ or } C] = P(A \text{ or } B) + P(C) \qquad (7)$$
$$= P(A) + P(B) + P(C)$$

A similar addition formula holds for the probability of the union of any number of mutually exclusive events.

For any event A

$$P(A') = 1 - P(A) \qquad (8)$$

This follows from the fact that (A' or A) $= I$ and (A' and A) $= \emptyset$ so by (2) and (4).

$$1 = P(I) = P(A' \text{ or } A) = P(A') + P(A), \text{ which gives (8)}$$

For any two events A and B

$$P(B) = P(B \text{ and } A) + P(B \text{ and } A') \qquad (9)$$

This follows from (4) and the fact that $B = [(B \text{ and } A) \text{ or } (B \text{ and } A')]$, where the two events in parentheses are mutually exclusive.

Example 11
A card is chosen at random from a standard deck of 52. Consider the following events and their probabilities.

$$A = \text{the card is a heart} \qquad P(A) = \frac{13}{52} = \frac{1}{4}$$

$$B = \text{the card is a diamond} \qquad P(B) = \frac{13}{52} = \frac{1}{4}$$

$$C = \text{the card is an ace} \qquad P(C) = \frac{4}{52} = \frac{1}{13}$$

By (4), since the events A, B are mutually exclusive,

$$P(A \text{ or } B) = P(A) + P(B) = \frac{1}{4} + \frac{1}{4} = \frac{1}{2}$$

However, it is *not* true that

$$P(A \text{ or } C) = P(A) + P(C) = \frac{1}{4} + \frac{1}{13} = \frac{17}{52}$$

since the events A, C are not mutually exclusive. The formula that applies in this case is (6).

$$P(A \text{ or } C) = P(A) + P(C) - P(A \text{ and } C) = \frac{1}{4} + \frac{1}{13} - \frac{1}{52} = \frac{16}{52}$$

in agreement with formula 1 applied directly.

Example 12

Two cards are drawn successively and at random from a deck of 52, the first card being returned and the deck reshuffled before the second card is drawn (this is called *sampling with replacement*). What is the probability that at least one of the two cards will be an ace?

The outcome space I of this experiment consists of the $N = 52 \cdot 52$ equally likely ways of successively drawing two cards. If A_1 is the event that the first card is an ace and A_2 that the second card is an ace, then since $\#(A_1) = 4 \cdot 52$ and $\#(A_2) = 52 \cdot 4$,

$$P(A_1) = \frac{4 \cdot 52}{52 \cdot 52} = \frac{1}{13}, \ P(A_2) = \frac{52 \cdot 4}{52 \cdot 52} = \frac{1}{13}$$

The two events A_1, A_2 are not mutually exclusive; in fact

$$P(A_1 \text{ and } A_2) = \frac{4 \cdot 4}{52 \cdot 52} = \left(\frac{1}{13}\right)^2 = \frac{1}{169}$$

Hence by (6)

$$P(\text{at least 1 ace}) = P(A_1 \text{ or } A_2) = P(A_1) + P(A_2) - P(A_1 \text{ and } A_2)$$
$$= \frac{2}{13} - \frac{1}{169} = \frac{25}{169}$$

As is often the case in probability theory, this problem can be solved in more than one way. The event "at least one ace" is the complement of the event "neither card is an ace," and hence by formula 8

$$P(\text{at least 1 ace}) = 1 - P(A_1' \text{ and } A_2') = 1 - \frac{48 \cdot 48}{52 \cdot 52}$$
$$= \frac{400}{2704} = \frac{25}{169}$$

The latter method of solution permits an immediate generalization to finding the probability of obtaining at least one ace in any given number n of successive draws, the card drawn being replaced and the deck reshuffled after each draw. For n such draws

$$P(\text{at least one ace}) = 1 - \left(\frac{48}{52}\right)^n = 1 - \left(1 - \frac{1}{13}\right)^n$$

where $1/13$ is the probability of getting an ace on any single draw.

More generally, if some event A has the probability p of occurring on a single trial, and if n successive trials are made under the same conditions, the probability that the event A will occur *at least once* in the n trials is

$$1 - (1 - p)^n$$

Thus, in n tosses of a fair coin, the probability of obtaining heads at least once is $1 - (1/2)^n$, and in n rolls of a fair die the probability of obtaining at least one 6 is $1 - (5/6)^n$.

Example 13

A fair coin is tossed twice. Let $C =$ one head and one tail, and $D =$ head on first toss. Then by (9)

$$P(C) = P(C \text{ and } D) + P(C \text{ and } D')$$
$$= P(HT) + P(TH) = \frac{1}{4} + \frac{1}{4} = \frac{1}{2}$$

Example 14

Two fair dice are rolled. Let $E =$ the sum of the spots is at least 4. Since $E' = \{(1.1), (1,2), (2,1)\}$, we have by (8)

$$P(E) = 1 - P(E') = 1 - \frac{3}{36} = \frac{33}{36} = \frac{11}{12}$$

The direct computation of $P(E)$ by formula 1 would require counting the 33 individual outcomes in E, instead of the three outcomes in E'.

PROBLEMS 2.3

1. One student is chosen at random from a class that contains 18 freshmen, 10 sophomores, 8 juniors, and 14 seniors. Let F represent the event "a freshman is chosen." Similarly, let S, J, and A represent the corresponding events for sophomores, juniors, and seniors, respectively. Find $P(F), P(S), P(J)$, and $P(A)$.

2. A precinct containing 1000 registered voters has 230 Republicans, 380 Democrats, 370 Independents, and 20 American Party members. Let R be the event that a voter chosen at random in this precinct is a Republican. Similarly, let D, In, and A be the corresponding events for the other parties. Find $P(R), P(D), P(In)$, and $P(A)$.

3. A fair die is tossed once. Let A be the event "a number divisible

by 3 appears." Let B be the event "a number smaller than 4 appears." Find $P(A)$ and $P(B)$. Compute $P(A$ or $B)$ and $P(A$ and $B)$ by using (1).

4. A fair coin is tossed four times. Find the number of outcomes in the outcome space of this experiment. Let A be the event "three or more heads appear in the four tosses." Let B be the event "an even number of heads appears in the four tosses." Find by (1), $P(A)$, $P(B)$, $P(A$ or $B)$, and $P(A$ and $B)$.

5. A person has three nickels and three dimes, and chooses two coins at random. Find the number of outcomes in the outcome space. Let A be the event "the sum of the two coins is more than 10 cents." Let B be the event "both coins have the same value." Find by (1), $P(A)$ and $P(B)$.

6. A jar contains four red balls and two white balls. We randomly pick two balls from the jar in a single draw. Find the number of outcomes in the outcome space of this experiment. Let A be the event "both balls are the same color," and B, "at least one of the two balls is red." Find by (1), $P(A)$ and $P(B)$.

7. Toss a coin $n = 10$ times and record $m =$ the number of times a head appears. Compute m/n and compare with $P(A)$ where A is the event "a head appears in one toss of a fair coin." Repeat with $n = 50$, $n = 100$, and $n = 200$. Comment on your results in relation to (1).

8. Toss a die $n = 100$ times and record $m =$ the number of tosses in which a six appears. Compute m/n and compare with $P(A)$ where A is the event "a six appears in one toss of a fair die." Repeat with $n = 200$. Comment on your results in relation to (1).

9. In problem 1, find $P(S$ or $J)$, $P(F$ or $A)$, and $P(S$ or $F)$ directly by (1) and also by (4). Find $P(F$ or S or $J)$ first by (1) and then by (7).

10. In problem 2, find $P(R$ or $D)$, $P(R$ or $In)$, and $P(D$ or $In)$ by using first formula 1 and then (4). Find $P(R$ or D or $A)$ by (1) and by (7).

11. The probabilities that a student will get an A, B, C, D, or F in a certain course are .17, .26, .40, .11, .06, respectively.
   a. What is the probability of a student getting an A or B?
   b. What is the probability of a student not getting an F? (Hint: Use formula 8.)
   c. What is the probability of a student not getting an A or B?

12. In problem 1, find $P(F')$, $P(J')$, and $P(F$ or $J)$.

13. A carton of eight light bulbs has one defective bulb. If two bulbs are chosen at random, find the probability that

   a. the first bulb drawn is defective.

   b. the second bulb drawn is defective.

   c. at least one of the two bulbs drawn is defective. (Hint: Use (a) and (b) and (9).)

14. Two cards are drawn successively without replacement from a shuffled deck. What is the probability that the second card drawn will be red? (Hint: Use formula 9 and observe that the first card must be red or black.)

2.4 A More General Definition of Probability

The "classical" definition of probability (formula 1) is applicable only to experiments with a *finite number of equally likely outcomes*. Thus, in a single toss of a fair die, $P(\text{even number}) = 3/6 = 1/2$, since there are six equally likely outcomes of which three are even numbers, and in repeated tosses the relative frequency (that is, the proportion of times) with which an even number appears should be close to 1/2. For a loaded die, however, the long-run relative frequency with which an even number appears may differ considerably from 1/2. The same would be true for the long-run relative frequency of heads in tossing an unsymmetrical coin, such as the 1964-D (Denver) penny, in which the edge is not at right angles to the faces.

    To treat such cases, suppose that the outcome space I of an experiment consists of some number N of individual outcomes $\{a_1, \ldots a_N\}$, but that intuition or experience indicates that they cannot be considered equally likely. Suppose also that in some number n of trials under the same conditions we observe that

$$\begin{aligned}
\text{outcome } a_1 \quad \text{occurs} \quad & m_1 \text{ times} \\
\text{outcome } a_2 \quad \text{occurs} \quad & m_2 \text{ times} \\
\vdots \qquad\qquad\qquad & \vdots \\
\text{outcome } a_N \quad \text{occurs} \quad & m_N \text{ times}
\end{aligned}$$

with $m_1 + \ldots + m_N = n$. The ratio $f_i = m_i/n$, the relative frequency of the outcome a_i in the n trials, may then be taken as an *empirical estimate* of the probability with which a_i would occur in a conceptually infinite series of trials. (Of course, this estimate would be subject to change with further experience as the number n of observed trials increases.) The numbers $f_1, \ldots, f_N$ sum to 1. The relative frequency of occurrence of any event A (that is, subset of I) during the n observed trials will be given by the sum, over all the outcomes a_i in A, of the corresponding f_i values. Accordingly, we make the following generalization of definition 4.

Definition 6
Let the outcome space I of an experiment consist of N elements $\{a_1, a_2, \ldots, a_N\}$, and let $p_1, p_2, \ldots, p_N$ be any non-negative numbers that sum to 1 (p_i might represent the idealized long-run relative frequency with which the particular outcome a_i will occur). For any event A (that is, subset of I) its *probability* is defined as follows:

$P(A) =$ the sum of all the p_i for which the corresponding   (10)
   outcome a_i belongs to the set A

When $p_i = 1/N$ for each $i = 1, 2, \ldots, N$, this reduces to the equal likelihood definition (formula 1).

Example 15
A gambler has prepared a loaded die so that in the long run the six faces come up with the frequencies shown in figure 2.5. The outcome space I of one roll of this die consists of the six elements $\{1,2,3,4,5,6\}$, with respective probabilities summing to 1. Then by formula 10 the event $A = $ (even number) will have the probability

$$P(A) = .18 + .16 + .20 = .54$$

while the event $A' = $ (odd number) will have the probability

$$P(A') = .13 + .18 + .15 = .46 = 1 - P(A)$$

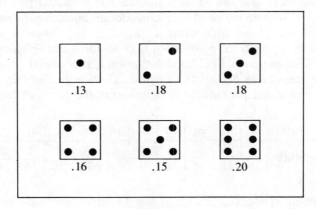

FIGURE 2.5
Probabilities for a loaded die

In many cases both the equal likelihood formula (1) and the more general formula (10) can be applied to the same experiment by properly redefining the outcome space.

Example 16
A student is chosen at random (that is, in such a way that each student has an equal chance of being selected) from an undergraduate college that consists of 34 percent freshmen, 27 percent sophomores, 20 percent juniors, and 19 percent seniors. If a_1 denotes that the student chosen is a freshman, a_2 a sophomore, a_3 a junior, and a_4 a senior, then the outcome space may be defined as the four-element set $I = \{a_1, a_2, a_3, a_4\}$, with $p_1 = .34$, $p_2 = .27$, $p_3 = .20$, and $p_4 = .19$, summing to 1. We can then compute by formula 10 the probability of any event (that is, subset of I). For example, if A is the event that the student chosen is not a freshman, then

$$P(A) = p_2 + p_3 + p_4 = .27 + .20 + .19 = .66 = 1 - p_1$$

In this example, the "equally likely" outcome space has as elements all students in the college. The new outcome space I, however, has only four elements, $a_1, \ldots, a_4$, which are not equally likely. Both outcome spaces give the same probabilities for events involving membership in the four college classes, but for such events, the outcome space I with fewer elements is simpler to work with.

Example 17
In example 4, which involved rolling a pair of fair dice, the outcome space was taken to be the $6 \cdot 6 = 36$ equally likely individual outcomes. (See figure 2.1.) If we are interested only in the sum of the numbers on the two dice, and not in *how* this sum is obtained (for example, $2 + 4$ or $3 + 3$), then we need only consider an outcome space I which consists of the 11 possible sums $a_2, a_3, \ldots, a_{12}$. Then $p_2 = P(\text{sum} = 2) = 1/36$, $p_3 = 2/36$, $p_4 = 3/36$, and so forth, these values being obtained from the equal likelihood definition of probability by summing along the respective diagonals in figure 2.1. We thus obtain the new outcome space and probability assignment in the sense of formula 10

Outcome (sum)	a_2	a_3	a_4	a_5	a_6	a_7	a_8	a_9	a_{10}	a_{11}	a_{12}
Probability	$\frac{1}{36}$	$\frac{2}{36}$	$\frac{3}{36}$	$\frac{4}{36}$	$\frac{5}{36}$	$\frac{6}{36}$	$\frac{5}{36}$	$\frac{4}{36}$	$\frac{3}{36}$	$\frac{2}{36}$	$\frac{1}{36}$

This outcome space $\{a_2, \ldots, a_{12}\}$ has 11 unequally likely outcomes, whereas the outcome space given earlier in figure 2.1 has 36 equally likely outcomes. The new space is simpler to work with if, as in some games of chance, we are interested only in the sum of the numbers on the two dice and not in how this sum was obtained. Either space can be used for computing probabilities for sums. For example, if C is the event that the sum is even, then from formula 10

$$P(C) = p_2 + p_4 + p_6 + \ldots + p_{12}$$

$$= \frac{1}{36} + \frac{3}{36} + \frac{5}{36} + \frac{5}{36} + \frac{3}{36} + \frac{1}{36} = \frac{18}{36} = \frac{1}{2}$$

The same result is obtained by using the equal likelihood definition where

$$P(C) = \frac{\#(C)}{\#(I)} = \frac{18}{36} = \frac{1}{2}$$

It is important to observe that all the general formulas 2–9 of probability that hold for the equal likelihood definition 1 continue to hold for the more general definition 10. We leave the detailed verification of this fact to the reader.

When there is neither a compelling reason for regarding the individual outcomes of an experiment as equally likely, nor any possibility of observing a long series of trials performed under the same experimental conditions, then any assessment of the probability of an event must be largely subjective. Thus in 1975 we can give only a subjective answer to the question "What is the probability that a cure for the common cold will be found by 1980?"

PROBLEMS 2.4

1. In problem 1, section 2.3, define an outcome space with four unequally likely outcomes, and list the corresponding probabilities of these four outcomes. Find the probability of the events $C =$ "the student is a lower classman (F or S)," and $B =$ "the student is not a freshman," by using formula 10.

2. In problem 2, section 2.3, define an outcome space with four unequally likely outcomes, and list the corresponding probabilities. Find the probability of the events (R or D) and $(In)'$ using (10).

3. A box contains four balls labeled 1, 2, 3, and 4. A ball is drawn at random from the box and the number is recorded. The ball is replaced, a second ball is drawn at random, and its number is recorded. How many possible outcomes are there, considering each pair of numbers as an outcome? List these outcomes as outcome space I'. Define another outcome space $I = (a_2, a_3, \ldots, a_8)$, where $a_i =$ the sum of the two numbers drawn ($i = 2, 3, \ldots, 8$).

Find $p_i = P(a_i)$ for outcome space I and show that $p_1 + \ldots + p_8 = 1$. Using outcome space I, compute by formula 10 the probability of the events A = the sum is an even number," and B = "the sum is greater than or equal to 5." Verify your calculations of $P(A)$ and $P(B)$ by recalculating them from the equal likelihood formula 1 using the outcome space I'.

4. A card is drawn at random from a standard deck. Let C be the event "the card is a club" and F be the event "the card is a face card (king, queen, or jack)." Find $P(C$ or $F)$ by (10).

5. A student is picked at random from a class of 24 students, of which 15 are women, 9 are men, 10 are graduate students, and 14 are undergraduate students. Of the 14 undergraduates, 8 are women. Let W be the event "the student chosen is a woman" and U the event "the student chosen is an undergraduate." Find $P(W$ or $U)$ by (10).

6. In problem 4, find $P(C$ or $H)$ where H is the event "the card is a heart" by using (10). Why does the answer using (1) agree with that using (10)? Also, compute $P(H$ or $F)$ by (10). Why does $P(H$ or $F) \neq P(H) + P(F)$ in this case? Remark on these results in connection with (1) and (10).

7. In problem 5, find $P(U$ or $M)$ where M is the event "the student is a man," by using (10). Why does this answer agree with that obtained by using (1)? Compute $P(M')$ and $P(U$ or $W)$ and comment on this in relation to (1) and (10).

8. A county tabulation of workers by income and age gave the following:

Age \ Yearly income	Less than $5000	$5000 – $10,000	More than $10,000
18–30	210	270	120
31–50	210	360	230
over 50	120	140	140

Find the probability that a worker chosen at random from this county is

a. (30 or under) or (earns more than \$10,000).
b. (over 50) or (earns between \$5,000 and \$10,000 per year).
c. (30 or under) or (over 50).

9. A drug is administered to 100 persons—40 smokers and 60 non-smokers. Of the 100 persons, 20 had nausea; 10 of these were

smokers. Find the probability that a person chosen at random from this group

a. is a nonsmoker or had nausea.

b. is a smoker or had no nausea.

10. A die is tossed twice. Let A_1 be the event that a one appears on the first toss and A_2 be the event that a one appears on the second toss. Find $P(A_1)$ and $P(A_2)$. If A is the event that a one appears on either toss of the die, find $P(A)$ by using (10). (Hint: $A = A_1$ or A_2.) Also, find the probability of getting an even number on either toss of the die.

11. Let A, B, and C be three events. Then, $P(A$ or B or $C) = [P(A) + P(B) + P(C)] - [P(A$ and $B) + P(B$ and $C) + P(A$ and $C)] + P(A$ and B and $C)$.

   Draw a Venn diagram and explain why the above equation is true.

12. Using the formula in problem 11, compute the probability of the event $(A$ or B or $C)$ in problem 8, with A the event "30 or under" B the event "earns between \$5000 and \$10,000 per year," and C the event "over 50."

2.5 Conditional Probability

We begin by considering a simple example in which this concept arises.

Example 18

A study of the incomes of 5703 registered party members gave the following information.

Income Party	Low*	High	Totals
Republican	1337	1064	2401
Democratic	1916	756	2672
Totals	3253	1820	5073

Low income was defined as under \$10,000 per year.

Suppose that a person in this group is chosen at random. The probability that the person chosen will be a Democrat is then

$$P(\text{Dem.}) = \frac{2672}{5073} = .5267$$

Now suppose we are given the information that the person chosen has a low income. Then the probability that the person chosen is a Democrat becomes

$$P(\text{Dem.}|\text{Low}) = \frac{1916}{3253} = .5890 \tag{11}$$

This is called the *conditional probability* of being a Democrat, given low income. To compute it, the original outcome space of 5703 persons is replaced by the "restricted" or "reduced" outcome space consisting of the 3253 persons with low incomes.

It is important to observe that the *conditional probability* P(Dem. |Low) can be expressed as the *ratio of* two *unconditional probabilities.* To do this we simply divide numerator and denominator of the ratio in (11) by 5073, obtaining

$$P(\text{Dem.}|\text{Low}) = \frac{1916}{3253} = \frac{1916/5073}{3253/5073} = \frac{P(\text{Dem. and Low})}{P(\text{Low})}$$

This example illustrates the following general definition of conditional probability.

Definition 7
Let A and B be any two events for which $P(B) > 0$. The *conditional probability of the event* A, *given the event* B, is the ratio

$$P(A|B) = \frac{P(A \text{ and } B)}{P(B)} \tag{12}$$

The symbol $P(A|B)$ is read "the probability of A, given B"; it is the probability that the event A will occur when we restrict ourselves to just those outcomes of the experiment in question in which the event B occurs. (The ordinary, or "unconditional," probability $P(A)$ of an event A can be regarded as the conditional probability of A, given no information except that I is the outcome space, since by (12)

$$P(A|I) = \frac{P(A \text{ and } I)}{P(I)} = \frac{P(A)}{1} = P(A)$$

A conditional probability P(A|B) *may or may not be equal to the unconditional probability* P(A).

Example 19
A card chosen at random from a standard deck is observed to be red. What is the probability that it is (a) an ace, (b) a heart?

a. $P(\text{ace}|\text{red}) = \dfrac{P(\text{ace and red})}{P(\text{red})} = \dfrac{2/52}{26/52} = \dfrac{1}{13} = P(\text{ace})$

b. $P(\text{heart}|\text{red}) = \dfrac{P(\text{heart and red})}{P(\text{red})} = \dfrac{P(\text{heart})}{P(\text{red})} = \dfrac{13/52}{26/52} = \dfrac{1}{2}$

which is not equal to $P(\text{heart}) = \dfrac{13}{52} = \dfrac{1}{4}$

PROBLEMS 2.5

1. In an outcome space, the events A and B are such that $P(A) = .5$, $P(B) = .7$, and $P(A \text{ and } B) = .25$. Find $P(A|B)$ and $P(B|A)$.

2. In an outcome space, the events A, B, and C are such that $P(A) = .8$, $P(B) = .5$, $P(C) = .2$, $P(A \text{ and } B) = .2$, $P(B \text{ and } C) = .3$, and $P(A \text{ and } C) = .4$. Find $P(A|B)$, $P(B|A)$, $P(A|C)$, $P(C|A)$, $P(B|C)$, and $P(C|B)$.

3. A fair die is tossed once. Find the probability of the event A "a six appears," given the event B "an even number appears." Is $P(A) = P(A|B)$?

4. A card is drawn at random from a deck of 52. Find the probability of the event K "the card drawn is a king," given F "the card drawn is a face card." Is $P(K) = P(K|F)$?

5. Suppose that in the U.S. population over the age of 50, the probability of being overweight is .60 and the probability of being overweight and having heart disease is .30. Use (12) to find the probability of having heart disease, given that a person is above 50 and overweight. Similarly, if the probability of not being overweight and having heart disease is .05, find the probability of having heart disease given that a person is above 50 and not overweight.

6. Suppose the probability of an adult completing college and earning over $10,000 per year is .15. If the probability of an adult completing college is .20, what is the probability that an adult earns over $10,000 per year, given that he or she has completed college? If the probability of earning less than $10,000 per year and completing college is .05, find the probability of earning less than $10,000 given that college has been completed.

7. In problem 5, complete the following table of probabilities.

Event	B Overweight	B' Not overweight	Total
A Has heart disease	.30	.05	
A' No heart disease			
Total	.60		1.00

Using the results of this table, compute: $P(A|B)$, $P(A'|B)$, $P(A|B')$, $P(A'|B')$, $P(B|A)$, and $P(B|A')$.

8. In problem 6, complete the following table of probabilities by filling in the blank spaces.

Event	B Income $\geq$ $10,000	B' Income < $10,000	Total
A Completed college	.15	.05	.20
A' Not completed college			
Total	.25		1.00

Using the results of this table, compute: $P(B|A)$, $P(B'|A)$, $P(B|A')$, $P(B'|A')$, $P(A|B)$, and $P(A'|B')$.

9. Consider the following tabulation of students at a college.

GPA \ Sex	A_1 0.00 to 1.00	A_2 1.01 to 2.00	A_3 2.01 to 3.00	A_4 3.01 to 4.00
Male (M)	50	200	300	150
Female (F)	40	140	200	120

How many outcomes are in the restricted sample space if it is given that a person chosen at random from this college is male? female? Using these restricted sample spaces, compute: $P(A_i|M)$ and $P(A_i|F)$, $i = 1, 2, 3, 4$.

Recompute these using formula 12 and the original sample space of all students in the college.

10. Verify that if A and B are mutually exclusive events with $P(A) > 0$ and $P(B) > 0$, then $P(A|B) = 0$ and $P(B|A) = 0$.

2.6 The Probability of the Intersection of Two or More Events

Formula 12 furnishes a general method of computing the probability $P(A \text{ and } B)$ of the *intersection* of two events. If A and B are any two events in an outcome space I, then the probability of the event (A and B) can be obtained by either of the following formulas:

$$P(A \text{ and } B) = \begin{cases} P(B) \cdot P(A|B) \\ P(A) \cdot P(B|A) \end{cases} \qquad (13)$$

The first of these relations follows at once from (12), while the second follows from the first by interchanging A and B; $P(A$ and $B) = P(B$ and $A) = P(A) \cdot P(B|A)$.

If A, B, C are any three events of positive probability, then to compute $P(A$ and B and $C)$ we proceed by grouping events:

$$P(A \text{ and } B \text{ and } C) = P[(A \text{ and } B) \text{ and } C] = P(A \text{ and } B) \cdot P(C|A \text{ and } B)$$

(replacing A in the second formula of (13) by $(A$ and $B)$ and B by C)

$$= P(A) \cdot P(B|A) \cdot P(C|A \text{ and } B)$$

(by formula 13 again). Since the event $(A$ and B and $C)$ is the same for any interchange of the letters A, B, C, we see that $P(A$ and B and $C)$ may be evaluated in a total of six ways.

$$P(A \text{ and } B \text{ and } C) = \begin{array}{l} P(A) \cdot P(B|A) \cdot P(C|A \text{ and } B) \\ P(A) \cdot P(C|A) \cdot P(B|A \text{ and } C) \\ P(B) \cdot P(C|B) \cdot P(A|B \text{ and } C) \\ P(B) \cdot P(A|B) \cdot P(C|A \text{ and } B) \\ P(C) \cdot P(A|C) \cdot P(B|A \text{ and } C) \\ P(C) \cdot P(B|C) \cdot P(A|B \text{ and } C) \end{array}$$

The generalization to more than three events is now evident:

$$P(A_1 \text{ and } A_2 \text{ and } \cdots \text{ and } A_k)$$

$$= P(A_1) \cdot P(A_2|A_1) \cdots P(A_k|A_1 \text{ and } A_2 \text{ and } \cdots \text{ and } A_{k-1})$$

Example 20

A bowl contains five white and eight black chips. From it three chips are drawn successively at random, without replacement (this is called *sampling without replacement*). What is the probability that the first will be white and the second black and the third white? Define the events $A =$ first white, $B =$ second black, $C =$ third white. The desired probability is

$$P(A \text{ and } B \text{ and } C) = P(A) \cdot P(B|A) \cdot P(C|A \text{ and } B)$$

$$= \frac{5}{13} \cdot \frac{8}{12} \cdot \frac{4}{11} = \frac{160}{1716}$$

It is also true, for example, that

$$P(A \text{ and } B \text{ and } C) = P(B) \cdot P(C|B) \cdot P(A|B \text{ and } C)$$

but now the terms on the right hand side are much more difficult to compute, as the reader may verify.

PROBLEMS 2.6

1. Suppose that the probability of a person getting a cold in January is .10 and the probability of developing a sore throat given that the person has a cold is .40. Find the probability of getting both a cold and a sore throat.

2. If 42 percent of the students at a certain college work part-time and if 25 percent of the students who work part-time carry a reduced load of courses, what is the probability that a student will both work part-time and carry a reduced load of courses?

3. Two persons are chosen at random from a group of 20 students and five faculty members to form a subcommittee. What is the probability that both persons chosen are (a) students, (b) faculty members? (Hint: In (a), let A_1 be the event that the first member chosen is a student and A_2 the event that the second member chosen is a student. Use (13) to find $P(A_1$ and $A_2)$.)

4. If the U.S. Senate is composed of 60 Democrats and 40 Republicans, find the probability that a two-member committee chosen at random will consist of two (a) Republicans, (b) Democrats.

5. If two cards are chosen at random without replacement, find the probability that (a) both are hearts, (b) both are of the same suit.

6. A person takes two coins at random without replacement from a box containing five pennies, four nickels, and three dimes. Find the probability that
   a. both coins drawn are pennies.
   b. both coins drawn are dimes.
   c. both coins drawn have the same value.

2.7 Independent Events

Two events A, B sometimes have the property that $P(A) = P(A|B)$; *that is, the unconditional probability of* A *is equal to the conditional probability of* A, *given* B. In this case we say that A is *independent* of B. The condition $P(A) = P(A|B)$ reduces by (12) to $P(A) = P(A$ and $B)/P(B)$; that is, to $P(A$ and $B) = P(A) \cdot P(B)$. The latter equation would also be obtained if we had started by assuming that B is independent of A; in other words, that $P(B) = P(B|A)$. Thus A is independent of B if and only if B is independent of A, and the requirement for either is that $P(A$ and $B) = P(A) \cdot P(B)$. We therefore state

Definition 8

Two events A, B are *independent* if

$$P(A \text{ and } B) = P(A) \cdot P(B) \tag{14}$$

When this relation holds, $P(A) = P(A|B)$ and $P(B) = P(B|A)$. If (14) does not hold, A, B are said to be *dependent*, and for such events $P(A) \neq P(A|B)$ and $P(B) \neq P(B|A)$.

Intuitively, two events A, B are independent when the probability that one will occur is not affected by the occurrence or nonoccurrence of the other. The distinction between independence and dependence is illustrated by the two cases of sampling with and without replacement.

Example 21

We draw one card from a shuffled deck of 52 cards, return the card, reshuffle the deck, and draw a second card (sampling with replacement). Let A_1 be the event "an ace appears on the first draw" and A_2 the event "an ace appears on the second draw." Since there are $52 \cdot 52$ different and equally likely outcomes of the total experiment, of which $4 \cdot 4$ belong to the event (A_1 and A_2),

$$P(A_1 \text{ and } A_2) = \frac{4 \cdot 4}{52 \cdot 52} = \left(\frac{4}{52}\right)\left(\frac{4}{52}\right) = \frac{1}{169} = P(A_1) \cdot P(A_2)$$

so A_1, A_2 are independent in the sense of definition 8. This example shows that definition 8 reflects the intuitive sense of the word *independent*, because replacing the card and reshuffling the deck ensures that the outcome of the second draw will not be affected by the outcome of the first.

Example 22

We draw two cards at random from a deck of 52, without replacing the first card (sampling without replacement). The probability that both cards are aces in this case is by (13) for the dependent events A_1, A_2

$$P(A_1 \text{ and } A_2) = P(A_1)P(A_2|A_1)$$
$$= \frac{4}{52} \cdot \frac{3}{51} = \frac{1}{13} \cdot \frac{1}{17} = \frac{1}{221}$$

Comparing this result with that obtained in example 21, where $P(2 \text{ aces}) = 1/169$, we see that we are less likely to get two aces in sampling without replacement than with replacement.

When each element of a population from which we draw a sample may have one or both of two attributes A, B, the independence of A and B is a delicate matter, as is shown by the following example.

Example 23

A bowl contains 100 chips, of which 60 are black and 40 are white. Of the 100 chips, 70 bear the number 0, and 30 the number 1. Moreover, 42 of the chips are both black and numbered 0. For a chip chosen at random from this bowl, the probability that the chip will be both numbered 0 (event A) and black (event B) is

$$P(A \text{ and } B) = \frac{42}{100} = .42$$

Here

$$P(A) = \frac{70}{100} = .7$$

and

$$P(B) = \frac{60}{100} = .6$$

so that

$$P(A \text{ and } B) = .42 = (.7)(.6) = P(A) \cdot P(B) \quad \text{(See figure 2.6.)}$$

Hence A, B are independent events by definition 8, and $P(A|B) = P(A)$.

Now suppose we have a second bowl just like the first except that instead of 42, 48 of the chips are both black and numbered 0. Then $P(A \text{ and } B) = .48$, while $P(A) = .7$ and $P(B) = .6$ as before. Since $.48 \neq (.7)(.6)$, (14) no longer holds. In this case the events A, B are *dependent*; if we know that B has occurred, this changes our assessment of the probability of A. In fact,

$$P(A|B) = \frac{P(A \text{ and } B)}{P(B)} = \frac{.48}{.60} = .8$$

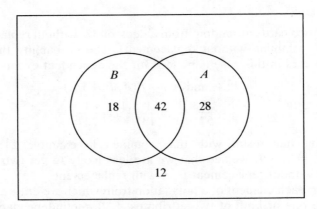

FIGURE 2.6
Bowl 1

The difference between the two bowls is that only for the first is the ratio

$$\frac{\#(A \text{ and } B)}{\#(B)} = \frac{42}{60} = \text{proportion of } black \text{ chips numbered 0}$$

equal to the ratio

$$\frac{\#(A)}{\#(I)} = \frac{70}{100} = \text{proportion of } all \text{ chips numbered 0}$$

so that restriction to the black chips does not alter the original proportion of chips numbered 0. (See figure 2.7.)

The following interpretation may make this example more meaningful:

> bowl = town;
> chip = adult inhabitant;
> event B = takes aspirin;
> event A = has frequent headaches.

If $P(A) < P(A|B)$ this suggests some causal connection between A and B, though not necessarily of the form "B tends to cause A."

Example 24
Suppose that four cards are drawn from a deck without replacement. What is the probability of getting four aces? Let A_1, A_2, A_3, and A_4 denote getting an ace on the first, second, third, and fourth draws, respectively. Then by the formula preceding example 20

$$P(A_1 \text{ and } A_2 \text{ and } A_3 \text{ and } A_4)$$

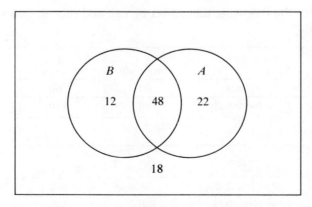

FIGURE 2.7
Bowl 2

$$= P(A_1)P(A_2|A_1)P(A_3|A_1 \text{ and } A_2)P(A_4|A_1 \text{ and } A_2 \text{ and } A_3)$$

so

$$P(4 \text{ aces}) = \frac{4}{52} \cdot \frac{3}{51} \cdot \frac{2}{50} \cdot \frac{1}{49} = \frac{1}{270{,}725}$$

Getting four aces in four draws is indeed a rare event.

Example 25

Suppose that there are n marksmen with the respective probabilities $p_1, \ldots, p_n$ of hitting the bullseye, and that the performance of each marksman is independent of that of the others. Then the probability $P(H)$ of the bullseye being hit (by at least one marksman) is

$$P(H) = 1 - P(H') = 1 - P(A_1' \text{ and } A_2' \text{ and } \ldots \text{ and } A_n')$$
$$= 1 - (1 - p_1)(1 - p_2) \ldots (1 - p_n)$$

For example, if each $p_i = .7$ and $n = 5$, then $P(H) = 1 - (.3)^5 = .99757$. (Compare with example 12.)

PROBLEMS 2.7

1. In which of the following cases are the two events independent?
   a. Head on first toss and head on second toss, in two tosses of a coin.
   b. Face card on first draw and face card on second draw, when two cards are drawn at random with replacement.
   c. The same as in (b) but without replacement.

2. Consider the following tabulation by age and race in two precincts of a city.

Race \ Age	A Under 30	A' 30 or over
B = Black	50	60
B' = Nonblack	100	120

Precinct 1

Race \ Age	A Under 30	A' 30 or over
B = Black	40	60
B' = Nonblack	90	140

Precinct 2

For each precinct find $P(A)$, $P(B)$, and $P(A$ and $B)$. Are A and B independent in both precincts?

3. Do problem 5, section 2.6, with replacement of the first card before the second is chosen. Does (14) hold for what happens on the two draws?

4. Do problem 6, section 2.6, with replacement of the first coin before the second is chosen. Does (14) hold for what happens on the two draws?

2.8 Bayes's Theorem

If A, B are any two events in an outcome space I, then by (12) and (13)

$$P(A|B) = \frac{P(A \text{ and } B)}{P(B)} = \frac{P(A)P(B|A)}{P(B)} \tag{15}$$

By (9) and (13) the denominator $P(B)$ is equal to

$$P(B) = P(B \text{ and } A) + P(B \text{ and } A') = P(A)P(B|A) + P(A')P(B|A') \tag{16}$$

Hence

$$P(A|B) = \frac{P(A)P(B|A)}{P(A)P(B|A) + P(A')P(B|A')} \tag{17}$$

This formula is often useful in applications when all the terms on the right-hand side are known and the left-hand side is the quantity of interest. (It is a special case of Bayes's Theorem, formula 24 below.)

As a simple example of the use of formulas 16 and 17 suppose that in a group of 1000 people 60 percent are women (A), 40 percent are men (A'), and B denotes the property of having blue eyes. If we know that $P(B|A) = .35$ (35 percent of the women are blue-eyed) and $P(B|A') = .55$ (55 percent of the men are blue-eyed), then by (15)

$$P(B) = (.60)(.35) + (.40)(.55) = .43$$

By (17)

$$P(A|B) = \frac{(.60)(.35)}{.43} = \frac{.21}{.43} \cong .49$$

so that approximately 49 percent of those in the group having blue eyes are women. (See figure 2.8.)

Example 26
A simple and quick diagnostic test for diabetes registers either "positive" or "negative." From past experience it is known that (a) if the

subject has diabetes, the test will register "negative" with probability .10, whereas (b) if the subject is free from diabetes, the test will register "positive" with probability .05.

Thus the test is subject to the two *error probabilities*:

$p_1 = P(\text{test negative}|\text{diabetes present}) = .10$

    $= \text{probability of a "false negative"}$

$p_2 = P(\text{test positive}|\text{diabetes absent}) = .05$

    $= \text{probability of a "false positive"}$

Suppose that in a given population of individuals the incidence of diabetes is 6 percent. A person is selected at random from this population and tested.

a. What is the probability that the test will be positive?
b. Given that the test is positive, what is the probability that the person has diabetes?

Answers
a. Let A = diabetes present, A' = diabetes absent, and B = test positive. Then by (16)

$$P(B) = P(A) \cdot P(B|A) + P(A') \cdot P(B|A')$$
$$= (.06)(.90) + (.94)(.05) = .054 + .047 = .101$$

b. By (15) $P(\text{diabetes present}|\text{test positive})$

$$= P(A|B) = \frac{P(A) \cdot P(B|A)}{P(B)} = \frac{.054}{.101} \cong .535$$

Thus, there is an approximately 53 percent chance that a person who tests positive, will in fact have diabetes.

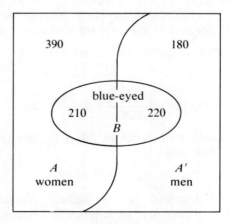

FIGURE 2.8

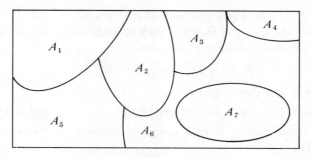

FIGURE 2.9
A partition of *I* into seven events

We shall now give a more general form of relations (16) and (17).

Definition 9

A *partition* of the outcome space *I* of an experiment is any collection of events $[A_1, A_2, \ldots, A_r]$ in which each individual outcome of *I* belongs to one and only one of the events $A_1, \ldots, A_r$; that is, in which the events $A_1, A_2, \ldots, A_r$ are *jointly exhaustive*

$$(A_1 \text{ or } A_2 \text{ or } \ldots A_r) = I \tag{18}$$

and *mutually exclusive*

$$(A_i \text{ and } A_j) = \emptyset \text{ for every } i \neq j \tag{19}$$

Note that if *A* is any event, then $[A, A']$ forms a partition of *I*. Likewise, if *A*, *B* are any two events, then $[(A \text{ and } B), (A \text{ and } B'), (A' \text{ and } B), (A' \text{ and } B')]$ forms a partition of *I*. (See figure 2.9.)

Example 27

Two dice are thrown and A_i denotes the event "the sum $= i$." Then $[A_2, A_3, \ldots, A_{12}]$ forms a partition of *I*.

Example 28

An experiment consists of choosing a person at random from a given group of individuals *I* categorized into 10 mutually exclusive and jointly exhaustive age groups (where $x =$ age of person chosen):

$$A_1 = \{0 \leq x < 10\}$$
$$A_2 = \{10 \leq x < 20\}$$
$$\vdots$$
$$A_9 = \{80 \leq x < 90\}$$
$$A_{10} = \{x \geq 90\}$$

Then $[A_1, \ldots, A_{10}]$ is a partition of I.

From (18) and (19) together with the addition property of probability (7) we see that for any partition $[A_1, \ldots, A_r]$

$$P(A_1) + P(A_2) + \ldots + P(A_r) = 1 \tag{20}$$

Also, if B is any event, then since

$$B = [(B \text{ and } A_1) \text{ or } (B \text{ and } A_2) \text{ or } \ldots \text{ or } (B \text{ and } A_r)]$$

is a representation of B as a union of *mutually exclusive* events, it follows that

$$P(B) = P(B \text{ and } A_1) + P(B \text{ and } A_2) + \ldots + P(B \text{ and } A_r) \tag{21}$$

(Formula 20 is the special case $B = I$.) From (21), using the fact from (13) that

$$P(B \text{ and } A_i) = P(A_i) \cdot P(B|A_i)$$

we have the generalization of (16) given by

$$P(B) = P(A_1) \cdot P(B|A_1) + \ldots + P(A_r) \cdot P(B|A_r) \tag{22}$$

for any event B and any partition $[A_1, \ldots, A_r]$ of I. The relation (22) is useful in practice when each term on the right-hand side is known and $P(B)$ is to be computed.

For an arbitrary partition $[A_1, \ldots, A_r]$ and any event B, since

$$P(A_i|B) = \frac{P(A_i \text{ and } B)}{P(B)} = \frac{P(A_i)P(B|A_i)}{P(B)} \tag{23}$$

we have from (22) that for each $i = 1, \ldots, r$

$$P(A_i|B) = \frac{P(A_i)P(B|A_i)}{P(A_1)P(B|A_1) + \ldots + P(A_r)P(B|A_r)} \tag{24}$$

This is a generalization of (17), in which the partition is $[A, A']$.

The relation (24), *Bayes's Theorem*, shows how the *unconditional* probabilities $P(A_i)$ of the events of any partition $[A_1, \ldots, A_r]$ are changed into *conditional* probabilities $P(A_i|B)$ once the additional information is available that an event B has occurred. Bayes's Theorem is the basis of statistical decision theory in some situations, as we shall see in the next section. Here we give a simple example of its use.

Example 29

Let D, R, and In represent the events that a voter chosen at random is a Democrat, Republican, or Independent, with $P(D) = .40$, $P(R) = .25$, and $P(In) = .35$. (We assume that $[D, R, In]$ constitutes a partition of the outcome space.) Let B be the event that a voter answers Yes to the question "Do you approve of how the (Republican) President is doing his job?" Suppose that 15 percent of the Democrats, 80 percent of the Republicans, and 40 percent of the Independents do approve. If a voter chosen at random answers Yes to the above question, what are the respective conditional probabilities of the voter's being a Democrat, Republican, or Independent? By (24)

$$P(D|B) = \frac{P(D) \cdot P(B|D)}{P(D) \cdot P(B|D) + P(R) \cdot P(B|R) + P(In) \cdot P(B|In)}$$

$$= \frac{(.40)(.15)}{(.40)(.15) + (.25)(.80) + (.35)(.40)}$$

$$= \frac{.06}{.06 + .20 + .14} = .15$$

Similarly

$$P(R|B) = \frac{.20}{.06 + .20 + .14} = .50 \qquad \text{and}$$

$$P(In|B) = \frac{.14}{.06 + .20 + .14} = .35$$

A comparison of the unconditional and conditional probabilities is shown below.

Probability of voter being a	Democrat	Republican	Independent	Total probability
Before answering	.40	.25	.35	1.00
After answering Yes	.15	.50	.35	1.00

PROBLEMS 2.8

1. Two coins are tossed, and A_i denotes the event "i heads appear in the two tosses," $i = 0, 1, 2$. Show that $[A_0, A_1, A_2]$ is a three-element partition of the outcome space. Find $P(A_i)$, $i = 0, 1, 2$, and show that $P(A_0) + P(A_1) + P(A_2) = 1$.

2. If a card is drawn at random from a deck of 52, and H, D, C, S represent the events that the card drawn is a heart, diamond, club, or spade, respectively, show that $[H, D, C, S]$ is a four-element partition of the outcome space. Find $P(H), P(D), P(C),$ and $P(S)$ and verify that (20) holds.

3. Suppose that in a group of people, 30 percent have blond hair (A_1), 45 percent have brown hair (A_2), and 25 percent have black hair (A_3). Let B denote the property of having brown eyes. If $P(B|A_1) = .30$ (30 percent of blond-haired people have brown eyes),

$P(B|A_2) = .50$, and $P(B|A_3) = .70$, find $P(B)$. Use Bayes's formula to find $P(A_i|B)$, $i = 1, 2, 3$.

4. Suppose that in a group of persons, 20 percent are heavy smokers (A_1), 35 percent are light smokers (A_2), and 45 percent are non-smokers (A_3). Let B be the property that a person in this group has high blood pressure. If $P(B|A_1) = .4$, $P(B|A_2) = .3$, and $P(B|A_3) = .2$, find $P(B)$. Use Bayes's formula to find $P(A_i|B)$, $i = 1, 2, 3$.

5. The following table gives data for a group of students (1) by class and (2) by response to the question "Do you feel that most of your college courses are relevant to your needs?"

Answer \ Class	Freshman	Sophomore	Junior	Senior
Yes	96	105	116	130
No	102	99	104	71
Don't know	117	62	43	32

Using these data, find the following probabilities for students in this group.

a. being a freshman, given that the student answers Yes. The same for sophomore, junior, and senior.

b. being a freshman, given that the student answers Don't Know. The same for sophomore, junior, and senior.

6. Consider the following tabulation of a group of adults by age and income in a certain city.

Age \ Income	Under $7000	$7000 to $12,000	Over $12,000
18–30	82	140	63
31–50	107	268	174
Over 50	73	182	157

Using these data, find the probabilities of

a. Income under $7,000, given that the person is in the 18–30 age group. The same for the other two income groups.

b. Income over $12,000, given that the person is in the over-50 age group. The same for the other two income groups.

7. Suppose that a person is presented with one of two jars selected at random, and then draws two balls at random from that jar. If jar 1 has five black balls and two white balls and jar 2 has two black balls and five white balls, find the probability that

a. the two balls came from jar 1, given that both are black.
b. the two balls came from jar 2, given that both are black.

8. Suppose that you are given two dice, one of which is a standard die and one of which has ones on all six sides. You are blindfolded, asked to pick one die at random, and toss it twice. Both tosses are ones; find

a. the conditional probability that the die was the standard die.
b. the conditional probability that the die had all ones.

2.9 Two Examples of Probability in Decision Making

Example 30
A manufacturer wishes to ascertain whether a newly developed product will be preferred to the old product already on the market. The new product is tested by asking a randomly chosen sample of eight users to try each of the two products for a week and then express a preference. Suppose all eight prefer the new product. How strong is this evidence for a general preference for the new product? Denote by p the unknown proportion of users in the general population who would prefer the new product. Let A_i be the event "user i prefers the new product," $i = 1, 2, \ldots, 8$; then the event $A = (A_1$ and $\ldots$ and $A_8)$ is the event that "all eight users prefer the new product." Assume that the events A_i are independent of each other. (This will be the case if the population from which the sample of eight was chosen is so large that the removal of any seven persons does not appreciably affect the proportion preferring the new product, and if the persons in the sample are not influenced by each other.) Then

$$P(A) = P(A_1 \text{ and } \ldots \text{ and } A_8) = P(A_1) \ldots P(A_8) = p^8$$

which equals $1/2^8 = 1/256$ when $p = 1/2$, and is even less when $p < 1/2$.

Based on this evidence the manufacturer might reasonably decide that the new product is generally preferred to the old one (that is, that $p > 1/2$), *since the chance of observing a unanimous preference for the new product when in fact they are equally preferred is only 1 in 256, and is even less when the old product is preferred to the new one.*

Example 31
Suppose that a woman names a certain man as the father of her child. He denies paternity, and is required to take a blood test. Assume that the child has a blood type that is not shared by his mother, and could

only come from his father. Then if the man does not have the type in question he is definitely not the father, while if he does have the type the probability of his being the father is increased, although the contrary possibility is not excluded. We shall show how to estimate the probability p that the woman's assertion of the man's paternity is true, even though at first this might seem to be an impossible task.

Let the blood type in question be called T, with a known relative frequency f_T of occurrence in the population. Consider the group of all alleged fathers who have taken a blood test in similar cases when the child has blood type T and the mother does not. Then by (16), letting A = mother's assertion is true, A' = mother's assertion is false, B = alleged father has blood type T

$$P(B) = P(\text{alleged father has blood type } T) \tag{25}$$
$$= P(A) \cdot P(B|A) + P(A') \cdot P(B|A')$$
$$= p \cdot 1 + (1 - p) \cdot f_T$$

This follows since, if the mother's assertion is true, the alleged father must have blood type T, whereas if the mother's assertion is false, his chance of having type T will (presumably) be the same as the frequency f_T of blood type T in the population. Solving (25) for p we find that

$$p = \frac{P(\text{alleged father has blood type } T) - f_T}{1 - f_T} \tag{26}$$

Now f_T is known from population statistics, while the term P(alleged father has blood type T) can be estimated by the relative frequency in which alleged fathers have been found to have blood type T in such cases over a number of years. Hence p can be estimated.

Knowing p, the unconditional or *prior* probability of paternity before the man's blood type is known, we can now compute the conditional or *posterior* probability of paternity, given that an alleged father's blood is of type T, by (17). The result is

$$P(A|B) = \frac{P(A)P(B|A)}{P(A)P(B|A) + P(A')P(B|A')} = \frac{p \cdot 1}{p \cdot 1 + (1 - p) \cdot f_T}$$

Since $0 < f_T < 1$, the denominator is always less than $p + (1 - p) = 1$, so the last fraction is greater than p. For example, if T is a blood type for which $f_T = .2$, and if $p = .7$, then the posterior probability of paternity for the alleged father of a child of blood type T when the mother is not of type T is

$$0 \quad \text{if the alleged father's blood type is not } T$$

$$\frac{.7}{.7 + (.3)(.2)} = \frac{70}{76} \cong .92 \quad \text{if his blood type is } T$$

PROBLEMS 2.9

1. Would you believe that a coin is fair if five tosses all result in heads? (Hint: Compute the probability of five heads in five tosses of a fair coin.) What if there are 10 heads in 10 tosses?

2. Suppose that you are presented with a jar and told that it contains 20 black balls and three white balls. You are allowed to draw two balls at random without replacement. What might you conclude if both balls are white? (Hint: Compute the probability of getting this result.) What would you conclude if in three draws you get three white balls?

3. A certain disease is present in 5 percent of the persons screened by a clinic. If a person has the disease, the screening test is positive with a probability of .95; and if the person does not have the disease the screening test is positive with a probability of .10 (that is, there is a 10 percent chance of a false positive on the test). Suppose that a person has a positive screening test. What is the probability that he or she has the disease?

4. Suppose that 40 percent of the students at a certain college are women. Seventy percent of the women feel discriminated against at this college, and 30 percent of the men feel that women are discriminated against. Find the probability that a person who feels that women are discriminated against is a woman.

Random Variables

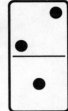

3 Random Variables

The results of experiments are usually recorded in numerical form. For example: in drug testing the experimenter may record the *number of patients whose symptoms are relieved*; in agricultural experiments, the *yield per acre*; and in studies of cloud seeding, the *amount of precipitation*. These numbers are the result of experiments, and can be thought of as numerical outcomes, or numerical values associated with outcomes. In chapter 2 we studied the probabilities of outcomes or events in general, whether numerical in nature or not. In this chapter we shall see that the behavior of a numerical outcome, or *random variable*, is summarized by what is called its *probability distribution*, two important characteristics of which are the *mean* and the *variance*.

3.1 Random Variables

Definition 1
Let $I = \{a_1, a_2, \ldots\}$ be the outcome space of an experiment, and let the symbol x denote any specific rule that assigns a definite *number* $x(a)$ to each element a of I. Then x is called a *random variable associated with the experiment*.

Example 1
If a family with three children is selected at random from a group of such families, *the number of male children* among the three is a random variable that can take any of the possible values 0, 1, 2, and 3, depending on the particular family chosen. The outcome space

$$I = \{MMM, MMF, MFM, FMM, MFF, FMF, FFM, FFF\} \quad (1)$$

has $2 \cdot 2 \cdot 2 = 2^3 = 8$ elements, where the successive letters M and F indicate whether the first, second, or third child is male or female. If a denotes any of the eight outcomes listed in (1) we may define $x = x(a)$ as the number of male children associated with that outcome. Thus, $x(MMM) = 3$, $x(MMF) = x(MFM) = x(FMM) = 2$, $x(MFF) = x(FMF) = x(FMF) = x(FFM) = 1$, and $x(FFF) = 0$. Here x is a random variable with the four numerical values 0, 1, 2, 3.

Example 2
One member of a class of 30 students is chosen at random. The outcome space consists of the 30 students, denoted by $a_1, \ldots, a_{30}$. Let $y(a)$ be the random variable which assigns to each student a his or her GPA. For example, if student a_1 has a GPA of 3.41, student a_2 a GPA of 2.68, then $y(a_1) = 3.41$, $y(a_2) = 2.68$. Here y is a random variable with values lying within the interval $0 \leq y \leq 4$.

Random variables $x, y, \ldots$ are used to record numerically any relevant aspects of the outcome of an experiment. In example 1, if only the *number* of each sex is of interest, and not the *order* of sex by birth, then $x(a)$ records that aspect of the outcome a which is of interest. In example 2, only the GPA y of the student chosen may be of interest, not what courses he took, and so on.

These examples illustrate two different types of random variables that occur in practice. In example 1, x can assume any one of the finite set of values (0, 1, 2, 3). In example 2, y can take on, in principle, any one of the infinitely many numerical values between and including 0 and 4.

Definition 2
A random variable that can take on only a *finite* number of distinct values is called a *discrete random variable*. A random variable that can take on *any value within some interval of numbers* is called a *continuous random variable*.

Example 3
A coin is tossed until heads appears for the first time, or until 100 consecutive tails appear. The number of tosses needed is indicated

by x. Because the only possible values of x are 1, 2, 3, . . . , 100, x is a *discrete random variable*.

Example 4
An experiment consists of recording the random variable y, the weight in pounds of a person chosen at random from some population of adults. The value of y can in principle be any positive number, such as 162.38. (In reality, the practical range of y is from, say, 20 lbs. to perhaps 500 lbs.) Here y is a *continuous random variable* if weights can be measured with complete accuracy.

PROBLEMS 3.1

1. Identify each of the following random variables as discrete or continuous. Give the possible values of the random variables.
    a. The sum in tossing two dice.
    b. The grade point average of a student.
    c. The weight loss of a mouse on an experimental drug.
    d. The number of defective parts in a batch of 1000.
    e. The number of people answering Yes to a given question in a survey of 1500 people.

2. Identify each of the following random variables as discrete or continuous. Give the possible values.
    a. The number of bacterial colonies on a petri plate.
    b. The income of a person in a survey.
    c. The time involved for a monkey to do a given task in a psychological experiment.
    d. The number of auto licenses issued in a certain day in Illinois.
    e. The tensile strength of a newly developed alloy.

3. In a sample of 40 college students, the question is asked, "Do you feel that professors are generally good teachers?" The possible answers are Yes and No, and $x =$ number of Yes answers. What are the possible values of the random variable x? What kind of random variable is x?

4. Let $x =$ height of a person chosen at random from a certain population. What are the possible values of x? What kind of random variable is x?

5. Suppose a family selected at random has four members, and $x =$ the number of members having a cold. List the outcomes a in the outcome space and write $x(a)$ for each outcome a in the outcome space. Write each of the events $\{x=0\}$, $\{x=1\}$, etc., as a set of outcomes in this space.

6. In a survey of two households, the number of cars owned per household is recorded. With 0, 1, 2, 3 as the only possible numerical outcomes per household, and with $x_1 =$ number of cars in the first household surveyed, and $x_2 =$ number of cars in the second household surveyed, list the possible outcomes of this survey if the outcome space consists of the sum of the possible pairs of values for these two households. In other words, $x = x_1 + x_2$, the sum of cars for the two households.

3.2 The Probability Distribution of a Discrete Random Variable

In example 1 we may think of $\{x = 0\}$, $\{x = 1\}$, $\{x = 2\}$, and $\{x = 3\}$ as events in the outcome space (1) of the experiment. For example, $\{x = 1\}$ comprises the three outcomes MFF, FMF, FFM. As such, the event $\{x = 1\}$ has a *probability* attached to it, the probability of the event {MFF, FMF, FFM}. Suppose that male and female children are equally likely, and that the sexes of the children are independent of each other. Then the eight outcomes listed in (1) are equally likely, and hence the event $\{x = 1\}$, comprising three such outcomes, has the probability $p_1 = P\{x = 1\} = 3/8$. Similarly, $p_0 = P\{x = 0\} = 1/8$, $p_2 = P\{x = 2\} = 3/8$, $p_3 = P\{x = 3\} = 1/8$. The list of all the different *values* of the discrete random variable x, together with their associated *probabilities*, is called the *probability distribution of* x. (See figure 3.1.)

Definition 3
Let x be a discrete random variable defined on an outcome space I, and let the possible values of x be $b_1, \ldots, b_k$, with the corresponding probabilities $p_1 = P\{x = b_1\}, \ldots, p_k = P\{x = b_k\}$, summing to 1. Then the *probability distribution* of x is given by the table

$$x: \quad \begin{array}{c|c|c|c|c|c|c} \text{Prob.} & p_1 & p_2 & \ldots & p_i & \ldots & p_k \\ \hline \text{Value} & b_1 & b_2 & \ldots & b_i & \ldots & b_k \end{array} \qquad (2)$$

Passing from the underlying outcome space I of the experiment and the individual probabilities of the various outcomes, to the probability distribution (2) of some random variable x associated with the experiment, we abstract from all details of the experiment other than the different values b_i that x takes on and the respective probabilities p_i associated with these values. For example, if we choose at random one person from any specified population I, and if x denotes that person's age to the nearest year (with $x = 100$ if the person's age exceeds 100), then the probability distribution (2) of x is displayed by the table

$$x: \frac{\text{Prob.}}{\text{Value}} \begin{array}{||c|c|c|c|c|c|c||} p_0 & p_1 & \ldots & p_i & \ldots & p_{100} \\ 0 & 1 & \ldots & i & \ldots & 100 \end{array}$$

where $p_i = $ (number of people in I with $x = i$)/(total number of people in I), and $p_0 + p_1 + \ldots + p_{100} = 1$

Example 5

A fair die is rolled, and $x = $ the number obtained. The probability distribution of x is

$$x: \frac{\text{Prob.}}{\text{Value}} \begin{array}{||c|c|c|c|c|c||} \frac{1}{6} & \frac{1}{6} & \frac{1}{6} & \frac{1}{6} & \frac{1}{6} & \frac{1}{6} \\ 1 & 2 & 3 & 4 & 5 & 6 \end{array}$$

First child	Second child	Third child	x = no. of males	Probability of x
M	M	M	3	$\frac{1}{8}$
		F	2	$\frac{1}{8}$
	F	M	2	$\frac{1}{8}$
		F	1	$\frac{1}{8}$
F	M	M	2	$\frac{1}{8}$
		F	1	$\frac{1}{8}$
	F	M	1	$\frac{1}{8}$
		F	0	$\frac{1}{8}$

$P\{x = 3\} = \frac{1}{8}$

$P\{x = 2\} = \frac{3}{8}$

$P\{x = 1\} = \frac{3}{8}$

$P\{x = 0\} = \frac{1}{8}$

The probability distribution of x				
Probability	$\frac{1}{8}$	$\frac{3}{8}$	$\frac{3}{8}$	$\frac{3}{8}$
Value	0	1	2	3

FIGURE 3.1

The random variable x of example 1 and its probability distribution

Example 6

Two fair dice are rolled, and $x =$ the sum of the two numbers. Here x has the possible values 2, 3, . . . , 12. Since $\{x=2\} = \{(1, 1)\}$, $\{x=3\} = \{(1, 2), (2, 1)\}, \ldots, \{x = 12\} = \{(6, 6)\}$, the probability distribution of x is

x:

Prob.	$\frac{1}{36}$	$\frac{2}{36}$	$\frac{3}{36}$	$\frac{4}{36}$	$\frac{5}{36}$	$\frac{6}{36}$	$\frac{5}{36}$	$\frac{4}{36}$	$\frac{3}{36}$	$\frac{2}{36}$	$\frac{1}{36}$
Value	2	3	4	5	6	7	8	9	10	11	12

Example 7

A fair coin is tossed twice, and $x =$ the number of heads obtained. Then x has the probability distribution

x:

Prob.	$\frac{1}{4}$	$\frac{1}{2}$	$\frac{1}{4}$
Value	0	1	2

PROBLEMS 3.2

1. A fair coin is tossed once, and $x =$ number of heads in the single toss. Find the probability distribution of x.

2. A card is drawn at random from a deck of 52 cards, and $x =$ number on the card (ace counts 1, face card counts 10). Find the probability distribution of x.

3. A jar contains five balls, three numbered with a 1, one numbered with a 2, and one numbered with a 3. If one ball is chosen at random from this jar, and $x =$ the number on the ball, find the probability distribution of x.

4. A die is labeled with a one on one side, a two on two sides, and a three on three sides. If $x =$ the number that appears on the die, give the probability distribution of x.

5. The following table gives the ages of the students in a certain high school:

Age	14	15	16	17	18	19
No. of students	60	100	130	120	70	20

If $x =$ age of a student chosen at random from this high school, find the probability distribution of x.

6. An insurance company has its clerical employees grouped by years of college education.

Years of college	0	1	2	3	4
No. of employees	80	30	20	10	60

If x = number of years of college education of a person chosen at random from these employees, find the probability distribution of x.

7. If, in problem 3, two balls are chosen with replacement, find the probability distribution of x = sum of the two balls chosen.

8. If the die in problem 4 is tossed twice, find the probability distribution of x = sum of the numbers in the two tosses.

9. In each of the following distributions find the missing probability.

   a. x:

Prob.	$\frac{1}{2}$	$\frac{1}{3}$	?
Value	0	1	2

   b. x:

Prob.	$\frac{1}{8}$	$\frac{1}{4}$	?	$\frac{1}{4}$
Value	1	2	3	4

   c. x:

Prob.	.3	.1	?
Value	-1	0	1

10. Explain why each of the following cannot represent a probability distribution.

   a. x:

Prob.	$\frac{1}{4}$	$-\frac{1}{4}$	$\frac{1}{4}$
Value	0	1	2

   b. x:

Prob.	.1	.1	.4	.5	.1
Value	1	2	3	4	5

   c. x:

Prob.	.1	-.3	.6	.6
Value	0	1	2	3

3.3 The Mean Value of a Discrete Random Variable

The mean value of a random variable x is a number that in a sense locates a "central value" of the probability distribution of x. Let x be any discrete random variable associated with some experiment, taking on values $b_1, \ldots, b_k$ with respective probabilities $p_1, \ldots, p_k$ summing to 1, and having the probability distribution (2).

Definition 4
The *mean value* μ_x of the random variable x is the number

$$\mu_x = b_1 \cdot p_1 + \ldots + b_k \cdot p_k \qquad (3)$$

obtained by multiplying each value that x can take on by its associated probability, and summing over all such values. (The symbol μ_x is read "mu sub x.") Instead of writing μ_x we shall for typographical reasons sometimes write m.v. (x) to denote the mean value of a random variable x.

The random variable x of example 1 has the mean value m.v. $(x) = \mu_x = 0 \cdot 1/8 + 1 \cdot 3/8 + 2 \cdot 3/8 + 3 \cdot 1/8 = 12/8 = 1.5$. The x in example 5 has the mean value $m.v.(x) = \mu_x = 1 \cdot 1/6 + 2 \cdot 1/6 + 3 \cdot 1/6 + 4 \cdot 1/6 + 5 \cdot 1/6 + 6 \cdot 1/6 = 21/6 = 3.5$. The x of example 6 has the mean value $m.v.(x) = \mu_x = 2 \cdot 1/36 + 3 \cdot 2/36 + 4 \cdot 3/36 + \ldots + 12 \cdot 1/36 = 252/36 = 7$. We note from these examples that the mean value μ_x may or may not be one of the possible values that x can assume.

Example 8
In three tosses of a fair coin, let x = the total number of heads. The probability distribution of x is the same as that for x in example 1, so $\mu_x = 1.5$.

Example 9
Two cards are drawn without replacement from a shuffled pack of five red cards and three black cards, and x = the number of red cards drawn. The possible values of x are 0, 1, 2. The probability distribution and mean value of x are obtained below.

First draw	Second draw	Number of red cards (x)	Probability of x
R	R	2	$\frac{5}{8} \cdot \frac{4}{7} = \frac{20}{56}$
	B	1	$\frac{5}{8} \cdot \frac{3}{7} = \frac{15}{56}$
B	R	1	$\frac{3}{8} \cdot \frac{5}{7} = \frac{15}{56}$
	B	0	$\frac{3}{8} \cdot \frac{2}{7} = \frac{6}{56}$

$$\mu_x = \frac{0 \cdot 6 + 1 \cdot 15 + 1 \cdot 15 + 2 \cdot 20}{56} = \frac{70}{56} = 1.25$$

We shall now indicate why the value μ_x defined by (3) is in fact a reasonable way of assigning a "central value" to the probability distribution (2) of x. Suppose that the probabilities $p_1, \ldots, p_k$, which can be any positive numbers summing to 1, are of the form

$$p_1 = \frac{m_1}{N}, p_2 = \frac{m_2}{N}, \ldots, p_k = \frac{m_k}{N}$$

where N is some (possibly very large) positive integer and m_1, m_2, $\ldots, m_k$ are positive integers that together sum to N. We place in a bowl N chips so that

m_1 chips are labeled with the number b_1 (4)
m_2 chips are labeled with the number b_2
   ⋮
m_k chips are labeled with the number b_k

If we now draw at random one chip from this bowl and let x denote the number on it, then x will be a random variable with the given probability distribution (2). Moreover, the *average value* of x (i.e., the arithmetic mean of the numbers on the N chips in the bowl) is

$$\frac{m_1 b_1 + m_2 b_2 + \ldots + m_k b_k}{N} = b_1 \cdot p_1 + \ldots + b_k \cdot p_k = \mu_x$$

since m_1 of the chips bear the number b_1, m_2 bear the number b_2, and so forth.

In this manner, starting with any experiment in which we are concerned with a discrete random variable x, we can construct a bowl model in which the value of x is represented by the number on a chip randomly drawn from a bowl of proper composition; the mean value μ_x of the random variable x is then the ordinary average of all the numbers on the chips in the bowl. If the numbers on the chips represent prizes in a lottery, then the "fair" price to pay for the privilege of drawing one chip at random (that is, of making one observation of the random variable x) is μ_x, the average value of the equally likely prizes.

We conclude this section by stating three simple and useful facts about mean values.

1. If c is any constant, then by assigning to each outcome of an experiment the fixed numerical value c we define a "degenerate" random variable with probability distribution concentrated at the single value c.

$$c: \quad \frac{\text{Prob.} \;\|\; 1}{\text{Value} \;\|\; c}$$

The mean value of c is by (3) $\mu_c = c \cdot 1 = c$, as common sense would indicate. Thus, *for any constant* c, *the mean value of* c *is just* c *itself*,

$$\mu_c = c \tag{5}$$

In terms of the bowl model, if all the chips in the bowl are labeled with the value c, then the average of these values is likewise c.

2. If c is any constant and x is a random variable with probability distribution (2), then by assigning to each outcome of the experiment the new value $x + c$ we obtain a random variable with the following probability distribution.

$$x + c: \quad \begin{array}{c|c|c|c|c} \text{Prob.} & p_1 & p_2 & \ldots & p_k \\ \hline \text{Value} & b_1 + c & b_2 + c & \ldots & b_k + c \end{array} \tag{6}$$

Its mean value by (3) is therefore

$$\mu_{x+c} = (b_1 + c) \cdot p_1 + \ldots + (b_k + c) \cdot p_k$$
$$= (b_1 \cdot p_1 + \ldots + b_k \cdot p_k) + c(p_1 + \ldots + p_k) = \mu_x + c$$

since $p_1 + \ldots + p_k = 1$. Thus, *for any constant* c, *the mean value of the random variable* x + c *is equal to the mean value of* x *plus the constant* c,

$$\mu_{x+c} = \mu_x + c \tag{7}$$

In terms of the bowl model, adding the same number c to the value on each chip increases the average of these values by c.

3. If c is any constant and x a random variable with probability distribution (2), then cx is also a random variable, with probability distribution.

$$cx: \quad \begin{array}{c|c|c|c|c} \text{Prob.} & p_1 & p_2 & \ldots & p_k \\ \hline \text{Value} & cb_1 & cb_2 & \ldots & cb_k \end{array} \tag{8}$$

and mean value

$$\mu_{cx} = cb_1 \cdot p_1 + \ldots + cb_k \cdot p_k = c(b_1 \cdot p_1 + \ldots + b_k \cdot p_k) = c\mu_x$$

Thus, *for any constant* c, *the mean value of* cx *is equal to* c *times the mean value of* x,

$$\mu_{cx} = c\mu_x \tag{9}$$

The bowl interpretation of this formula is similar to that described in number 2 above, since multiplying the value on each chip by c multiplies the average of these values by c.

PROBLEMS 3.3

1 – 6. Find the mean value of x for problems 1–6 in section 3.2.

7. In problem 7, section 3.2, find the *m.v.* of x and $y = 3x + 2$.

8. In problem 8, section 3.2, find the *m.v.* of x and $y = 2x - 4$.

3.4 The Variance of a Discrete Random Variable

The mean value μ_x of a random variable gives some information about the probability distribution of x, but no idea of how distant the various values of x lie from the "central value" μ_x. For example, if each student brings to a class exactly three books, then the mean number of books brought by a randomly selected student is 3, with no variation. In another class, however, the mean might also be 3 but with some students bringing none, some one, and so forth. To measure the amount of dispersion of the values of a random variable x about its mean value μ_x we introduce

Definition 5
The *variance* σ_x^2 of a random variable x is the number

$$\sigma_x^2 = (b_1 - \mu_x)^2 \cdot p_1 + (b_2 - \mu_x)^2 \cdot p_2 + \ldots + (b_k - \mu_x)^2 \cdot p_k \quad (10)$$

obtained by subtracting μ_x from each value of x, *squaring the difference, multiplying that figure by its corresponding probability, and, finally, summing all such products.* (The symbol σ_x^2 is read "sigma squared sub x.") Instead of writing σ_x^2 we shall for typographical reasons sometimes write $var(x)$ to denote the variance of a random variable x.

The variance of x is, in fact, simply the mean value of the random variable $(x - \mu_x)^2$, the squared distance of x from μ_x. This is seen by applying formula 3, since the random variable $(x - \mu_x)^2$ has the probability distribution

$$(x - \mu_x)^2 : \frac{\text{Prob.}}{\text{Value}} \left\|\begin{array}{c} p_1 \\ (b_1 - \mu_x)^2 \end{array}\right. \left|\begin{array}{c} \cdots \\ \cdots \end{array}\right| \left.\begin{array}{c} p_k \\ (b_k - \mu_x)^2 \end{array}\right. \quad (11)$$

Thus we can write

$$var(x) = \sigma_x^2 = m.v. \; [(x - \mu_x)^2]$$

If we expand each of the terms on the right-hand side of (10)

$$(b_i - \mu_x)^2 \cdot p_i = b_i^2 p_i - 2\mu_x b_i p_i + (\mu_x)^2 p_i$$

and carry out the summation over i, we obtain from the definition (3) of μ_x and the fact that the p's sum to 1 the useful relation

$$\sigma_x^2 = b_1^2 \cdot p_1 + \ldots + b_k^2 \cdot p_k - 2\mu_x \cdot \mu_x + (\mu_x)^2 \quad (12)$$

$$= m.v.(x^2) - [m.v.(x)]^2$$

In other words, *the variance of* x *is the mean value of* x² *minus the square of the mean value of* x. This provides a convenient way of computing σ_x^2, as shown below, where the values are written in vertical columns for ease of addition.

(13)

x	x^2	p	$x \cdot p$	$x^2 \cdot p$
b_1	$b_1^{\,2}$	p_1	$b_1 \cdot p_1$	$b_1^{\,2} \cdot p_1$
b_2	$b_2^{\,2}$	p_2	$b_2 \cdot p_2$	$b_2^{\,2} \cdot p_2$
$\vdots$	$\vdots$	$\vdots$	$\vdots$	$\vdots$
b_k	$b_k^{\,2}$	p_k	$b_k \cdot p_k$	$b_k^{\,2} \cdot p_k$
Sums		1	μ_x	μ_{x^2}

$$\sigma_x^{\,2} = \mu_{x^2} - (\mu_x)^2$$

Since the mean value (3) of a random variable x is a weighted sum of x values, it is measured with the same unit as x itself; thus if x represents a length in centimeters then μ_x will also be measured in centimeters. However, the variance $\sigma_x^{\,2}$ of x as defined by (10) is a weighted sum of the *squared* differences of x from μ_x, and hence its unit of measurement will be the square of that of x [(cm^2) in the example just given]. On the other hand, σ_x, *the positive square root of* $\sigma_x^{\,2}$, has the same unit of measurement as that of x itself.

Definition 6
The *standard deviation* σ_x of a random variable x is the positive square root of its variance. For typographical reasons we shall sometimes write σ_x as *s.d.* (x).

Example 10
If $x =$ the number obtained in one roll of a fair die, then from the table of example 5 (page 60) we have

$$\mu_x = \frac{1}{6}(1 + 2 + \ldots + 6) = \frac{21}{6} = \frac{7}{2} = 3.5$$

$$\sigma_x^{\,2} = \frac{1}{6}(1^2 + 2^2 + \ldots + 6^2) - \left(\frac{7}{2}\right)^2 = \frac{91}{6} - \frac{49}{4} = \frac{70}{24} = \frac{35}{12} \cong 2.92$$

$$\sigma_x = \sqrt{\frac{35}{12}} \cong 1.71$$

If y denotes a random variable taking on only the two values 1 and 6 with equal probabilities 1/2, 1/2, then

$$\mu_y = \frac{1}{2}(1 + 6) = \frac{7}{2} = 3.5$$

$$\sigma_y^{\,2} = \frac{1}{2}(1^2 + 6^2) - \left(\frac{7}{2}\right)^2 = \frac{37}{2} - \frac{49}{4} = \frac{50}{8} = \frac{25}{4} = 6.25$$

$$\sigma_y = 2.5$$

Thus x and y have the same mean value 3.5, but since the values of y

are in general farther from 3.5 than those of x, the "dispersion" of y as measured by its variance or standard deviation exceeds that of x.

Example 11

In example 8 we saw that if x = number of heads in three tosses of a fair coin, then $\mu_x = 1.5$. From the distribution of x given in figure 3.1 we have by (10) that

$$\sigma_x^2 = (0 - 1.5)^2 \cdot \frac{1}{8} + (1 - 1.5)^2 \cdot \frac{3}{8}$$

$$+ (2 - 1.5)^2 \cdot \frac{3}{8} + (3 - 1.5)^2 \cdot \frac{1}{8} = \frac{6}{8} = .75$$

Alternatively, the use of (12) gives

$$m.v.(x^2) = 0^2 \cdot \frac{1}{8} + 1^2 \cdot \frac{3}{8} + 2^2 \cdot \frac{3}{8} + 3^2 \cdot \frac{1}{8} = \frac{24}{8} = 3$$

Therefore, $\sigma_x^2 = 3 - (1.5)^2 = .75$, as before.

In subsequent chapters we shall frequently need to compute the variance of random variables. These computations are facilitated by the following simple but important general rules, analogous to the numbered rules in section 3.3 (see page 64–65). The formal proofs of these rules are left to the reader.

4. If c is any constant, then $\sigma_c^2 = 0$ **(14)**

5. If c is any constant, then $\sigma_{x+c}^2 = \sigma_x^2$ **(15)**

6. If c is any constant, then $\sigma_{cx}^2 = c^2 \sigma_x^2$ **(16)**

In words, *the variance of a constant is 0, the variance of* x + c *is the same as the variance of* x, *and the variance of* cx *is* c² *times the variance of* x. Since the standard deviation σ_x is the square root of the variance, it follows that *the standard deviation of a constant is 0, the standard deviation of* x + c *is the same as that of* x, *and the standard deviation of* cx *is* |c| *times that of* x.*

As a consequence of these rules, we have for the mean value and variance of any *linear function* a + bx of a random variable x, where a and b are constants

$$m.v.(a + bx) = \mu_{a+bx} = a + b\mu_x \tag{17}$$

$$s.d.(a + bx) = \sigma_{a+bx} = |b|\sigma_x \tag{18}$$

---

*|b| denotes the *absolute value* of b, and is equal to b for $b \geq 0$ and to $-b$ for $b < 0$. It occurs in (18) because whether b is positive or negative, $\sqrt{b^2} = |b|$ is the positive square root of b^2.

For example, if $\mu_x = 10$ and $\sigma_x = 2$, then the random variable $y = (5/9)(x - 32) = -160/9 + 5x/9$ has

$$\mu_y = -\frac{160}{9} + \frac{5}{9} \cdot 10 = -\frac{110}{9}, \ \sigma_y = \frac{5}{9} \cdot 2 = \frac{10}{9}.$$

PROBLEMS 3.4

1–8. Find the variance and standard deviation in problems 1–8, section 3.3.

9. For each of the following distributions, find the mean value and standard deviation.

a. x:

Prob.	.2	.2	.2	.2	.2
Value	−2	−1	0	1	2

b. x:

Prob.	.3	.15	.1	.15	.3
Value	−2	−1	0	1	2

c. x:

Prob.	.1	.2	.4	.2	.1
Value	−2	−1	0	1	2

Discuss the meaning of σ_x with regard to (a), (b), and (c) above.

10. For each of the following distributions, find the mean value and standard deviation.

a. x:

Prob.	$\frac{1}{4}$	$\frac{1}{4}$	$\frac{1}{4}$	$\frac{1}{4}$
Value	0	1	2	3

b. x:

Prob.	$\frac{3}{8}$	$\frac{1}{8}$	$\frac{1}{8}$	$\frac{3}{8}$
Value	0	1	2	3

c. x:

Prob.	$\frac{3}{20}$	$\frac{6}{20}$	$\frac{9}{20}$	$\frac{2}{20}$
Value	0	1	2	3

Discuss the meaning of σ_x with regard to (a), (b), and (c) above.

11. Let x = the number of hours per week (to the nearest hour) spent at a part-time job by a student chosen at random from a certain population of university students. If x has a mean value of 15 hours and a standard deviation of 4 hours, what are the mean value and standard deviation of the weekly income y of this population of students if $y = 2x + 3$?

12. Let x = the number of heads in nine tosses of a fair coin. Then x has mean value 4.5 and standard deviation 1.5. If one engages in a gambling game in which one is paid $2 for every head that appears in the nine tosses and it costs $10 to enter the game, find the mean value and standard deviation of the random variable $y =$ amount of money gained in such a game. (Hint: $y = 2x - 10$.)

13. If x is a random variable with a mean value of 5 and a variance of 4, find the mean value, variance, and standard deviation of each of the following random variables:

a. $2x$ d. $0 \cdot x + 4$
b. $6x - 5$ e. $-x + 2$
c. $x + 2$ f. $bx - 1$ (b is a constant)

14. If x is a random variable with a mean value of -20 and a standard deviation of 5, find the mean value, variance, and standard deviation of each of the following random variables:

a. $x + 3$ d. $-2x - 3$
b. $2x - 6$ e. $0 \cdot x - 4$
c. 5 f. $cx + d$ (c and d are constants)

3.5 Chebyshev's Inequality

We have seen that while the mean value μ_x serves to locate the "central value" of the probability distribution of a random variable x, the standard deviation σ_x measures the amount of "dispersion" of the values of x about its mean value. This rather vague statement is given a more concrete meaning by the following theorem.

Theorem 1 (Chebyshev's inequality)
For any constant $c > 0$

$$P\{|x - \mu_x| \geq c\sigma_x\} \leq \frac{1}{c^2} \qquad (19)$$

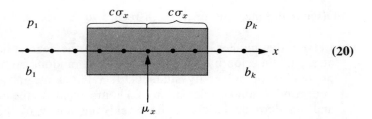

$$(20)$$

The inequality (19) has the following geometrical interpretation. Plot the various values b_i that x can assume on a number axis, each labeled with its corresponding probability p_i, as shown above. Compute μ_x and σ_x^2, and with μ_x as the center draw a rectangular box extending a distance $c\sigma_x$ on each side of μ_x, with c equal to any desired constant > 0. The quantity on the left-hand side of (19) is the probability that when the experiment defining x is performed, the observed x value will lie outside the box; it is just the sum of the p_i's associated with those b_i values that lie outside the box. Theorem 1 states that *no matter what the nature of the probability distribution of* x, *the probability that* x *will lie outside the box from* $\mu_x - c\sigma_x$ *to* $\mu_x + c\sigma_x$ *is at most equal to* $1/c^2$. By choosing a c that is sufficiently large, we can make $1/c^2$ as close to 0 as we please. For example, if we know only that $\mu_x = 12$ and $\sigma_x = 2$, then choosing, say, $c = 3$ will ensure by (19) that

$$P[|x - 12| \geq 3 \cdot 2] = P[\{x \geq 18\} \text{ or } \{x \leq 6\}] \leq \frac{1}{9} = .111 \ldots$$

whereas choosing $c = 5$ will ensure that

$$P[|x - 12| \geq 5 \cdot 2] = P[\{x \geq 22\} \text{ or } \{x \leq 2\}] \leq \frac{1}{25} = .04$$

In most cases the inequality (19) is rather crude, and the left-hand side will usually be considerably smaller than $1/c^2$. The virtue of the inequality (19) is that it always gives at least an upper bound to the actual probability of the event $\{|x - \mu_x| \geq c\sigma_x\}$.

Proof of Theorem 1
By the definition (10) of $\sigma_x{}^2$

$$\sigma_x{}^2 \geq \Sigma^*(b_i - \mu_x)^2 p_i \tag{21}$$

where the symbol Σ^* denotes summation over just those values b_i that lie outside the box. Now, for each such value

$$(b_i - \mu_x)^2 \geq c^2\sigma_x{}^2 \tag{22}$$

since any b_i outside the box is distant at least $c\sigma_x$ from the center μ_x of the box. From (21) and (22) we have

$$\sigma_x{}^2 \geq c^2\sigma_x{}^2 \, \Sigma^* \, p_i = c^2\sigma_x{}^2 \cdot P[\{|x - \mu_x| \geq c\sigma_x\}] \tag{23}$$

Dividing (23) by $c^2\sigma_x{}^2$ on both sides gives (19).

PROBLEMS 3.5

1. Let x be a discrete random variable with the mean value $\mu_x = 10$ and $\sigma_x{}^2 = 9$. Use (19) to find a bound on the probability that
   a. $P(|x - 10| \geq 6)$
   b. $P(|x - 10| \geq 9)$

2. Let x be a discrete random variable with the mean value $\mu_x = 0$ and $\sigma_x^2 = .5$. Use (19) to find a bound on the probability that

   a. $P(|x| \geq 1)$
   b. $P(|x| \geq 2)$

3. Let x be a discrete random variable with the distribution

$x:$

Prob.	.01	.02	.07	.15	.20	.10	.20	.15	.07	.02	.01
Value	-5	-4	-3	-2	-1	0	1	2	3	4	5

For this distribution show that $\mu_x = 0$ and $\sigma_x = 2$. Compare the bound in (19) with direct computation for

   a. $P(|x| \geq 2)$ **c.** $P(|x| \geq 4)$
   b. $P(|x| \geq 3)$ **d.** $P(|x| \geq 5)$

3.6 Random Sampling from a Probability Distribution

Scientific experiments that involve random phenomena are usually performed more than once to reveal as much as possible about the true probability distribution of whatever is being measured. For example, a traffic engineer concerned with the volume of morning rush-hour traffic at a particular intersection might observe the intersection during a two-minute interval for each of 10 work days, and record the number of cars arriving. Suppose that the results for 10 actual days observed turn out to be $x_1 = 42$, $x_2 = 31$, $x_3 = 54$, $x_4 = 23$, $x_5 = 35$, $x_6 = 26$, $x_7 = 43$, $x_8 = 20$, $x_9 = 39$ and $x_{10} = 31$. Let $x =$ the number of cars arriving at the intersection during a randomly chosen two-minute interval during the morning rush hour. Then x is a random variable, and the values $x_1, \ldots, x_{10}$ given above are those which actually occurred in 10 repeated trials of the experiment of counting cars during a two-minute interval. Now suppose we can assume that the probability distribution (2) that governs the behavior of x (here, the values $b_1, b_2, \ldots$ are 0, 1, . . .) is the same for each day, and that observations taken on different days do not influence each other. Then the observations $\{x_1, \ldots, x_{10}\}$ taken in this manner by the engineer are called a *random sample* from the probability distribution (2) of x; each x_i has the *same probability distribution* (2), and all the x_i values are *mutually independent*, as defined below.

Definition 7
Discrete random variables $\{x_1, \ldots, x_n\}$ are said to be *mutually independent* if for any possible values $x_1^*, \ldots, x_n^*$ of $x_1, \ldots, x_n$,

$$P[\{x_1 = x_1^*\} \text{ and } \{x_2 = x_2^*\} \text{ and } \ldots \text{ and } \{x_n = x_n^*\}] \qquad \textbf{(24)}$$

$$= P\{x_1 = x_1^*\} \cdot P\{x_2 = x_1^*\} \ldots P\{x_n = x_n^*\}$$

Suppose, for example, that a ball in a fair roulette wheel can fall into any one of 37 slots, numbered from 0 to 36. The wheel is spun three times. Let x_i = the number that appears on the ith spin, for $i = 1, 2, 3$. Then $\{x_1, x_2, x_3\}$ are independent random variables, since the outcomes of any past spins do not affect the probabilities for the next spin. For instance,

$$P[\{x_1 = 0\} \text{ and } \{x_2 = 0\} \text{ and } \{x_3 = 1\}]$$
$$= P\{x_1 = 0\} \cdot P\{x_2 = 0\} \cdot P\{x_3 = 1\} = \frac{1}{37} \cdot \frac{1}{37} \cdot \frac{1}{37}$$

so the probability of getting two 0's followed by a 1 is $1/(37)^3$

Definition 8
Taking a *random sample* of size n from the probability distribution (2) of a random variable x consists of making n trials of the experiment of observing x and recording the successive observed values $\{x_1, \ldots, x_n\}$. It is assumed that (a) the x values are mutually independent (24), and (b) each x_i has the same probability distribution (2) as x.

The random variables $\{x_1, \ldots, x_n\}$ are then said to be *independent* and *identically distributed*.

As an example, let a fair coin be tossed three times. Random variables $\{x_1, x_2, x_3\}$ are defined as

$$x_i = \begin{cases} 1 \text{ if heads appears on the } i\text{th toss} \\ 0 \text{ if tails appears on the } i\text{th toss} \end{cases}$$

Each x_i has the same probability distribution, given by

$$x: \frac{\text{Prob.}}{\text{Value}} \begin{array}{|c|c|} \frac{1}{2} & \frac{1}{2} \\ \hline 1 & 0 \end{array} \tag{25}$$

and $\{x_1, x_2, x_3\}$ are *mutually independent*, since the coin at any toss neither "remembers" what it did in past tosses nor "foresees" what it will do in future tosses. Thus, $\{x_1, x_2, x_3\}$ constitute a *random sample* of size 3 from the probability distribution (25).

Probabilities of joint events involving independent random variables are found by applying (24). For example,

$$P(3 \text{ heads}) = P[\{x_1 = 1\} \text{ and } \{x_2 = 1\} \text{ and } \{x_3 = 1\}]$$
$$= P\{x_1 = 1\} \cdot P\{x_2 = 1\} \cdot P\{x_3 = 1\}$$
$$= \frac{1}{2} \cdot \frac{1}{2} \cdot \frac{1}{2} = \frac{1}{8}$$

The probabilities of other events are computed similarly.

The concept of a random sample assumes that the experiment in question is conducted so that the sample values $\{x_1, \ldots, x_n\}$ are independent representatives of the probability distribution under study. In statistics we use such samples to make inferences about some characteristic of an unknown probability distribution, such as its mean value. Thus, in the example discussed above, the engineer may want to know the mean value μ_x of the arrival rate x of cars in a randomly chosen two-minute interval during the rush-hour at the intersection in question. He may never know this mean value exactly, but a sample will help in estimating it, and the information in the sample will be useful in planning traffic-control strategy.

Our standard conceptual model for statistical inference in random sampling from an unknown probability distribution will be the following. A bowl contains some number N of chips. Each chip is marked with one of a set of values $b_1, \ldots, b_k$. The proportion of chips in the bowl bearing the number b_i is $p_i =$ (number of chips marked b_i)/(total number N of chips in the bowl), so that $p_1 + \ldots + p_k = 1$. The true values of these proportions p_i are unknown to us. If we thoroughly mix the chips in the bowl, draw one blindly ("at random"), and observe the number x on it, then x is a random variable with the probability distribution (2), since $p_i = P\{x = b_i\}$. If we continue to draw n chips at random from this bowl, *replacing the chip drawn each time and thoroughly mixing the chips before the next draw,* then the successive numbers $\{x_1, x_2, \ldots, x_n\}$ on the n chips drawn will form a random sample of size n from the probability distribution of x, since (a) the random variables x_i are mutually independent, and (b) each x_i has the same probability distribution as x. By observing the actual values $\{x_1, \ldots, x_n\}$ obtained, we hope to be able to form some picture of the precise nature of the unknown (to us) composition of the bowl; that is, of the unknown probability distribution (2) of x. We may, for example, be interested in estimating from the sample values $\{x_1, \ldots, x_n\}$ the value of μ_x or of σ_x^2.

Note that: (a) The evidence concerning (2) contained in a random sample $\{x_1, \ldots, x_n\}$ is not affected by the hypothetical or actual total *number* N of balls in the bowl. Only the *proportions* p_i with which the different values b_i occur govern the behavior of the sampling process. (b) The evidence concerning (2) in the sample will never be completely conclusive, since because of chance variations the various values b_i will usually occur in the *sample* with proportions somewhat different from the p_i in the probability distribution (2) or, as we shall say, the *population*. (c) However, the larger the *sample size* n, the more accurately the sample values $\{x_1, \ldots, x_n\}$ will permit us to estimate the nature of the unknown probability distribution (2), and of any parameter characteristic of it, for example, μ_x or σ_x^2. How estimates and inferences concerning an unknown probability distribution or population are to be made from the evidence in a sample will be our chief concern in the chapters that follow. Before entering in later chapters into these questions of statistical inference concerning an unknown probability distribution, we shall discuss in the remainder of this chapter three important distributions that occur in practice: the *binomial*, *hypergeometric*, and *Poisson* distributions.

PROBLEMS 3.6

1. Suppose that an experimenter has put four rats on an experimental diet. For the ith rat, the experimenter records

$$x_i = \begin{cases} 1 & \text{if the } i\text{th rat gains weight} \\ 0 & \text{if the } i\text{th rat loses weight} \end{cases}$$

Assuming the weight gains for the rats are in fact independent of each other, do the x's form a random sample? Why? If the probability that $P(x_i = 1) = 2/3$ for $i = 1, 2, 3$, and 4, find P (all rats gain weight) by using the notion of random sampling.

2. Suppose that a fair die is tossed three times and x_i = the number which appears on the ith toss of the die, $i = 1,2,3$. Do the x's form a random sample? Why? Find the probability of all faces showing a 1 by using the notion of random sampling.

3. Let x be a random variable with the probability distribution

$$x: \quad \begin{array}{c|c|c|c} \text{Prob.} & .5 & .3 & .2 \\ \hline \text{Value} & 0 & 1 & 2 \end{array}$$

If a random sample x_1, x_2, x_3 is taken from this distribution, find the probability of the following events:

   a. $(x_1 = 0)$ and $(x_2 = 2)$ and $(x_3 = 2)$
   b. (all $x_i = 0$)
   c. (sum of the $x_i = 3$)

4. Let x be a random variable with the probability distribution

$$x: \quad \begin{array}{c|c|c|c} \text{Prob.} & .3 & .4 & .3 \\ \hline \text{Value} & -1 & 0 & 1 \end{array}$$

If a random sample x_1 and x_2 is taken from this distribution, find the probability of the following events:

   a. $(x_1 = 1)$ and $(x_2 = -1)$
   b. $(x_1 = x_2)$
   c. $(x_1 + x_2 = 0)$

5. A jar contains ten balls; six labeled 0, and four labeled 1. Suppose two balls are chosen from the jar at random without replacement.

If $x_1 =$ the number on first ball drawn and $x_2 =$ the number on the second ball drawn, show that x_1 and x_2 are not mutually independent. If the first ball is replaced before the second is drawn, show that x_1 and x_2 are mutually independent. In each case, find the probabilities

a. $P(x_1 = x_2 = 0)$, $P(x_1 = 0)$, $P(x_2 = 0)$
b. $P(x_1 = x_2 = 1)$, $P(x_1 = 1)$, $P(x_2 = 1)$

Discuss your findings in (a) and (b) in relation to the notion of a random sample from a probability distribution.

3.7 The Binomial Distribution

A random variable y that occurs very frequently in applications is *the total number of occurrences of a particular event* A *in a given number* n *of successive independent trials of an experiment,* where the probability of the occurrence of A in each trial is some constant p between 0 and 1. The values that y can assume are 0, 1, 2, . . . , n. We shall see that the corresponding probabilities $p_0, p_1, \ldots, p_n$ can be computed from a knowledge of p and n.

If we call the occurrence of A a "success" and the nonoccurrence of A (that is, the occurrence of A') a "failure," then the formal definition of y is as follows.

Definition 9
A *binomial random variable* y is one that arises from the following experimental procedure:

1. A number of trials n are made that can result in either "success" or "failure."
2. The trials are mutually independent.
3. The probability of success in each trial is a constant p, and the probability of failure is $q = 1 - p$.
4. The random variable $y =$ the total number of successes in the n trials.

If we record $\{x_1, \ldots, x_n\}$, where by definition

$$x_i = \begin{cases} 1 & \text{if the } i\text{th trial is a success} \\ 0 & \text{if the } i\text{th trial is a failure} \end{cases} \tag{26}$$

then $\{x_1, \ldots, x_n\}$ is a random sample, as defined in the preceding section, from the two-valued distribution

$$x: \frac{\text{Prob.}}{\text{Value}} \begin{array}{|c|c} p & q \\ \hline 1 & 0 \end{array} \qquad (q = 1 - p) \tag{27}$$

and the binomial random variable y can be written as the sum $y = x_1 + \ldots + x_n$ of the n independent single-trial random variables (26), each of which has the same probability distribution (27).

The "bowl model" for generating a binomial random variable y is as follows. A bowl contains N chips, of which a are numbered 1 and $N - a$ are numbered 0. From this bowl, n chips are drawn one at a time, with replacement. Let y = the total number of chips numbered 1 among the n chips drawn, and let a chip numbered 1 be called a "success" and a chip numbered 0 a "failure". Then y is a binomial random variable with n trials and success probability $p = a/N$ for each single trial.

If in this experiment the chips are drawn *without replacement*, then y does not have a binomial distribution, since the probability of obtaining a success on the ith trial depends on the results of the preceding trials. However, when the total number n of trials is sufficiently small compared to the population size N, the dependence on preceding trials is so slight that it can be ignored for practical purposes, and we can assume for simplicity's sake that the trials are independent, as in sampling with replacement.

Example 12
A die is tossed 10 times and the number y of times in which a 3 appears is recorded. If the die is fair, y will have a binomial distribution with $n = 10$ and $p = 1/6$. The population from which the sample of 10 is drawn is conceptually infinite, consisting of all the tosses that will ever be made with that die.

Example 13
One thousand army recruits chosen at random are tested to see whether they have 20-20 vision, and the number y who do is recorded. Then y has a binomial distribution with $n = 1000$, but (in the absence of reliable previous data) an unknown value of p.

Example 14
A sample of 200 is drawn at random from the records of all the fires reported in New York City during 1974, and y is the number of cases in which arson was established as the cause.

In most examples such as these, one or more of the elements of definition 9 are subject to question. Nevertheless, the assumption of a binomially distributed random variable y is often useful as an approximation of reality. Note that in examples 13 and 14, the n trials are, strictly speaking, dependent, but n is so small compared to the population size N that we can ignore, for practical purposes, this dependence and assume independent trials. In general, if the sample size is less than 5 percent of the population size, the independence assumption is a good approximation to the real situation.

We now state the chief characteristics of the binomial random variable of definition 9.

a. The mean value μ_y and the variance σ_y^2 are given by

$$\mu_y = np \qquad \sigma_y^2 = npq \qquad (28)$$

b. The probability $p_i = P\{y = i\}$ is given by the formula

$$p_i = \frac{n!}{i!(n-i)!} p^i q^{n-i} \quad (i = 0, 1, \ldots, n) \qquad (29)$$

where $n!$ (read "n factorial") is an abbreviation for the product $1 \cdot 2 \cdot 3 \ldots n$ of all the positive integers from 1 to n inclusive. It is also mathematically convenient to define $0! = 1$, and this convention will be followed throughout the text.

The coefficient of $p^i q^{n-i}$ in (29) is also written as

$$\frac{n!}{i!(n-i)!} = \binom{n}{i} \qquad (30)$$

(It is equal to the number of different subsets of i objects that can be formed from a set of n distinct objects.) We compute $\binom{n}{i}$ by forming the ratio

$$\begin{aligned}
\binom{n}{i} &= \frac{1 \cdot 2 \cdots n}{[1 \cdot 2 \cdots i] \cdot [1 \cdot 2 \cdots (n-i)]} \\
&= \frac{n(n-1)(n-2) \cdots (n-i+1)}{1 \cdot 2 \cdot 3 \cdots i}
\end{aligned} \qquad (31)$$

Observe that by (30)

$$\binom{n}{n-i} = \frac{n!}{(n-i)![n-(n-i)]!} = \frac{n!}{(n-i)!i!} = \binom{n}{i} \qquad (32)$$

Formulas 28 and 29 will be established later. For the moment we shall assume their validity, pausing only to show by direct evaluation that they hold for $n = 1$ and $n = 2$.

For $n = 1$, we have $y =$ the number of successes in one trial. By (29)

$$p_0 = \binom{1}{0} p^0 q^1 = \frac{1!}{0!1!} q = q = P\{x = 0\}$$

$$p_1 = \binom{1}{1} p^1 q^0 = \frac{1!}{1!0!} p = p = P\{x = 1\}$$

Hence

$$\mu_x = 0 \cdot q + 1 \cdot p = p$$

$$\sigma_x^2 = \mu_{x^2} - (\mu_x)^2 = 0^2 \cdot q + 1^2 \cdot p - p^2 = p - p^2 = p(1-p) = pq$$

is conformity with (28).

For $n = 2$ we have $y =$ the number of successes in two trials. A tree diagram of outcomes gives

First Trial	Second Trial	$x = $ no. of S's	Probability of x
S —	S	2	$p \cdot p = p^2$
	F	1	$p \cdot q$
F —	S	1	$q \cdot p$
	F	0	$q \cdot q = q^2$

and hence

$$P\{x=0\} = q^2, \ P\{x=1\} = 2pq, \ P\{x=2\} = p^2$$

This agrees with (29), since

$$p_0 = \binom{2}{0} p^0 q^2 = \frac{2!}{0!2!} p^2 = q^2$$

$$p_1 = \binom{2}{1} p^1 q^1 = \frac{2!}{1!1!} pq = 2pq$$

$$p_2 = \binom{2}{2} p^2 q^0 = \frac{2!}{2!0!} p^2 = p^2$$

From these probabilities we compute

$$\mu_y = 0 \cdot q^2 + 1 \cdot 2pq + 2 \cdot p^2 = 2pq + 2p^2 = 2p(q+p) = 2p$$

$$\mu_{y^2} = 0^2 \cdot q^2 + 1^2 \cdot 2pq + 2^2 \cdot p^2 = 2pq + 4p^2$$

Hence by (12)

$$\sigma_y^2 = \mu_{y^2} - (\mu_y)^2 = 2pq + 4p^2 - (2p)^2 = 2pq$$

Thus for $n = 2$ the values of μ_y and σ_y^2 are in agreement with the general formulas (28).

Example 15

We draw a single card from a deck of 52, and note whether it is black or red. This experiment is repeated six times, the chosen card being replaced and the deck reshuffled each time. What is the probability distribution of the random variable $y =$ the total number of black cards drawn? Here y has a binomial distribution with $n = 6$ and p (probability of getting a black card in a single draw) $= 1/2$. (The trials are independent, since the card is returned and the deck reshuffled after each draw.) From (29) we have

$$p_0 = p_6 = \frac{6!}{0!6!} \left(\frac{1}{2}\right)^0 \left(\frac{1}{2}\right)^6 = 1 \cdot \left(\frac{1}{2}\right)^2 = \frac{1}{64}$$

$$p_1 = p_5 = \frac{6!}{1!5!} \left(\frac{1}{2}\right)^1 \left(\frac{1}{2}\right)^5 = 6 \cdot \left(\frac{1}{2}\right)^6 = \frac{6}{64}$$

$$p_2 = p_4 = \frac{6!}{2!4!} \left(\frac{1}{2}\right)^2 \left(\frac{1}{2}\right)^4 = 15 \cdot \left(\frac{1}{2}\right)^6 = \frac{15}{64}$$

$$p_3 = \frac{6!}{3!3!} \left(\frac{1}{2}\right)^3 = 20 \cdot \left(\frac{1}{2}\right)^6 = \frac{20}{64}$$

As a check on our computations we note that

$$p_0 + \ldots + p_6 = \frac{1}{64} + \frac{6}{64} + \frac{15}{64} + \frac{20}{64} + \frac{15}{64} + \frac{6}{64} + \frac{1}{64} = 1$$

From (28), $\mu_y = 3$, $\sigma_y^2 = 6 \cdot 1/2 \cdot 1/2 = 1.5$

Example 16

Suppose that 10 percent of the people in the present U.S. population are allergic to ragweed. If three persons are chosen at random from this population, and $y =$ the number of people allergic to ragweed among them, then y has a binomial distribution with $n = 3$ trials and success probability $p = .10$ (here "success" is being allergic to ragweed). (29) yields

$$p_0 = \frac{3!}{0!3!} (.1)^0 (.9)^3 = .729$$

$$p_1 = \frac{3!}{1!2!} (.1)^1 (.9)^2 = .243$$

$$p_2 = \frac{3!}{2!1!} (.1)^2 (.9)^1 = .027$$

$$p_3 = \frac{3!}{0!3!} (.1)^3 (.9)^0 = .001$$

From (28), $\mu_y = .3$ and $\sigma_y^2 = .27$

Prob.	.0010	.0098	.0439	.1172	.2051	.2461	.2051	.1172	.0439	.0098	.0010
Value	0	1	2	3	4	5	6	7	8	9	10

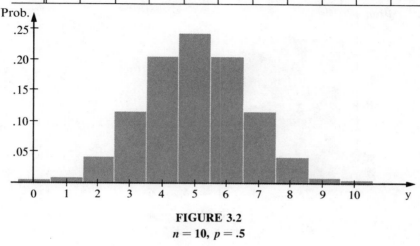

FIGURE 3.2
$n = 10, \ p = .5$

In figure 3.2 we have illustrated the distribution of a binomial random variable y ($n = 10$ and $p = .5$) by drawing rectangles that are centered at each of the y values and have heights proportional to their respective probabilities of occurrence.

For this distribution, $\mu_y = np = 5$, $\sigma_y^2 = npq = 10/4 = 2.5$, $\sigma_y \cong 1.6$. We note that Chebyshev's inequality (19) gives for $c = 2$ that

$$P\{|y - 5| \geq 2(1.6)\} \leq .25$$

whereas in fact this probability is

$$P\{y = 0, 1, 9, \text{ or } 10\} = p_0 + p_1 + p_q + p_{10} \cong .022$$

In figure 3.3 we have illustrated the distribution of a binomial random variable with $p = .3$ and $n = 8$ by drawing rectangles centered at each of the y values with heights proportional to their respective probabilities of occurrence.

For this distribution, $\mu_y = np = 2.4$ and $\sigma_y^2 = npq = 1.68$, $\sigma_y \cong 1.3$. Here Chebyshev's inequality (19) gives for $c = 2$ that

$$P\{|y - 2.4| \geq 2(1.2)\} \leq .25$$

whereas in fact this probability is $P\{y = 5, 6, 7, 8\} \cong .066$.

Comparing figures 3.2 and 3.3 we note a symmetry in figure 3.2 ($p_0 = p_{10}$, $p_1 = p_9$, etc.) that is not present in figure 3.3. The binomial distribution is symmetric in this way only when $p = .5$.

We give now the general proof of (29). The event $\{y = i\}$ can hap-

Prob.	.0576	.1977	.2965	.2541	.1361	.0467	.0100	.0012	.0001
Value	0	1	2	3	4	5	6	7	8

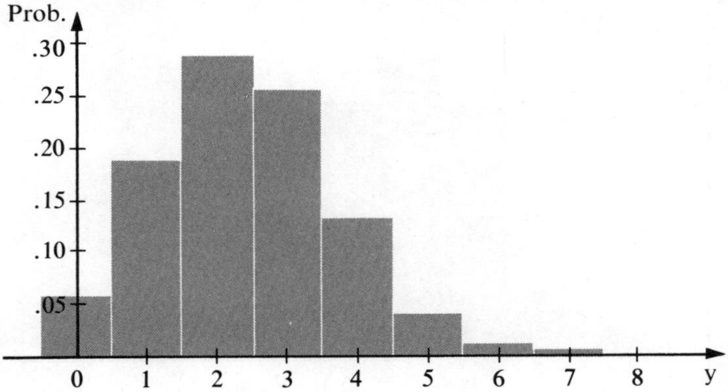

FIGURE 3.3

$n = 8$, $p = .3$

pen in many ways, according to *which i* of the n trials are successes. For each of these ways the probability is $p^i q^{n-i}$ by the independence assumption of definition 9. Hence $P\{y = i\} = \binom{n}{i} p^i q^{n-i}$, where $\binom{n}{i}$ denotes the number of different subsets of i elements that can be chosen from the set $\{1, 2, \ldots, n\}$ of trials to be the successes. Now, the number of ways of making i different choices *in order* from the set $\{1, 2, \ldots, n\}$ is $n(n-1)(n-2) \ldots (n-i)$, since the first choice can be made in n ways, then the second in $(n-1)$ ways, and so forth. But each fixed subset containing i of the numbers $\{1, 2, \ldots, n\}$ can be ordered in $i(i-1)(i-2) \ldots 1 = i!$ ways, since the first can be any one of the i members of the subset, and so on. Hence $n(n-1) \ldots (n-i) =$ the number of *ordered* subsets of i of the numbers $\{1, 2, \ldots, n\} = i! \cdot$ (the number of such subsets) $= i! \binom{n}{i}$, so

$$\binom{n}{i} = \frac{n(n-1) \ldots (n-i)}{i!} = \frac{n!}{i!(n-i)!}$$

Hence as stated by (29).

$$P\{y = i\} = \frac{n!}{i!(n-i)!} p^i q^{n-i}$$

Let y be a binomial random variable with n trials and success probability p, and let i be any given integer between 0 and n. Since the events $\{y = 0\}$, $\{y = 1\}$, . . . , $\{y = i\}$ are mutually exclusive (33)

$$P\{y \leq i\} = P\{y = 0\} + P\{y = 1\} + \ldots + P\{y = i\}$$

$$= \sum_{j=0}^{i} p_j = \sum_{j=0}^{i} \frac{n!}{j!(n-j)!} p^j q^{n-j}$$

The function $B(i; n, p) = P\{y \leq i\}$ is called the *cumulative distribution function* of y. Some values of this function are given in appendix table 4.

Example 17

A multiple-choice test consists of 25 questions, each of which has five possible answers. A student choosing answers at random has probability 1/5 of answering any given question correctly. What is the probability that such a student will get (a) five or fewer answers correct? (b) more than 10 answers correct?

a. Let y = number of correct answers obtained. Then y has a binomial distribution with $n = 25$ and $p = 1/5 = .2$. From appendix table 4, $P\{y \leq 5\} = B(5; 25, .2) = .617$.

b. Since the event $\{y > 10\}$ is the complement of the event $\{y \leq 10\}$,

$$P\{y > 10\} = 1 - P\{y \leq 10\} = 1 - B(10; 25, .2) = 1 - .994 = .006$$

Thus a student who guesses at random has only six chances out of 1000 to get a mark better than 40 percent ($10/25 = .4$) on the test. On the other hand, the student has 617 chances in a thousand to get a mark of 20 percent or below.

If a single binomial probability $p_i = P\{y = i\}$ is required, it can be obtained from the tables of $B(i; n, p)$ by taking the difference

$$P\{y = i\} = B(i; n, p) - B(i - 1; n, p) \text{ for } i = 1, 2, \ldots, n,$$
$$P\{y = 0\} = B(0; n, p)$$

For $n = 20$ and $p = .2$,

$$P\{y = 8\} = B(8; 20, .2) - B(7; 20, .2) = .9900 - .9679 = .0221,$$
$$P\{y = 0\} = B(0; 20, .2) = .0115$$

PROBLEMS 3.7

1. For each of the following, state whether the random variable does or does not have a binomial distribution. For those random variables that do not have a binomial distribution, explain which of the properties (1–4) of definition 9 fail to hold.

   a. y = number of heads in 10 tosses of a coin.

   b. $y =$ number of aces in five cards dealt from a newly shuffled deck.

   c. $y =$ number of babies having blue eyes out of 10 births, assuming the births are independent of each other.

   d. $y =$ the time it takes an athlete to run one mile.

2. For each of the following, state whether the random variable does or does not have a binomial distribution. For those random variables that do not have a binomial distribution, explain which of the properties (1–4) of definition 9 fail to hold.

   a. $y =$ the number of ones in five tosses of a fair die.

   b. $y =$ the income of a full-time employee sampled from a population of employees.

   c. $y =$ the number of defective items in a sample of 8 items from a shipment of 100 items, of which 5 are defective.

   d. $y =$ the number of mice showing toxic side effects in a group of 20 mice injected with an experimental drug.

3. Suppose that 20 percent of all drivers in Tennessee have had at least one traffic violation within the last year. If five of these drivers are sampled, find the probability distribution of $y =$ number in the sample of 5 with at least one traffic violation in the last year, by using (29). Draw the distribution of y as in figures 3.2 and 3.3. Find the mean and variance of y.

4. If 60 percent of all TV viewers watched the last Super Bowl, find the probability distribution of $y =$ number of viewers who watched this game in a sample of six such viewers by using (29). Draw the distribution of y as in figures 3.2 and 3.3. Find the mean value and variance of y.

5. If 5 prizes are awarded at random to a group of 50 persons, 20 of whom are women, and any person may receive any number of prizes, find the probability that

   a. all prizes are won by women.

   b. all prizes are won by men.

   c. at least one prize is won by a woman.

   d. exactly three women win prizes.

6. A single card is drawn from a deck of cards, and it is noted whether or not the card is a face card. If this experiment is repeated four times, the chosen card being replaced and the deck reshuffled each time, find the probability that

   a. all cards drawn are face cards.

   b. no cards drawn are face cards.

   c. exactly two of the cards drawn are face cards.

d. at least one card drawn is a face card.

7. Suppose that penicillin is 80 percent effective in curing a bacterial infection. If 20 patients having this infection are treated with penicillin, find the probability, by appendix table 4, that

   a. 15 or more patients are cured.
   b. fewer than seven patients are cured.
   c. $4 \leq y \leq 15$, where $y =$ number of the 20 patients cured.
   d. exactly 17 patients are cured.

8. If 30 percent of those over 65 in the United States are below the poverty income level, find the probability, using appendix table 4, that in a sample of 25

   a. fewer than 10 are below this income level.
   b. more than five are below this income level.
   c. between five and 15 (inclusive) are below this income level.
   d. exactly seven are below this income level.

9. A student takes a true-false test of 25 questions. Assuming that his answers to the questions are independent of each other and are randomly chosen, find the probability of his getting 20 or more correct. Based on your calculations, what might you conclude if the student has 20 or more correct answers?

10. A sample of 20 people are asked to try two different toothpastes (brand A and brand B) for a one-month period. Find the probability that more than 15 people will prefer brand A to brand B if in reality they are equally likely to be preferred. Based on your calculations, what might you conclude regarding the relative preference for brand A and brand B if more than 15 prefer brand A to brand B?

11. Verify the formulas in (28) by direct computation of the probability distribution, its mean value, and variance, for $n = 2, 3, 4$, and 5 and $p = 1/2$.

12. Verify the formulas in (28) by direct computation of the probability distribution, its mean value, and variance, for $n = 2, 3$, and 4 and $p = 1/3$.

3.8 The Law of Large Numbers for the Binomial Distribution

Let A denote some particular event associated with an experiment, with the probability $p = P(A)$. We have seen that the *relative frequency* with which A occurs in a large number n of independent trials may be regarded as an empirical measurement of the possibly unknown probability p. The reason for this is that *when* n *is large the relative frequency will usually be close to* p. One mathematical formulation of this rather vague statement is the "law of large numbers," which we shall now derive.

In any given number n of independent trials of an experiment, the total number of times that an event A will occur is a random variable y having a binomial distribution with mean value $\mu_y = np$ and variance $\sigma_y^2 = npq$, where $q = 1 - p$. The relative frequency of success (that is, of the occurrence of A) in the n trials is the random variable $\hat{p} = y/n$, which by (9) and (16) has the mean value and variance

$$\mu_{\hat{p}} = \frac{1}{n}\,\mu_y = \frac{1}{n}\cdot np = p \qquad \sigma_{\hat{p}}^2 = \frac{1}{n^2}\,\sigma_y^2 = \frac{1}{n^2}\cdot npq = \frac{pq}{n}$$

Applying Chebyshev's inequality (19) to $x = \hat{p}$ gives for any constant $c > 0$

$$P\left\{|\hat{p} - p| \geq c\cdot\sqrt{\frac{pq}{n}}\right\} \leq \frac{1}{c^2}$$

If in this inequality we put

$$\epsilon = c\sqrt{\frac{pq}{n}}, \text{ so that } c = \epsilon\sqrt{\frac{n}{pq}}$$

it can be written in the equivalent form

$$P\{|\hat{p} - p| \geq \epsilon\} \leq \frac{pq}{n\epsilon^2} \tag{34}$$

Now $pq = p(1 - p) \leq 1/4$ for all values $0 \leq p \leq 1$ (see page 169 for a graph of the function $p(1 - p)$ for $0 \leq p \leq 1$). Hence no matter what the value of p

$$P\{|\hat{p} - p| \geq \epsilon\} \leq \frac{1}{4n\epsilon^2} \tag{35}$$

This inequality is valid for any positive constant ϵ, no matter how small. By taking a sufficiently large n, we can make the right-hand side of (35) as small as we please. This is the content of

The Law of Large Numbers for Relative Frequency

In n *independent trials of an experiment in which a given event* A *occurs with constant probability* p *at each trial, the probability that the relative frequency* $\hat{p}$ *of the occurrence of* A *in the* n *trials (* $\hat{p}$ *is a random variable) will differ from the (constant)* p *by more than any* $\epsilon > 0$ *satisfies the inequality (35). Hence, this probability can be made as small as we please by taking a sufficiently large* n.

For example, if from a bowl containing a proportion p of white chips we draw n chips at random with replacement and denote by $\hat{p}$ the proportion of times a white chip appears, then choosing $\epsilon = .02$ in (35) we find that, irrespective of the true value of p.

$$P\{|\hat{p} - p| \geq .01\} \leq \frac{2500}{4n} = \frac{625}{n} \tag{36}$$

Thus, in n independent trials the probability that the proportion of times in which a white chip is drawn (this proportion is a random variable with values between 0 and 1) will differ from the (constant) proportion p of white chips in the bowl by as much as .02 or more cannot exceed the value $625/n$. For example, for $n = 12,500$ the right hand side of (36) becomes $625/12,500 = 1/20 = .05$, while for $n = 62,500$ it becomes $625/62,500 = .01$.

For a large n each of the possible values of $\hat{p}$, $0 = 0/n, 1/n, 2/n, \dots,$ $i/n, \dots, n/n = 1$, will have a small probability individually. This probability will be largest in the neighborhood $\hat{p} \cong p$, and will decrease so rapidly as $\hat{p}$ departs appreciably from p that the total probability associated with all values $\hat{p} = i/n$ for which $|i/n - p| \geq \epsilon$ will be $\leq 1/4 n\epsilon^2$, which tends to 0 as n increases. If we draw a graph of the probability distribution of $\hat{p}$, making the unit in the vertical direction large to display the probabilities more clearly, then for a large n it will have the following general appearance.

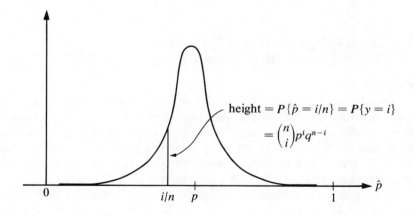

$$\text{height} = P\{\hat{p} = i/n\} = P\{y = i\}$$
$$= \binom{n}{i}p^i q^{n-i}$$

Briefly stated, for a large n the *relative frequency* $\hat{p}$ of success in n independent trials is *almost certain* to be close to the *probability* p of success in a single trial.

PROBLEMS 3.8

1. Find the mean value and variance of

$$\hat{p} = \frac{y}{n} = \frac{\text{relative frequency of heads in}}{n \text{ tosses of a fair coin}}$$

for $n = 10, 20, 100$, and 500. Compute $P(|\hat{p} - .5| \geq .1)$ for $n = 10$ and 20 using appendix table 4. For $n = 100$, this probability is .016. Find an upper bound for this probability for $n = 10, 20, 100$, and 500 using (35). Discuss the meaning of these results.

2. Find the mean value and variance of

$$\hat{p} = \frac{y}{n} = \frac{\text{relative frequency of four, five,}}{\text{and six in } n \text{ tosses of a fair die}}$$

for $n = 15, 25, 200$, and 800. Compute $P(|\hat{p} - .5| \geq .05)$ for $n = 15$ and 25, using appendix table 4. For $n = 200$, this probability is .1789. Find an upper bound for this probability for $n = 15, 25, 200$, and 800, using the inequality (34).

3. A pollster wishes to find the probability p of candidate A being preferred, based on a sample of n voters of which y prefer A. (a) If he uses the relative frequency $\hat{p} = y/n$ as his guess for p, find an upper bound for $P(|\hat{p} - p| \geq .03)$ if $p = .5$ using (35). (b) How large must n be if he wants the probability of error to be $\leq .05$? (Hint: Let $\epsilon = .03$ in (35) and make $(1/4n \epsilon^2) = .05$.) Repeat (a) and (b) with .01 in place of .03.

3.9 The Hypergeometric Distribution (Sampling Without Replacement)

Example 20
A manufacturer buys fuses in lots of $N = 50$. To check the quality of each lot he tests to destruction (and hence *without replacement*) $n = 3$ randomly chosen items from the lot, and counts $y =$ the number of defective items in the sample. If $y = 0$ he accepts the lot; otherwise he rejects it. What is the probability $P\{y = 0\}$ of accepting the lot if in fact it contains $a = 0, 1, 2, \ldots$ defective items?

More generally, suppose a bowl contains a chips labeled 1 and b chips labeled 0, with $N = a + b$ chips in all. We choose without replacement some number n, $1 \leq n \leq N$, of these chips in such a way that each of the $\binom{N}{n}$ subsets consisting of n of the N chips has the same probability $1/\binom{N}{n}$ of being chosen. This is called a *random sample of size* n *drawn without replacement from the finite population of* N *chips.* Let $y =$ the number of chips labeled 1 among the n chips chosen. Then y, which takes on some integer value between 0 and the smaller of a and n, is said to have a *hypergeometric distribution.* We shall show that for this distribution

$$P\{y = i\} = \frac{\binom{a}{i}\binom{b}{n-i}}{\binom{N}{n}}, \text{ where } \begin{cases} i = 0, 1, \ldots, n \ (\text{if } n \leq a) \\ i = 0, 1, \ldots, a \ (\text{if } n > a) \end{cases} \quad (37)$$

We recall that the symbol $\binom{n}{i}$ defined by (30) gives the number of different subsets with i members that can be formed from a set of n distinct elements. Hence, we can obtain exactly i chips labeled 1 in $\binom{a}{i}$ ways, and $n - i$ chips labeled 0 in $\binom{b}{n-i}$ ways. There are therefore $\binom{a}{i} \cdot \binom{b}{n-i}$ ways in all of choosing n chips from the bowl such that exactly i are labeled 0, out of the total of $\binom{N}{n}$ equally likely ways of choosing any n chips. Formula 37 thus follows from the equal likelihood definition of probability.

If we write out this formula explicitly, using (31), it becomes

$$P\{y = i\} = \frac{\dfrac{a(a-1)\ldots(a-i+1)}{1 \cdot 2 \ldots i} \cdot \dfrac{b(b-1)\ldots(b-n+i+1)}{1 \cdot 2 \ldots (n-i)}}{\dfrac{N(N-1)\ldots(N-n+1)}{1 \cdot 2 \ldots n}}$$

$$= \frac{n!}{i!(n-i)!} \cdot \frac{a(a-1)\ldots(a-i+1)}{N(N-1)\ldots(N-i+1)}$$

$$\cdot \frac{b(b-1)\ldots(b-n+i+1)}{(N-i)(N-i-1)\ldots(N-n+1)}$$

If n (and hence i) *is small compared to* N, then this is approximately equal to

$$\frac{n!}{i!(n-i)!} \cdot \left(\frac{a}{N}\right)^i \cdot \left(\frac{b}{N}\right)^{n-i} = \binom{n}{i} p^i q^{n-i}$$

where $p = a/N$ and $q = b/N = 1 - p$. Hence in this case the hypergeometric probability (37) differs little from the binomial probability (29), with $p = a/N =$ probability of getting a ball labeled 1 in a single trial.

Returning to example 20, for $N = 50$ and $n = 3$ we have by (37)

$$P\{y = i\} = \frac{\binom{a}{i}\binom{50 - a}{3 - i}}{\binom{50}{3}}$$

for $i = 0, 1, \ldots$ up to the smaller of a and 3, where $a =$ number of defective items in the lot of 50. For example, if $a = 10$ then

$$P\{y = 0\} = \frac{\binom{10}{0}\binom{40}{3}}{\binom{50}{3}} = \frac{\binom{40}{3}}{19,600} = \frac{9880}{19,600} = .504 \qquad (38)$$

$$P\{y - 1\} = \frac{\binom{10}{1}\binom{40}{2}}{\binom{50}{3}} = \frac{(10)(780)}{19,600} = \frac{7800}{19,600} = .398$$

$$P\{y = 2\} = \frac{\binom{10}{2}\binom{40}{1}}{\binom{50}{3}} = \frac{(45)(40)}{19,600} = \frac{1800}{19,600} = .092$$

$$P\{y = 3\} = \frac{\binom{10}{3}\binom{40}{0}}{\binom{50}{3}} = \frac{\binom{10}{3}}{\binom{50}{3}} = \frac{120}{19,600} = .006$$

Thus the manufacturer, who accepts a lot of 50 only if no defective items are found in a three-item sample without replacement, runs about a 50 percent chance of accepting a lot even when it contains 10 defectives.

As a check on the arithmetic, note that from the values (38)

$$P\{0 \le y \le 3\} = \frac{19,600}{19,600} = 1$$

We find by (38) that the mean value and variance of y are

$$\mu_y = \frac{0 \cdot 9880 + 1 \cdot 7800 + 2 \cdot 1800 + 3 \cdot 120}{19,600} = \frac{11,760}{19,600} = \frac{3}{5}$$

and

$$\sigma_y^2 = \mu_{y^2} - (\mu_y)^2 = \frac{0 \cdot 9880 + 1 \cdot 7800 + 4 \cdot 1800 + 9 \cdot 120}{19,600} - \frac{9}{25}$$

$$= \frac{9024}{19,600} = \frac{564}{1225} = .46$$

In the general case it can be shown that the mean value and variance of the hypergeometric distribution (37) are given by

$$\mu_y = n \cdot \frac{a}{N} \tag{39}$$

$$\sigma_y{}^2 = n \cdot \frac{a}{N} \cdot \frac{b}{N} \cdot \left(\frac{N-n}{N-1}\right) \tag{40}$$

These formulas are identical with those for the binomial y that would be obtained by sampling *with* replacement from the same bowl, except for the factor $(N-n)/(N-1)$ in (40), called the *finite population correction factor for the variance* in sampling without replacement. When N is large compared to n this factor is almost 1, as it must be, since then the difference between sampling with and without replacement is negligible. In example 20, (39) and (40) give

$$\mu_y = 3 \cdot \frac{10}{50} = \frac{3}{5} \quad , \quad \sigma_y{}^2 = 3 \cdot \frac{10}{50} \cdot \frac{40}{50} \cdot \frac{47}{49} = \frac{564}{1225}$$

in agreement with the direct evaluation obtained previously.

PROBLEMS 3.9

1. A forensics club has ten members; four women, and six men. Three members are chosen at random to represent the club at its national convention. Let $y =$ the number of women among the three chosen members. Find the probability distribution of y.

2. A manufacturer of TV sets buys tubes in lots of 24 and tests a sample of three tubes from each lot. If a lot contains two defective tubes, compute the probability distribution of $y =$ the number of defective tubes in the sample of three tubes.

3. If three cards are chosen at random from a standard deck, find the probability that
   a. all cards chosen are red.
   b. all cards chosen are face cards (K, Q, J).
   c. at least one card chosen is a face card.
   d. all three cards chosen are aces.
   e. the three cards chosen form three of a kind.

4. Suppose the U.S. Senate is composed of 58 Democrats and 42 Republicans. If three senators are chosen at random to be on a TV panel discussion, find the probability that
   a. all senators chosen are Democrats.
   b. all senators chosen are of the same party.
   c. at least one Republican is chosen.
   d. at least one senator from each party is chosen.

5. In problem 1, find the *m.v.* and variance of y by (39) and (40).

6. In problem 2, find the *m.v.* and variance of y by (39) and (40).

3.10 The Poisson Distribution

When y is a binomial random variable, representing the number of successes in n independent trials with a single-trial success probability p, we have seen that the mean value and variance of y are given by the simple formulas

$$\mu_y = np \qquad \sigma_y^2 = np(1 - p) \tag{41}$$

although the individual probabilities $p_i = P\{y = i\}$ have the rather complicated form

$$p_i = \binom{n}{i} p^i (1-p)^{n-i}; \quad i = 0, 1, \ldots, n \tag{42}$$

For large values of n these values are difficult to compute.

Suppose now that n is very large but p is very near 0, and let the product of n and p be denoted by

$$\lambda = np \tag{43}$$

Then the equations (41) can be written in the form

$$\mu_y = \lambda \qquad \sigma_y^2 = \lambda \left(1 - \frac{\lambda}{n} \right) \tag{44}$$

If λ is held constant while n increases and p tends to 0 (so that $p = \lambda/n$ for $n = 1, 2, 3, \ldots$) then as n increases, the variance σ_y^2 will tend to the constant $\sigma_y^2 = \lambda$. *Thus for a binomial* y *with* n *large,* p *near* 0, *and* np $= \lambda$, *the mean value and variance of* y *will both be approximately equal to* λ.

For example, let $\lambda = 2$. Then a binomial y with

$$n = 4, p = .5 \text{ will have } \mu_y = 2, \sigma_y^2 = 2(1 - 2/4) = 1.000$$
$$n = 10, p = .2 \text{ will have } \mu_y = 2, \sigma_y^2 = 2(1 - 2/10) = 1.600$$
$$n = 20, p = .1 \text{ will have } \mu_y = 2, \sigma_y^2 = 2(1 - 2/20) = 1.800$$
$$n = 40, p = .05 \text{ will have } \mu_y = 2, \sigma_y^2 = 2(1 - 2/40) = 1.900$$
$$n = 100, p = .02 \text{ will have } \mu_y = 2, \sigma_y^2 = 2(1 - 2/100) = 1.960$$

Since as n increases and $np = 2$ is held fixed both μ_y and σ_y^2 tend to a limit, we naturally ask whether the individual probabilities (42) tend to limiting values involving λ and i alone. It can be shown that this is indeed the case. *When* np $= \lambda$ *and* n *is large, then for any fixed value of* i *the probability*

$$p_i = P\{y = i\} = \binom{n}{i} p^i (1 - p)^{n-i} = \binom{n}{i} \left(\frac{n}{\lambda} \right)^i \left(1 - \frac{n}{\lambda} \right)^i$$

tends to a limiting value given by the mathematical expression

$$e^{-\lambda} \cdot \frac{\lambda^i}{i!} \tag{45}$$

where $e = 2.718 \ldots$ is a constant that occurs frequently in higher mathematics. The values of (45) are available in tables. We show below the approach of $P\{y = i\}$ to the limiting value (45) as n increases for the particular case $np = \lambda = 2$ discussed above. The tabulated values are those of $P\{y = i\}$ with $p = 2/n$, so that $np = 2$.

Values of $P\{y = i\}$ *for* np = 2 *as* n *increases*

n \ i	0	1	2	3	4	5	6	7	8
4	.06250	.25000	.31500	.25000	.06250	0	0	0	0
10	.10737	.27844	.30197	.20133	.08808	.02642	.00551	.00078	.00008
20	.12158	.27017	.28518	.19012	.08978	.03192	.00886	.00197	.00036
40	.12851	.27055	.27778	.18511	.09012	.03415	.01099	.00268	.00058
100	.13262	.27065	.27342	.18227	.09021	.03535	.01142	.00313	.00074
$\vdots$	$\vdots$	$\vdots$	$\vdots$	$\vdots$	$\vdots$	$\vdots$	$\vdots$	$\vdots$	$\vdots$
$e^{-2} \cdot \frac{2^i}{i!}$	.13534	.27067	.27067	.18045	.0902	.03609	.01203	.00344	.00086

For any positive constant λ, a random variable y such that

$$P\{y = i\} = e^{-\lambda} \cdot \frac{\lambda^i}{i!} \text{ for } i = 0, 1, 2, \ldots \tag{46}$$

is said to have a *Poisson distribution with the parameter* λ. The value λ is simultaneously the *mean value* and the *variance* of this random variable:

$$\mu_y = \lambda \qquad \sigma_y^2 = \lambda \tag{47}$$

Values of the *cumulative distribution function*

$$P(i, \lambda) = P\{y \le i\} = \sum_{j=0}^{i} e^{-\lambda} \cdot \frac{\lambda^i}{i!} \tag{48}$$

are given in appendix table 5. To find any individual probability (46) we use the relations

$$P\{y \le i\} = P\{y \le i\} - P\{y \le i - 1\} \tag{49}$$
$$= P(i; \lambda) - P(i - 1; \lambda); i = 1, 2, \ldots$$
$$P\{y = 0\} = P(0; \lambda)$$

The Poisson distribution often arises in practice in counting the total number y of "rare events", that is, the number of occurrences of an event of small probability p, in n independent trials. Knowing only the mean value λ of y, we can then find the probability of any given number 0, 1, 2, . . . of occurrences of the event by (46).

Example 21
Suppose that y, the number of deaths per day in the United States caused by a certain rare disease, follows a Poisson distribution with mean value $\lambda = 3$. The probability distribution of y can be obtained by using (49) and appendix table 5 with $\lambda = 3$.

y:

Prob.	.050	.149	.224	.224	.168	.101	.050	.022	.008	.003	.001	.000	. . .
Value	0	1	2	3	4	5	6	7	8	9	10	11	

For example,

$$P\{y = 4\} = P\{4; 3\} - P\{3; 3\} = .815 - .647 = .168$$

while

$$P\{y > 8\} = 1 - P\{y \le 7\} = 1 - .988 = .012$$

Example 22
It is known that if bacteria are grown on a culture plate with a total area A, and if $y =$ the number of bacterial colonies in a randomly chosen small area a of the plate, then y has a Poisson distribution with mean value $\lambda = (a/A) \cdot$ (the total number of colonies on the plate). Suppose that $\lambda = 5.5$; find the probability that (a) three or fewer colonies will be found in the area; (b) more than eight colonies will be found in the area; and (c) between two and nine colonies inclusive will be found in the area.
We calculate these probabilities using appendix table 5; here $\lambda = 5.5$ and

a. $P\{y \le 3\} = P(3; 5.5) = .2017$

b. $P\{y > 8\} = 1 - P\{y \le 7\} = 1 - P(7; 5.5) = 1 - .8095 = .1905$

c. $P\{2 \le y \le 9\} = P\{y \le 9\} - P\{y \le 1\} = P(9; 5.5) - P(1; 5.5)$
    $= .9462 - .0266 = .9196$

The reason that y has a Poisson distribution in the above example is as follows. If the total area of the plate is A and if there are n colonies in all, then with a uniform distribution of location for each colony, the probability that any given colony will be found in a given small area a will be a/A. If the colonies act independently of one another, then the number y of colonies that will be found in this small area will have a binomial distribution with n trials and the probability $p = a/A$ of "success" in a single trial. The mean value of the number of colonies in the small area a will then be $\lambda = np = (a/A) \cdot n$. If n is large and a/A is small, the binomial y will therefore have (approximately) a Poisson distribution with the parameter λ.

The same argument shows that if a batch of raisin cookies is made by randomly mixing a large number n of raisins into a volume of dough A that is large compared to the volume of a single cookie a, then the number y of raisins in a randomly selected cookie from the batch will have a Poisson distribution with the parameter $\lambda = (a/A) \cdot n$. Since $A/a =$ the number of cookies in the batch, we see that the parameter λ has the value $\lambda = n/(A/a) =$ the average number of raisins per cookie for the batch. If, say, $\lambda = 3$, then from example 21 we can see that the probability that a randomly selected cookie will have exactly three raisins is .224, while the probability that it will have fewer than three is $.050 + .149 + .224 = .423$.

PROBLEMS 3.10

1. Let $y =$ the number of colds a person chosen at random has in a given calendar year. If y has a Poisson distribution with $\lambda = 4$, find the probability that a person chosen at random has in the year

   a. exactly four colds.
   b. exactly three colds.
   c. at least one cold.
   d. more than eight colds.

2. Let $y =$ the number of breakdowns of an electronic computer during an interval of t hours. The random variable y will have a Poisson distribution with mean $m.v.\lambda = t \cdot$ (number of breakdowns per hour). Suppose $\lambda = 1$ for $t = 48$, a two-day period. Find the probability that

   a. no breakdown will occur in a 48-hour period.
   b. exactly one breakdown will occur in a 48-hour period.
   c. at least one breakdown will occur in a 48-hour period.
   d. more than four breakdowns will occur in a 48-hour period.

3. In problem 1, find the mean value and variance of y by (47).

4. In problem 2, find the mean value and variance of y by (47).

5. The number of car accidents in a given month at a certain intersection is known to follow a Poisson distribution with a $m.v.$ $\lambda = 2.5$. Find the probability that

   a. exactly one accident occurs in the month.

b. at least one accident occurs in the month.

c. more than 10 accidents occur in the month.

Suppose that more than 10 accidents are observed in the month. Considering the probability in (c), might one suspect that $\lambda = 2.5$ is not true?

6. If a person enters a lottery 1000 times, and his chance of winning each time is one in a thousand, then y = number of times he wins in the lottery has a Poisson distribution (approximately) with the mean value $\lambda = 1000 \, (1/1000) = 1$. (See (41).) Find the probability that in the 1000 times

a. no wins occur.

b. at least one win occurs.

c. five or more wins occur.

Statistical Inference for the Binomial Distribution

4 Statistical Inference for the Binomial Distribution

In section 3.7 we discussed the probability distribution of a binomial random variable y. For example, in 20 tosses of a fair coin the total number of heads y has a binomial distribution with the parameters $n = 20$ and $p = .5$. From appendix table 4, the probability of obtaining 15 or more heads is $P(y \geq 15) = 1 - P(y \leq 14) = 1 - .979 = .021$.

This computation is, of course, valid only when the true probability p of heads in a single toss is exactly .5. In *statistical inference*, however, we have to reverse this process, and from an *observed* value of y make a judgment about a probability p which is *unknown*. Such judgments, of course, can never be certain, but we shall see how the degree of uncertainty associated with them can be evaluated.

For example, suppose that a stranger invites us to gamble on repeated tosses of his coin; we win a dollar for each tail that appears and lose a dollar for each head. This would be a fair, though risky, game if $p = .5$ for his coin. Since we do not know p, we deem it prudent to test his coin by tossing it a few times. Suppose that in 20 trial tosses, heads appears 15 times. As we have just seen, the probability of obtaining 15 or more heads in 20 tosses of a fair coin is .021. We would therefore be justified in suspecting that the coin is biased in favor of heads, and hence in refusing to play. In so doing, we would be making a "statistical inference" about the unknown value of p.

Again, suppose that we have all the ballots for two candidates, A and B, before us. We want to find out who won the election without tallying all the ballots. To this end we take a random sample of 100 ballots, and observe that 59 are for candidate A. Clearly, .59 is a reasonable estimate of candidate A's proportion of the total vote, based on this sample. But how reliable an estimate is it? In particular, how safe would it be to conclude that candidate A won the election; that is, that the unknown proportion p of the total vote for candidate A is $> .5$? Computation shows that the probability of getting at least 59 ballots for candidate A if $p = .5$ is

$$P\{y \geq 59\} = \sum_{i=59}^{100} \binom{100}{i}\left(\frac{1}{2}\right)^i\left(1 - \frac{1}{2}\right)^{100-i}$$

$$= \frac{(100)!}{2^{100}} \sum_{i=59}^{100} \frac{1}{(i!)(100 - i)!} = .045$$

Moreover, this probability is even smaller if $p < .5$. Thus, if we make it a *rule* in such situations to guess that a candidate has won if, and only if, in a random sample of 100 votes, the candidate receives 59 or more, then our chance of being wrong is at most $.045 + .045 = .09$. (It is double the value .045, since the preceding reasoning applies also to candidate B.)

   Statistical inference is concerned with finding rules for making reasonable judgments from a sample about the unknown structure of the population from which the sample is drawn, and of assessing the degree of reliability of these judgments. We restrict ourselves in this chapter to the simple but important case of the binomial distribution with unknown parameter p.

4.1 Point Estimation for the Binomial Distribution

Example 1

A drug that sometimes produces toxic side effects is given to n mice, and y are observed to be toxically affected. If y has a binomial distribution with n trials, and the probability p of each mouse being affected is unknown, what will be a good estimate of the true value of p? Of course, the true p could have any value between 0 and 1, but on the basis of what has been observed in the sample of n, a reasonable estimate of p is the *sample proportion* affected; that is, $\hat{p} = y/n$.

   In general, if y is binomially distributed with a known sample size n but an unknown parameter p, we shall estimate p by $\hat{p} = y/n$. Since $\hat{p}$ varies from one sample of n to another, it is a *random variable*. How good an estimator of the unknown parameter p is it?

   Two good properties of the estimator $\hat{p} = y/n$ are

1. $\hat{p}$ is an *unbiased* estimator of p.
2. $\hat{p}$ is a *consistent* estimator of p.

1. Unbiasedness

We can easily find the mean value of the probability distribution of $\hat{p}$. Since $\hat{p} = y/n$ and $\mu_y = np$, it follows that $\mu_{\hat{p}} = 1/n \cdot \mu_y = 1/n \cdot np = p$. Thus *whatever the value* of p

$$\mu_{\hat{p}} = p \tag{1}$$

The probability distribution of the observable random variable $\hat{p}$ is therefore such that its *mean* value is equal to the unknown constant p that it is attempting to estimate. This is expressed by saying that $\hat{p}$ is an *unbiased* estimator of the parameter p.

2. Consistency

The variance of $\hat{p}$, a measure of the dispersion of $\hat{p}$ about its mean value p, is equal to

$$\sigma_{\hat{p}}^2 = \frac{1}{n^2} \cdot \sigma_y^2 = \frac{1}{n^2} \cdot npq = \frac{pq}{n} \tag{2}$$

This quantity approaches zero as n increases. Hence, for a large n the probability distribution of $\hat{p}$ is highly concentrated about its mean value p. *The probability that $\hat{p}$ will deviate from p by more than any fixed amount $\epsilon > 0$, no matter how small, approaches zero as n becomes larger and larger.* This property of $\hat{p}$ is called *consistency*. In general, if a sample estimator (here $\hat{p}$) of some population parameter (here p) has the property that for any fixed positive number ϵ the probability approaches 0 as n increases so that the estimator will differ from the true value of the parameter by as much as ϵ, then the estimator is said to be *consistent*. In contrast to no. 1 above, consistency is a "large sample" property of an estimator.

To prove the consistency of $\hat{p}$, we observe that by Chebyshev's inequality, for any $c > 0$

$$P\left\{ |\hat{p} - p| \geq c \sqrt{\frac{pq}{n}} \right\} \leq \frac{1}{c^2} \tag{3}$$

Putting $\epsilon = c\sqrt{pq/n}$, so that $c^2 = n\epsilon^2/pq$, we obtain the following inequality, valid for any $\epsilon > 0$, $0 \leq p \leq 1$, and $n = 1, 2, \ldots$

$$P\{ |\hat{p} - p| \geq \epsilon \} \leq \frac{pq}{n\epsilon^2} \tag{4}$$

The consistency of $\hat{p}$ follows at once from (4), since $pq/n\epsilon^2$ approaches zero as n increases.

The inequality (4), although useful because of its simplicity and generality, is quite crude. For example, let $p = .5$ and $\epsilon = .1$. From binomial distribution tables we find for $n = 50, 100, 200$, and 300 the values

$\epsilon = .1, p = .5; n =$	50	100	200	300
$P\{\lvert p_n - .5\rvert \geq .1\}$	.203	.057	.006	.001
$\dfrac{pq}{n\epsilon^2} = \dfrac{25}{n}$	.5	.25	.125	.0833

A comparison of the last two rows of this table shows that $25/n$, the right-hand side of (4), in this case, is considerably larger than the left-hand side.

The example that follows shows that if $\hat{p}$ is sufficiently large it may be safe to conclude at least that $p > .5$.

Example 2

A random sample of 25 students at a large university responded to the question "Should marijuana be legalized?" with 18 Yes's and 7 No's. The point estimate $\hat{p} = y/n$ of the unknown proportion p of students at this university who would say Yes is thus

$$\hat{p} = \frac{18}{25} = .72$$

suggesting that more than half of all students would say Yes to this question. We now ask, what is the probability that $\hat{p} \geq .72$ if in fact $p = .5$? To compute this we use appendix table 4 for $n = 25$ and $p = .5$

$$P\{\hat{p} \geq .72\} = P\left\{\frac{y}{25} \geq .72\right\} = P\{y \geq 18\}$$

$$= 1 - P\{y \leq 17\} = 1 - .978 = .022$$

Thus if the students were evenly divided on the question, the estimate $\hat{p}$ of p would be as large or larger than the observed value $\hat{p} = .72$ only about one in 50 times. Moreover, if the population proportion p of students who would say Yes were less than .5, then clearly $P\{\hat{p} \geq .72\}$ would be even smaller than .022. It is therefore safe to decide in this case that the true proportion p of the total student population who would answer Yes exceeds .5. "Safe" here means: if we agree to assert that $p > .5$ only when at least 18 in a sample of 25 answer Yes, then when in fact $p \leq .5$ we shall make an erroneous assertion no more than 2.2 percent of the time.

PROBLEMS 4.1

1. A manufacturer tests 20 automobile tires and observes that y of the tires have a lifetime of more than 30,000 miles. If these 20 tires are a random sample from all tires that the manufacturer might produce, give a point estimator of the unknown probability that a

tire so produced will have a lifetime of more than 30,000 miles. What is the value of your point estimator if $y = 17$?

2. A poll of 25 voters showed that y of them answered Yes when asked "Do you feel the President is doing a good job in foreign policy matters?" Given that these 25 voters are a random sample from all U.S. voters (we may ignore the question of replacement here for all practical purposes), give a point estimator of the unknown proportion of U.S. voters who would answer Yes to the above question. What is the value of your point estimator if $y = 11$?

3. In problem 1, what is the mean and variance of the estimator $\hat{p} = y/20$ if the true probability of a tire so produced having a lifetime of more than 30,000 miles is .8? Compute the probability that $\hat{p}$ will be within .1 of the true value .8; that is, find $P(|\hat{p} - .8| \leq .1)$. Do the same for an error of .2.

4. In problem 2, what is the mean and variance of the estimator $\hat{p} = y/25$ if the true proportion of all voters answering Yes is .4? Compute the probability that $\hat{p}$ will be within .1 of the true value .4; that is, find $P(|\hat{p} - .4| \leq .1)$. Do the same for an error of .2.

5. A jar containing r red balls and b black balls is presented to you, and you are asked to estimate the proportion $p = r/(r + b)$ of red balls in the jar. If you are allowed to randomly sample with replacement from the jar n times and you observe y red balls, give a point estimator of p.

   If $r = 10$ and $b = 15$, find the mean and variance of your estimator for $n = 10, 25, 100, 400,$ and 1600. Does the mean change with n? Does the variance change with n? What is the value of your estimator if $n = 100$ and $y = 36$?

6. Suppose that an unknown proportion of all babies born in the U.S. have a certain minor birth defect. If in a random sample of n such births, y of the babies born are observed to have this birth defect, give a point estimator of this unknown proportion. If the unknown proportion is .10, find the mean and variance of your estimator for $n = 10, 25, 100, 400,$ and 1600. What does this say about your estimator? What is the value of your estimator if $n = 400$ and $y = 44$?

7. Use Chebyshev's inequality (4) to compute the upper bound for $P(|\hat{p} - p| \geq .1)$ given by $pq/n(.1)^2$ for the data of problem 5. Discuss what this says about the notion of consistency.

8. Using Chebyshev's inequality (4) compute the upper bound for $P(|\hat{p} - p| \geq .01)$ given by $pq/n(.01)^2$ for problem 6 for $n = 400$,

1600, 6400, and 10,000. Based on these calculations, would you say that $\hat{p}$ is a consistent estimator of p?

4.2 Interval Estimation for the Binomial Distribution

We have seen that the sample proportion of successes, $\hat{p} = y/n$, is a good point estimator of the unknown parameter p of a binomial distribution when the number n of trials is large. However, $\hat{p}$ is a random variable; its value varies from sample to sample and will not often be exactly equal to p. In fact, if $p = .5$ and, say, $n = 20$, we have by appendix table 4

$$P\{\hat{p} = p\} = P\left\{\frac{y}{n} = .5\right\} = P\{y = 10\} = .176$$

Hence, when $p = .5$ and we use the point estimator $\hat{p}$ to estimate p, we have only a 17.6 percent chance of being exactly correct. (If in fact $p = .49$, then in 20 trials there is *no* chance that $\hat{p} = p$.) This shows that *a point estimate of* p *alone has limited value;* to state only that $\hat{p} = y/n$ is our best guess of an unknown p leaves much to be desired. What we would prefer is a pair of numbers p_L and p_U, $p_L < p_U$, such that we can be quite sure that the unknown p will lie between them. We shall in what follows show how to assign lower and upper values p_L and p_U such that the event $\{p_L < p < p_U\}$ will have a high probability. More precisely, for a given number $0 < \alpha < 1$, usually small (say, .02 or .05), we shall find lower and upper estimators p_L and p_U in such a way that *whatever be the true but unknown value of the parameter p*

$$P\{p_L < p < p_U\} \cong 1 - \alpha \tag{5}$$

When (5) holds, the interval (p_L, p_U) is called an approximately *100(1 − α)% confidence interval* for the unknown parameter p, meaning that *the probability is about* $1 - \alpha$ *that in repeated samples of size* n *the interval* (p_L, p_U), *computed each time from the observed sample, will contain the true but unknown value of* p.

To construct p_L and p_U satisfying (5), we use an improved version of (3). As seen above, the left-hand side of (3) is considerably smaller than $1/c^2$ for a large n. The following "normal" approximation, however, will be found to be quite accurate for large values of n:

$$P\left\{|\hat{p} - p| \leq c\sqrt{\frac{pq}{n}}\right\} \cong \begin{array}{l} .50 \text{ for } c = .67 \\ .90 \text{ for } c = 1.65 \\ .95 \text{ for } c = 1.96 \\ .98 \text{ for } c = 2.33 \\ .99 \text{ for } c = 2.58 \end{array} \tag{6}$$

As a rule of thumb, the approximation (6) will be in error by no more than about .01 if n is so large that $np \geq 10$ and $nq \geq 10$. (This approximation is based on theory to be discussed in chapter 5.) The accuracy of the approximation will be illustrated by some special cases.

For example, let $p = .5$, $n = 10$, and $c = 1.96$, for which the right-hand side of (6) has the value .95. Then

$$\sqrt{\frac{pq}{n}} = .158$$

and by appendix table 4

$$P\left\{p - 1.96\sqrt{\frac{pq}{n}} < \hat{p} < p + 1.96\sqrt{\frac{pq}{n}}\right\}$$

$$= P\left\{.19 < \frac{y}{10} < .81\right\} = P\{2 \leq y \leq 8\} = .978$$

which even for this small n is not too far from .95. For $p = .5$ and $n = 20$

$$\sqrt{\frac{pq}{n}} = .112$$

and now

$$P\left\{p - 1.96\sqrt{\frac{pq}{n}} < \hat{p} < p - 1.96\sqrt{\frac{pq}{n}}\right\}$$

$$= P\{5.61 < y < 14.39\} = P\{6 \leq y \leq 14\} = .958$$

which is within .01 of .95. For values $n > 20$ the approximation by .95 is even closer.

We shall accept the approximations (6) as valid working tools for the statistician, and show how they may be used to construct confidence interval estimates for an unknown p.

The event in (6) for $c = 1.96$ is that $\hat{p} = y/n$ is distant less than $1.96\sqrt{pq/n}$ from p; this is equivalent to saying that p is distant less than $1.96\sqrt{pq/n}$ from $\hat{p}$. Hence (6) for $c = 1.96$ may be rewritten in the equivalent form

$$P\left\{\hat{p} - 1.96\sqrt{\frac{pq}{n}} < p < \hat{p} + 1.96\sqrt{\frac{pq}{n}}\right\} \cong .95 \tag{7}$$

Now we have seen that $\hat{p}$ is a consistent estimator of p, so that for a large n, $\hat{p}$ will with high probability differ little from p. Setting $\hat{q} = 1 - \hat{p} = 1 - y/n$ in (7), it follows that

$$P\left\{\hat{p} - 1.96\sqrt{\frac{\hat{p}\hat{q}}{n}} < p < \hat{p} + 1.96\sqrt{\frac{\hat{p}\hat{q}}{n}}\right\} \cong .95 \tag{8}$$

since almost surely $pq \cong \hat{p}\hat{q}$. But (8) is equivalent to the statement that (5) holds, with $\alpha = .05$ and

$$p_L = \hat{p} - 1.96\sqrt{\frac{\hat{p}\hat{q}}{n}} \qquad p_U = \hat{p} + 1.96\sqrt{\frac{\hat{p}\hat{q}}{n}}$$

We express this fact by saying that for a large n the interval

$$\left(\hat{p} - 1.96\sqrt{\frac{\hat{p}\hat{q}}{n}}, \hat{p} + 1.96\sqrt{\frac{\hat{p}\hat{q}}{n}}\right) \tag{9}$$

centered at the observed relative frequency $\hat{p} = y/n$, *is an approximately 95% confidence interval for the unknown probability* p. In repeated sampling the random interval (9) will sometimes be entirely to the left of p, sometimes entirely to the right of p, and sometimes will contain p; it is the latter event which has probability $\cong .95$ of occurring. Similarly, referring back to (6), *the interval*

$$\left(\hat{p} - 2.33\sqrt{\frac{\hat{p}\hat{q}}{n}}, \hat{p} + 2.33\sqrt{\frac{\hat{p}\hat{q}}{n}}\right) \tag{10}$$

is an approximately 98% *confidence interval for* p; since in repeated samples of size n this interval will contain p about 98% of the time. From (6) we can similarly construct 50%, 90%, and 99% confidence intervals for p; for example, in repeated large samples the interval

$$\left(\hat{p} - .67\sqrt{\frac{\hat{p}\hat{q}}{n}}, \hat{p} + .67\sqrt{\frac{\hat{p}\hat{q}}{n}}\right) \tag{11}$$

will cover the true value of p about 50 percent of the time. All these confidence intervals are centered at the point estimator $\hat{p} = y/n$ of p, and extend an equal distance on either side of $\hat{p}$.

Example 3

A number n of randomly selected users of plain aspirin are given a buffered form and asked if they prefer it to the plain. Let $y =$ the number of users who say Yes. Find a 95% confidence interval for $p =$ the unknown proportion of all users who would prefer the buffered form.

To do this we compute the 95% confidence interval (9). About 95% of the time p will lie within this interval; in other words, the double inequality

$$p_L = \hat{p} - 1.96\sqrt{\frac{\hat{p}(1 - \hat{p})}{n}} < p < \hat{p} + 1.96\sqrt{\frac{\hat{p}(1 - \hat{p})}{n}} = p_U$$

will hold.

Suppose that in fact for $n = 10{,}000$ the value of y is found to be 5000. Then the 95% confidence interval for p would be

$$(.5 - .0098, .5 + .0098) \cong (.49, .51)$$

Example 4

The motor vehicle department in Iowa wishes to estimate the proportion p of registered cars that are over five years old. A random sample of 50 cards from their files shows 15 cars to be over 5 years old. The 95% confidence interval for p given by (9) is then

$$p = \frac{15}{50} \pm \frac{1.96}{\sqrt{50}} \sqrt{\frac{15}{50}\left(1 - \frac{15}{50}\right)} = .3 \pm .127; \text{ i.e., } p_L = .173 \text{ to } p_U = .427$$

Clearly, a sample size n considerably larger than 50 would be necessary to get a reasonably narrow confidence interval for p.

Example 5

An anticancer drug is used on $n = 1380$ mice to see with what probability it will cause a "response" in tumor shrinkage, defined as a decrease of at least 50% in tumor size within 10 days. If $y = 566$ mice respond, construct the 98% confidence (10) interval for $p = $ the unknown response probability.

Here $\hat{p} = y/n = 566/1380 = .41$, and (10) becomes

$$p = .41 \pm 2.33\sqrt{\frac{(.41)(.59)}{1380}} = .41 \pm 2.33\sqrt{.000175}$$

$$= .41 \pm (2.33)(.0132) = .41 \pm .031; \text{ i.e., } .379 \text{ to } .441$$

This *particular* interval may or may not contain the true parameter p. However, in repeated samples about 98% of the intervals constructed by the above procedure will contain p. *Before* the experiment we are therefore $\cong 98\%$ sure that the interval to be obtained will contain the unknown parameter p.

PROBLEMS 4.2

1. Using the probability approximation (6), find the approximate probability of the event $\{41 \le y \le 59\}$ in $n = 100$ tosses of a fair coin, where $y = $ number of heads. Hint: The random variable y has mean $100 \cdot 1/2 = 50$ and standard deviation $\sqrt{100 \cdot 1/2 \cdot 1/2} = \sqrt{25} = 5$, and $\{41 \le y \le 59\} = \{40.2 < y < 59.8\}$.

2. Using the probability approximation (6), find the approximate probability of the event $\{101 \le y \le 139\}$ in $n = 720$ tosses of a fair die, where $y = $ number of tosses in which a six appears. Hint: y has a mean $(720)(1/6) = 120$ and a standard deviation $= \sqrt{(720)(1/6)(5/6)} = \sqrt{100} = 10$, and $\{101 \le y \le 139\} = \{100.4 < y < 139.6\}$.

3. A random sample of 1600 voters shows that 848 voters prefer candidate A over candidate B. Using (9), give an approximately

95% confidence interval for the proportion p of voters preferring candidate A to candidate B. Explain what this interval means.

4. A random sample of 400 University of Wisconsin students showed that 278 of them were in favor of legalized trial marriage (*Wisconsin State Journal*, Jan. 22, 1974). Based on these results, estimate by an approximately 95% confidence interval the proportion of all students favoring legalized trial marriages. Explain the meaning of the interval constructed.

5. In a random sample of 2500 sales of toothpaste, 550 were observed to be Brand X. Give an approximately 99% confidence interval for Brand X's proportion of sales.

6. In a group of 900 patients with lung cancer, 620 died within one year after diagnosis. If this represents a random sample of all such patients, construct a 98% confidence interval for the proportion of lung cancer patients who will die within one year of diagnosis.

7. (*Class exercise*) Each person in the class should toss a fair coin 20 times and construct a 90% confidence interval for the probability p of heads appearing, based on $y =$ the number of heads in the 20 tosses. Each person should report whether or not his interval contains $p = 1/2$. Record the proportion of times $p = 1/2$ was contained in the interval calculated. Discuss the meaning of the results in class.

4.3 One-Sided Hypothesis Testing for the Binomial Distribution

Example 6

After the St. Lawrence Seaway was constructed, lamprey eels began killing off the lake trout. Studies showed that 70 percent of young trout caught after the seaway was constructed had lamprey-eel marks on their flesh. A method was devised to reduce the lamprey-eel population by electrifying their spawning areas. After one year's trial, limnologists observed a random sample of young trout caught to determine whether the frequency of finding lamprey-eel marks had decreased appreciably. Unless the percentage could be shown to be less than .60, it was felt that this method of eel control should be regarded as ineffective. How few eel-marked trout would have to be observed to make it safe to infer that the method was effective; that is, that the probability of finding lamprey-eel marks on a randomly caught young trout had become less than .60?

Here we encounter a problem of *statistical hypothesis testing* for the binomial distribution. In the present case we wish to decide whether the hypothesis $p \geq .6$ is convincingly refuted by the data.

The hypothesis that we shall put on trial is called the *null hypothesis* H_0: $p \geq .6$. It is called a one-sided hypothesis because it consists of all values of the unknown parameter p on *one* side of the value .6. The negation of the null hypothesis is called the *alternative hypothesis*; here, H_1:$p < .6$. If there is convincing evidence from the sample that H_0 is false then the action of continuing or extending the control method will be taken; otherwise the method will be discontinued and other means sought to decrease p to a value below .6.

In testing any null hypothesis H_0 against an alternative hypothesis H_1, some random variable y associated with a sample is observed. A particular subset R of y values is chosen, and it is agreed to *reject* the null hypothesis H_0 in favor of the alternative H_1 if, and only if, y is observed to have one of the values in R; if y has any value not in R, the null hypothesis H_0 is considered to be not convincingly rejected by the sample. The region R is called the *critical region* of the test. *The problem of hypothesis testing thus reduces to the problem of choosing a suitable critical region R.*

In example 6, y has a binomial distribution with some known n and unknown parameter p, and the two hypotheses are $H_0 : p \geq .6$ and $H_1 : p < .6$. The possible values of y are $0, 1, \ldots, n$. It is intuitively obvious that *small values of* y *tend to support* H_1, *while large values of* y *support* H_0. Accordingly, we take as the critical region R for a test the set of integers $R = (0, 1, \ldots, a)$ up to and including some positive integer $a < n$, and *agree to reject* H_0 *in favor of* H_1 *only if* $0 \leq y \leq a$. In order to decide which value of a to use we must investigate the "operating characteristics" of tests based on various choices of a.

For any given test (here determined by the value of a) the probability of rejecting H_0, regarded as a function of the true value of p, is called the *power function of the test*; it is defined for all $0 \leq p \leq 1$ by the formula

$$P_p \text{ (reject } H_0) = \text{probability of rejecting } H_0 \text{ when} \qquad (12)$$
$$\text{the true parameter value is } p$$
$$= P_p\{0 \leq y \leq a\} = \sum_{i=0}^{a} \binom{10}{i} p^i (1-p)^{n-i}$$

Suppose, for example, that to simplify the computations we choose $n = 10$ and $a = 3$. Then P_p (reject H_0) $= P_p\{0 \leq y \leq 3\} = P_p\{y = 0\} + P_p\{y = 1\} + P_p\{y = 2\} + P_p\{y = 3\}$, and for $p = .0, .1, .2, \ldots, .9,$ 1.0. Appendix table 4 gives

TABLE 4.1
Power Function for Test of $H_0: p \geq .6$ vs $H_1: p < .6$ Using Critical Region $R = (0, 1, 2, 3)$, Based on a Sample of Size $n = 10$.

p	0	.1	.2	.3	.4	.5	.6	.7	.8	.9	1.0
P_p (reject H_0)	1.00	.987	.879	.650	.382	.172	.055	.011	.001	.000	.000

From this table the graph shown in figure 4.1 can be drawn.

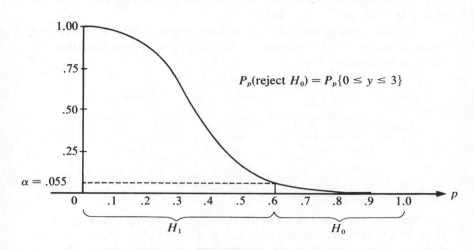

FIGURE 4.1
A Graph of the Power Function of Table 4.1; $R = (0, 1, 2, 3)$; $n = 10$

We see that, as is to be expected, the power function decreases from 1 to 0 as p increases from 0 to 1. The *maximum probability of rejecting H_0* for all those values $p \geq .6$ for which H_0 is in fact true is therefore attained at $p = .6$, and has the value .055. Thus, if p has any value $\geq .6$ (that is, if H_0 is true) the probability of (wrongly) rejecting H_0 is at most .055. For any given test (that is, critical region R) *the maximum value of the probability of rejecting the null hypothesis H_0 when it is in fact true is called the significance level of the test,* and is usually denoted by the letter α. By using the critical region $R = (0, 1, 2, 3)$ in this instance we are thereby testing H_0 at the significance level $\alpha = .055$.

Rejecting the null hypothesis H_0 when in fact it is true is called an error of type I. The significance level α of any test is the maximum probability of making a type I error when using the given test. We usually want a test to have a significance level $\alpha \leq .10$, so as to have a small probability of making a type I error.

Now let us consider the other possible type of error associated with testing the null hypothesis H_0 of example 6; that of *not rejecting* H_0 *when in fact it is false. This is called an error of type II.* For example, if the true value of p is .2, then the test with $n = 10$ and critical region $R = (0, 1, 2, 3)$ will reject $H_0 : p \geq .6$ with probability .879, as we see from table 4.1, and hence the type II error probability at $p = .2$ is $1 - .879 = .121$. Clearly, *the type II error probability for any* p *such that* H_1 *is true is equal to* $1 -$ *the power function of the test at* p. (Note that for p less than but close to .6, the type II error probability is close to $1 - \alpha = .945$.)

We may refer to the true value of the unknown parameter involved (here p) as the "State of Nature." The situation is then described by the four-fold table

Action taken State of nature	Reject H_0	Do not reject H_0
H_0 true	type I error	correct
H_0 false	correct	type II error

Suppose now that in example 6 we are unwilling to run a risk as large as $\alpha = .055$ of rejecting H_0 when it is in fact true. Clearly, we can decrease α by dropping some points from the critical region $R = (0, 1, 2, 3)$ that we used; that is, we can demand stronger evidence before we convict H_0 of being false. If, say, we use as our critical region only $R = (0, 1)$ then the power function becomes

$$P_p \text{ (reject } H_0) = P_p\{0 \leq y \leq 1\} = P_p\{y = 0\} + P_p\{y = 1\}$$

and the table and graph corresponding to table 4.1 and figure 4.1 are illustrated at the top of the facing page.

For this new test, the significance level (the maximum probability of rejecting $H_0 : p \geq .6$ when it is true) has decreased from $\alpha = .055$ to $\alpha = .002$. However, the price of achieving this desirable reduction is to decrease the entire power function, and hence to *increase* the probability of a type II error for values $p < .6$. For example, the critical region $R = (0, 1, 2, 3)$ had a type II error probability at $p = .2$ of .121, whereas for the critical region $R = (0, 1)$ the type II error probability at $p = .2$ is $= 1 - P_{.2}$ (reject H_0) $= 1 - .376 = .624$.

Suppose now that we are willing to work at a significance level α of about .05 but are unwilling to have a type II error probability as great as .121 when in fact $p = .2$. *Our only recourse then is to increase*

TABLE 4.2
Power Function for Critical Region $R = (0, 1)$; $n = 10$

p	0	.1	.2	.3	.4	.5	.6	.7	. . .	1.00
P_p (reject H_0)	1.00	.736	.376	.149	.046	.011	.002	.000	. . .	0

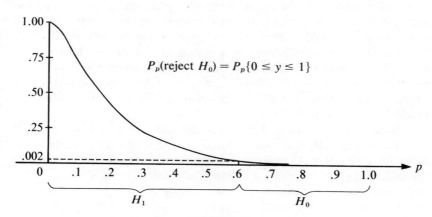

FIGURE 4.2
The Power function of table 4.2; $R = (0, 1)$

the sample size. If instead of $n = 10$ we take a sample of $n = 20$ and again use a critical region $R = (0, 1, 2, \ldots, a)$, the significance level will be

$$\alpha = P_{.6}\{0 \leq y \leq a\} = \sum_{i=0}^{a} \binom{20}{i}(.6)^i(.4)^{20-i}$$

Computation gives the numerical values

a	5	6	7	8	9
α	.002	.006	.021	.057	.128

Thus, choosing $n = 20$ and $a = 8$ gives a significance level $\alpha = .057$, which is about the same as the .055 for $n = 10$ and $a = 3$. But now the power function for the critical region $R = (0, 1, \ldots, 8)$

$$P_p(\text{reject } H_0) = P_p\{0 \leq y \leq 8\} = \sum_{i=0}^{8} \binom{20}{i}p^i(1-p)^{20-i}$$

can be shown from appendix table 4 to be

p	0	.1	.2	.3	.4	.5	.6	. . .	1
$P_p(\text{reject } H_0)$	1.00	1.00	.990	.887	.596	.252	.057	. . .	.000

and the type II error probability at $p = .2$ has fallen to $1 - .990 = .010$, as compared to $.121$ when $n = 10$. If we want even smaller type II error probabilities for $p < .6$ while keeping α about $.05$, we must take even larger values of n, and compute the significance level and power function for various values of a until we are satisfied with the general aspect of the power function obtained. Whenever the sample size n is under our control, these calculations of significance level and power function can be performed before we decide on the sample size, in order to ensure satisfactory performance characteristics of the test. If, on the other hand, n is not under our control, about the best we can do is first to choose a value of a for the given n, so that we can obtain an acceptable significance level α, and then to compute the power function, so that we can at least be aware of the type II error probabilities associated with the test.

Note that in example 6 with $n = 20$ and $a = 8$, if $y = 9$ the null hypothesis $H_0 : p \geq .6$ is not rejected, even though the sample point estimate $\hat{p} = 9/20 = .45$ of p is considerably less than $.6$. This illustrates the difference between point estimation (best numerical guess of an unknown parameter) and hypothesis testing (choice between one of two actions). In estimation, one is trying to get an approximate idea of the value of an unknown parameter (here p) regardless of the action to be taken. However, in hypothesis testing one is concerned only with the question of whether or not to take a certain action (here, implementing the eel control program). In so doing we guard against type I error by choosing the critical region to guarantee small probability ($\alpha = .057$) of error under the stated null hypothesis (here, $p \geq .6$).

Example 7

A statistician employed by a company manufacturing electronic devices wants to determine whether the chance that one of these devices will function for more than 2000 hours (the average use for a year) exceeds $.9$. (The company is considering giving a money-back one-year warranty, and does not want to have to refund the price more than $.10$ of the time.) He tests 25 items, and finds that after 2000 hours y of them are still functioning. Should he recommend that the company offer the warranty? Define p as the probability that a device will function for more than 2000 hours. The statistician can regard the problem as one of testing $H_0 : p \leq .9$ versus $H_1 : p > .9$. (The null hypothesis H_0 is that which it would be more serious to reject wrongly.) Since large values of y tend to discredit H_0, the natural critical region for the test is $R = (b, b + 1, \ldots, 25)$ for some integer b. The test criterion is therefore: Reject $H_0 : p \leq .9$ (and offer the warranty) if and only if $b \leq y \leq 25$.

The significance level α of this test is $\alpha =$ maximum probability of rejecting H_0 when it is true $= P_{.9}\{b \le y \le 25\}$.

If it is agreed that the company should take a risk α of only .05 to .10 of rejecting H_0 when it is true, b must then be chosen so that α lies between these limits. From appendix table 4 we see that for $b = 25$, $\alpha = 1 - .928 = .072$, so the statistician sets $b = 25$. He will therefore recommend giving the warranty if and only if $y = 25$. The probability of adopting a policy that will result in having to refund the price more than 10 percent of the time is then at most $\alpha = .072$.

In the general case, let y be a binomial random variable with n trials and unknown parameter p.

One-sided hypothesis tests for a binomial p:

Case 1. To test $H_0:p \le p_0$ versus $H_1:p > p_0$. The critical region is $R = \{b \le y \le n\}$ (reject H_0 if and only if $y \ge b$). The significance level of the test is

$$\alpha = P_{p_0}\{y \ge b\} = 1 - \sum_{i=0}^{b-1} \binom{n}{i} p_0{}^i (1 - p_0)^{n-i}$$

Case 2. To test $H_0:p \ge p_0$ versus $H_1:p < p_0$. The critical region is $R = \{0 \le y \le a\}$ (reject H_0 if and only if $y \le a$). The significance level of the test is

$$\alpha = P_{p_0}\{y \le a\} = \sum_{i=0}^{a} \binom{n}{i} p_0{}^i (1 - p_0)^{n-i}$$

After deciding what the null hypothesis is to be, we usually select the significance level α as some value between .01 and .10 so that rejection of H_0 when it is true will have a small probability. We control the value of α by choosing b in case 1 or a in case 2. For a given value α, if the power is too small for values of p under H_1, a larger sample size n must be chosen.

For values of n and p not given in appendix table 4, more extensive tables of the binomial distribution are available.

When n is large, the value of a or b for the above tests can be found by using the "normal" approximation to the binomial distribution; this will be discussed in detail in chapter 5. The result is that b in case 1 is $b \cong np_0 + z_\alpha\sqrt{np_0(1 - p_0)}$, while a in case 2 is $a \cong np_0 - z_\alpha\sqrt{np_0(1 - p_0)}$, where z_α is given by the following table as a function of the significance level α:

α	.10	.05	.02	.01
z_α	1.28	1.65	2.05	2.33

Example 8

A mail-order house has found in the past that about .15 of all customers place an order within three months after receiving a new catalog. In order to increase its volume of business, the house contemplates giving trading stamps with each order. For this to be profitable, an order rate of at least .20 must be achieved. Before adopting the trading-stamp policy, management surveys 2000 randomly chosen customers to see if the .20 rate can be attained.

Here the problem is that of testing $H_0: p \leq .2$ versus $H_1: p > .2$, based on the binomial random variable $y =$ number of customers out of the $n = 2000$ sampled who place an order within three months. Suppose that the house is willing to take only a .01 chance of adopting the trading-stamp policy (rejecting H_0 in favor of H_1) when in fact $p \leq .2$. Then $\alpha = .01$, and the test is

Reject $H_0: p \leq .2$ if $y \geq b$, where

$$b \cong np_0 + z_{.01}\sqrt{np_0(1 - p_0)} = (2000)(.2) + 2.33\sqrt{2000(.2)(.8)}$$
$$= 400 + 2.33\sqrt{320} \cong 442$$

If, for example, after three months only 424 of the 2000 customers have placed an order, then the house will not have enough evidence at the level of significance $\alpha = .01$ to reject $H_0: p \leq .2$, and will not adopt the trading-stamp policy. (Note, however, that the point estimate of p based on this sample is

$$\hat{p} = \frac{y}{n} = \frac{424}{2000} = .212$$

This is greater than .20, but the probability that $\hat{p}$ will be $\geq .212$ when in fact $p = .2$ exceeds the desired significance level .01.)

PROBLEMS 4.3

1. A candidate for office wishes to determine whether his proportion of the vote is no greater than .5, based on current voter attitudes. He wishes to test this hypothesis at some level of significance between .05 and .10, based on a sample of $n = 20$ voters. The alternative hypothesis is $H_1 : p > .5$, with null hypothesis $H_0 : p \leq .5$. (a) Find a rejection region of the form $R = (y \geq a) = (a, a + 1, \ldots, 20)$, $y =$ number of voters favoring him, where a satisfies the level of significance constraint. (b) Find a if the level of significance is to be less than .01.

2. Currently 30 percent of all autos on the highway in a certain state have a defect that could cause an accident. The state safety

council launches a campaign to encourage motorists to have their cars checked and repaired. After two months of the campaign, the council wishes to test whether the proportion p of cars with defects has been reduced. The null hypothesis is $H_0 : p \geq .30$ (no improvement) versus $H_1 : p < .30$ (reduced proportion). (a) Using a level of significance between .05 and .10, based on a random sample of $n = 25$ automobiles, find a rejection region of the form $R = (0, 1, \ldots, a) = (y \leq a)$, where $y =$ number of automobiles in the 25 having defects. (b) Do the same for a level of significance less than .01.

3. In problem 1, find the probability of a type II error for $p = .6$ and $p = .7$ for the test in (a) and (b).

4. In problem 2, find the probability of a type II error for $p = .2$ and $p = .1$ for the test in (a) and (b).

5. In problem 1, find a test with level of significance $\alpha = .05$ and $\alpha = .01$ using the table on page 113 if $n = 400$.

6. In problem 3, find a test with level of significance $\alpha = .05$ and $\alpha = .01$ using the table on page 113 if $n = 120$.

7. A person claims to have ESP and to be able to predict the outcome of a fair coin toss more than 60 percent of the time. (a) To test this claim at a level of significance of about .05, set up an appropriate rejection region for $H_0 : p \leq .6$ versus $H_1 : p > .6$, based on n tosses of a coin, for $n = 10$ and $n = 20$. (b) Do the same for $n = 100$ and $n = 400$ by using the table on p. 113. (c) Plot the power function of the tests derived in (a). (d) Find the probability of a Type II error for $p = .5$ for the tests derived in (a). (e) If $y = 12$ of $n = 20$ tosses are predicted correctly, would you agree that the person has ESP, based on your results in (b)? In coming to your conclusion, what type of error might you be making?

4.4 A Two-Sided Hypothesis Test of $p = .5$

A coin is tossed n times and we wish to test at level α whether the coin is fair. Here $H_0 : p = .5$ is the null hypothesis, while $H_1 : p < .5$ or $p > .5$ is the *two-sided* alternative hypothesis, where $p =$ probability of heads in a single toss.

Let $y =$ number of heads obtained in the n tosses. It is intuitively reasonable to reject H_0 in favor of H_1 when y is *either* rather small (suggesting that $p < .5$) *or* rather large (suggesting that $p > .5$). When $p = .5$ the two probabilities

$$P_{.5}\{y = i\} \text{ and } P_{.5}\{y = 20 - i\}$$

are equal. Hence it is reasonable to choose as the critical region R for the test one with the symmetric form

$$R = [\{0 \leq y \leq a\} \text{ or } \{n - a \leq y \leq n\}]$$

where a is some integer between 0 and $n/2$. For this critical region R, the significance level α is

$$\alpha = 2P_{.5}\{0 \leq y \leq a\} = 2 \cdot \frac{1}{2^n} \sum_{i=0}^{a} \binom{n}{i}$$

From appendix table 4 we find for $n = 20$, say, the numerical values

a	3	4	5	6	7	8
α	.002	.012	.042	.116	.262	.504

Thus, for $a = 5$, the significance level becomes .042; the chance of rejecting $H_0 : p = .5$ when it is true is about four in a hundred. The power function of this test is shown as the solid curve in figure 4.3.

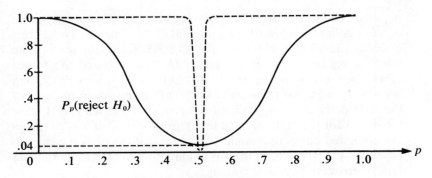

FIGURE 4.3
The power function of $R = (\{0 \leq y \leq 5\} \text{ or } \{15 \leq y \leq 20\})$; $n = 20$

Some numerical values of the power function of figure 4.3 are

p	0	.1	.2	.3	.4	.5	.6	.7	.8	.9	1
P_p (reject H_0)	1.00	.989	.804	.416	.128	.042	.128	.416	.804	.989	1.00

We see that if in fact $p = .9$ (or .1) the probability of rejecting H_0 is .989, and that the greater the distance of p from .5, the greater the probability of rejecting H_0. For a very large sample size n, we can make the power function have a value equal to, say, .01 at $p = .5$, yet rise so sharply as p departs from .5 that its value is very close to 1 at. say, $p = .51$ or .49 (the dotted curve in figure 4.3). *Such a test would rarely be useful* because of the very high probability that it would reject the null hypothesis $H_0 : p = .5$ even when the true value of p is only slightly different from its value $p = .5$ under H_0. Thus, if the sample size n is very large, an observed value of y will often be "highly significant" statistically for rejecting $H_0 : p = .5$ (that is, y may belong to an R for which, say, $\alpha = .01$) even though p is so close to .5 that the asserted deviation from H_0 is of little practical significance. This fact is often neglected in practice, with consequent error in the interpretation of large sample data.

In the general case, let y be any binomial random variable with n trials and an unknown success probability p for a single trial.

To test the null hypothesis $H_0 : p = .5$ versus the two-sided alternative $H_1 : p \neq .5$, the critical region is

$$R = \{0 \leq y \leq a\} \text{ or } \{n - a \leq y \leq n\} \tag{13}$$

for some integer a between 0 and n. The significance level is

$$\alpha = 2P_{.5}\{0 \leq y \leq a\} = 2 \cdot \frac{1}{2^n} \sum_{i=0}^{a} \binom{n}{i} \tag{14}$$

where $\alpha = $ the probability of rejecting H_0 when it is true.

When, for example, n is ≥ 20 we can use the approximation (6) with $p = .5$ to obtain α. To see how this is done, note that when $p = .5$, the probability in (6) with $\hat{p} = y/n$ is

$$P\left\{\frac{n}{2} - \frac{c\sqrt{n}}{2} < y < \frac{n}{2} + \frac{c\sqrt{n}}{2}\right\}$$

$$= 1 - P\left[\left\{0 \leq y \leq \frac{n}{2} - \frac{c\sqrt{n}}{2}\right\} \text{ or } \left\{\frac{n}{2} + \frac{c\sqrt{n}}{2} \leq y \leq n\right\}\right]$$

$$= 1 - P\{0 \leq y \leq a\} - P\{n - a \leq y \leq n\}$$

with $a = n/2 - c\sqrt{n}/2$. Hence, we have

A two-sided test of $H_0 : p = .5$ *for large* n:

$$\text{Reject } H_0 \text{ if } y \leq \frac{n}{2} - \frac{c\sqrt{n}}{2} \text{ or } y \geq \frac{n}{2} + \frac{c\sqrt{n}}{2} \tag{15}$$

where c is found from the table below as a function of $\alpha = P_{.5}$ (reject H_0):

$$\begin{array}{c||c|c|c|c} c & 1.65 & 1.96 & 2.33 & 2.58 \\ \hline \alpha & .10 & .05 & .02 & .01 \end{array} \qquad (16)$$

For example, if $n = 100$ and $\alpha = .02$, we take $c = 2.33$ and reject $H_0 : p = .5$ if

$$y \leq 50 - (2.33)(5) = 38.35, \text{ i.e., } y \leq 38; \text{ or}$$
$$y \geq 50 + (2.33)(5) = 61.65, \text{ i.e., } y \geq 62$$

If $n = 10$, we may use the exact rule (13). From appendix table 4

$$\begin{array}{c||c|c|c} a & 0 & 1 & 2 \\ \hline \alpha & .002 & .022 & .110 \end{array}$$

Therefore, if we again want α to be about .02, we choose $a = 3$ and reject H_0 if

$$y \leq 1 \text{ or } y \geq 10 - 1 = 9$$

If H_0 is rejected, large values of y suggest that $p > .5$, while small values suggest that $p < .5$. Thus, for $p > .5$ the probability that $0 \leq y \leq a$ cannot exceed $P_{.5}\{0 \leq y \leq a\}$, which is by (14) equal to $\alpha/2$.

Large-sample tests for $H_0 : p = p_0$ vs $H_1 : p \neq p_0$, where $p_0 \neq .5$, will be given in chapter 6. Note again the caution on page 117 against using very large sample tests of a "one-point" null hypothesis $H_0 : p = p_0$ vs $H_1 : p \neq p_0$.

PROBLEMS 4.4

1. A random sample of 100 births in a certain county is taken to see whether or not the birth ratio of males to females is 1 to 1. State the problem as a hypothesis-testing problem, giving the null and alternative hypotheses. Is the alternative hypothesis one-sided or two-sided?

2. A manufacturer tests a random sample of 200 items to determine whether or not 60 percent of the items have a lifetime of more than 200 usage hours. State the null and alternative hypotheses for the manufacturer's test. Is the alternative hypothesis one-sided or two-sided?

3. An auto insurance company samples 1000 of its customers to test whether or not 10 percent have had an accident within the last 12 months. State the null and alternative hypothesis for this situation. Is the alternative hypothesis one-sided or two-sided?

4. Suppose that six months ago a survey showed that 60 percent of the voters in the U.S. approved of the way the economy was functioning. A current survey of 500 is taken to check whether or not

attitudes have changed on this matter. State the null and alternative hypotheses. Is the alternative hypothesis one-sided or two-sided?

5. If a coin is tossed $n = 10$ times, find an $\alpha = .11$ level test of the hypothesis $H_0 : p = .5$ (the coin is fair) against the alternative $H_1 : p \neq .5$ (the coin is biased), where $p = $ probability of a head on a single toss. Do the same for $n = 20$ and $\alpha = .116$.

6. Test the hypothesis that the proportion of female births in a given hospital is $p = .5$, based on a sample of size $n = 15$ at level $\alpha = .036$. Do the same for $n = 25$ and $\alpha = .044$.

7. Plot the power function of the test in problem 5.

8. Plot the power function of the test in problem 6.

9. In problem 5, find the appropriate test if $n = 400$ and $\alpha = .10$. What conclusion would you reach if $y = 220$ heads are observed? In reaching this conclusion, what type of error might you be making?

10. In problem 6, find the appropriate test if $n = 100$ and $\alpha = .05$. What decision would you make if $y = 47$ female births in the 200 births? What type of error might you be making?

11. In a taste test of two brands of puddings, a sample of size $n = 900$ showed that y people preferred brand A to brand B. If $p = $ proportion of people preferring brand A to brand B, give an $\alpha = .02$ level test of $H_0 : p = .5$ against $H_1 : p \neq .5$. What decision would be reached if $y = 503$? What type of error might you be making?

4.5 The Sign Test

The results of the previous section lead to a simple but useful test for *comparing two populations* when measurements from the two populations occur in natural pairs.

Suppose we have N pairs of observations $\{(x_1, y_1), (x_2, y_2), \ldots , (x_N, y_N)\}$. We wish to test the null hypothesis

$$H_0 : P(x > y) = P(x < y)$$

vs the alternative H_1 that either

$$P(x > y) < P(x < y) \quad (y \text{ values usually larger}) \quad \text{or}$$
$$P(x > y) > P(x < y) \quad (x \text{ values usually larger})$$

To do this, we first eliminate all tied pairs (pairs for which $x_i = y_i$), and using the remaining untied pairs we test the hypothesis $H_0 : p^* = .5$ vs $H_1 : p^* \neq .5$, where p^* is the *conditional probability* $p^* = P(x < y | x \neq y)$. If $y =$ number of pairs for which $x_i < y_i$, then y has a binomial distribution with $n =$ number of untied pairs and parameter $p^* = .5$ under H_0. The test is therefore the same as the two-sided test of section 4.4:

The sign test. To test, for two jointly occurring random variables x and y,

$$H_0 : P(x < y) = P(x > y) \quad \text{vs}$$
$$H_1 : P(x < y) < P(x > y) \quad \text{or} \quad P(x < y) > P(x > y)$$

The *test statistic* is

$$y = \text{number of pairs for which } x_i < y_i$$
$$ = \text{number of } + \text{ signs of } y_i - x_i$$

The *critical region* for an α-level test with $n =$ number of untied pairs is

a. For $n \geq 20$:

$$\text{Reject } H_0 \text{ if } y \leq \frac{n}{2} - \frac{c\sqrt{n}}{2} \quad \text{or} \quad y \geq \frac{n}{2} + \frac{c\sqrt{n}}{2} \tag{17}$$

where c is determined as in (16) for a given value of α.

b. For $n < 20$:

$$\text{Reject } H_0 \text{ if } 0 \leq y \leq a \text{ or } n - a \leq y \leq n, \tag{18}$$

where a is chosen so that

$$\alpha = 2P(0 \leq y \leq a) = 2 \cdot \frac{1}{2^n} \sum_{i=0}^{a} \binom{n}{i} = 2B(a; n, .5)$$

where $B(i; n, p)$ is given in appendix table 4.

Example 9

A random sample of twelve sets of identical twins had the following birth weights (in lbs).

Set	1	2	3	4	5	6	7	8	9	10	11
First born (x_i)	6.2	4.7	5.8	5.0	7.1	5.3	3.8	4.1	5.3	6.1	5.6
Second born (y_i)	6.0	4.2	5.6	5.1	6.3	4.6	3.7	4.6	4.9	5.7	5.6
Sign	−	−	−	+	−	−	−	+	−	−	tie

To test the hypothesis H_0: first-born twin's weight is equally likely to be larger or smaller than second-born twin's weight, against the alternative H_1: first-born twin's weight more often exceeds (or is less than) the second-born twin's weight, we shall use the sign test. Here $n = 11 - 1 = 10$ and the critical region is

$$\text{Reject } H_0 \text{ if } y \le a \quad \text{or} \quad y \ge 10 - a$$

where from appendix table 4 and (18) the value of α is

a	0	1	2	3
α	.002	.022	.110	.344

Thus, if we want α to be between .05 and .15, we take $a = 2$ so that $\alpha = .110$, and reject H_0 if $y \le 2$ or $y \ge 8$. For the given data, $y = 2$, so we reject H_0. The evidence indicates that the first-born twin is more likely to have a higher weight.

Example 10

The IQ's of 26 randomly chosen married couples were:

Couple	1	2	3	4	5	6	7	8	9	10	11	12	13
Husband (x)	108	120	130	104	142	116	121	110	102	129	118	143	131
Wife (y)	115	127	123	94	145	128	144	101	110	115	106	131	140
Sign	+	+	−	−	+	+	+	−	+	−	−	−	+

Couple	14	15	16	17	18	19	20	21	22	23	24	25	26
Husband (x)	122	117	121	110	105	123	131	120	110	112	123	125	116
Wife (y)	122	104	135	107	114	134	126	110	102	125	114	126	123
Sign	tie	−	+	−	+	+	−	−	−	+	−	+	+

To test the hypothesis H_0: husband's IQ is equally likely to be greater or smaller than wife's, we use (17), since $n = 26 - 1 = 25$. For $\alpha = .05$ the critical region R of the test is

$$\text{Reject } H_0 \text{ if } y \le 12.5 - (1.96) \frac{\sqrt{25}}{2} \text{ or } y \ge 12.5 + (1.96) \frac{\sqrt{25}}{2}$$

or, equivalently, if $y \le 7$ or ≥ 18.

For the data shown, $y = 13$, and hence the evidence from this experiment is not sufficient at the $\alpha = .05$ level to justify claiming that there is a difference between the IQ's of husbands and wives.

We remark that the sign test is a "distribution free" statistical procedure, in the sense that no assumptions are made on the precise form of the distributions of the random variables x, y that are sampled. Several such procedures are discussed in chapter 11.

PROBLEMS 4.5

1. A random sample of 10 persons have their body temperature (T) recorded before and after an experimental drug is taken. Based on the results given below, test the hypothesis H_0: the before temperature is equally likely to be higher or lower than the after temperature, against the alternative hypothesis H_1: this is not so. Use the level of significance $\alpha = .022$.

Person	1	2	3	4	5	6	7	8	9	10
Before T	98.5	98.6	98.4	98.7	98.8	98.7	98.3	98.6	98.2	98.6
After T	98.6	98.8	98.5	98.6	98.9	99.0	98.5	98.7	98.4	98.9

State the rejection region of the test and the conclusion based on the above data.

2. A random sample of $n = 16$ pairs of shoes worn by right-handed people showed the following percentage of wear on the heels of the right and left foot. Based on this data, test the hypothesis H_0: the right heel of right-handed people is equally likely to have a higher or lower percentage of wear than the left heel, against the alternative hypothesis H_1: this is not so. Use a level of significance $\alpha = .036$.

Person	1	2	3	4	5	6	7	8
Left heel (%)	.20	.29	.30	.35	.30	.35	.33	.46
Right heel (%)	.24	.27	.31	.40	.36	.32	.35	.50

Person	9	10	11	12	13	14	15	16
Left heel (%)	.43	.22	.38	.36	.31	.24	.26	.40
Right heel (%)	.47	.28	.38	.41	.43	.29	.30	.36

State the rejection region of the test and the conclusion based on the above data.

3. An environmentalist wishes to check whether or not reduced speed lowers gasoline consumption. A sample of 40 cars is drawn. Each is driven 100 miles twice: once at 50 mph and once at 60 mph. The resulting consumption in gallons is given in the following table.

Car	Gallons at 50	Gallons at 60	Car	Gallons at 50	Gallons at 60
1	6.3	6.7	21	6.5	6.9
2	5.1	5.3	22	9.5	9.3
3	7.0	6.4	23	4.0	4.8
4	4.8	5.4	24	7.0	7.3
5	8.2	8.9	25	5.6	5.0
6	6.5	7.2	26	6.0	6.5
7	7.1	7.1	27	6.4	5.7
8	10.7	10.1	28	8.1	8.4
9	5.4	5.8	29	6.2	6.2
10	6.7	6.5	30	7.5	7.7
11	8.5	8.9	31	5.1	5.4
12	5.8	5.8	32	6.7	5.9
13	9.3	9.9	33	10.3	10.8
14	5.9	6.3	34	5.5	5.5
15	6.2	6.8	35	6.8	6.3
16	4.0	4.6	36	7.3	8.2
17	9.1	9.7	37	8.1	8.2
18	6.1	5.2	38	4.4	5.2
19	5.8	6.5	39	6.6	6.7
20	7.4	8.3	40	6.9	6.2

Using a level of significance $\alpha = .05$, test the hypothesis H_0: the 50 mph. speed is equally likely to have a larger or smaller gas consumption than the 60 mph. speed for the 100 miles driven, against the alternative H_1: this is not so. State the rejection region of the test and the conclusion based on the above data.

4. A random sample of 26 students at a certain university showed the following GPA's for the first and second semesters.

Student	1	2	3	4	5	6	7	8	9
GPA (sem. 1)	3.18	2.74	3.00	1.50	2.62	2.10	3.27	4.00	2.90
GPA (sem. 2)	3.01	2.58	3.42	1.87	2.08	2.43	3.12	4.00	3.71

Student	10	11	12	13	14	15	16	17	18
GPA (sem. 1)	3.45	2.67	2.00	2.88	4.00	2.80	2.05	3.02	3.05
GPA (sem. 2)	3.18	3.01	2.78	2.62	2.71	3.17	2.05	3.28	2.68

Student	19	20	21	22	23	24	25	26
GPA (sem. 1)	1.47	2.10	2.21	2.00	3.18	1.70	1.50	3.15
GPA (sem. 2)	1.92	2.18	3.16	1.25	3.54	2.24	0.98	2.71

Using a level of significance $\alpha = .05$, test the hypothesis H_0: the GPA in the first semester is equally likely to be higher or lower than the GPA in the second semester for a student at this university, against the alternative hypothesis H_1: this is not so. State the rejection region of the test and the conclusion based on the above data.

4.6 Concluding Remarks on Significance Levels

In testing a null hypothesis H_0 vs an alternative hypothesis H_1, based on the value of a random variable y in an observed sample, we used the following procedures.

1. We first determined a reasonable critical region R, such that H_0 is to be rejected if y belongs to R.

2. We computed the significance level α associated with each such R, and chose a particular R for which α was suitably small.

3. We then observed y, and rejected H_0 if, and only if, y belonged to R. Thus, the critical region R and its associated significance level α were fixed in advance of the experiment.

There is, however, another way of proceeding. After step 1 we may simply observe y and announce its value, *together with the significance level α of the smallest critical region of the class considered to which y belongs.*

An example will clarify this general point. In example 7, the statistician used the critical region $R = \{b \leq y \leq 25\}$ to test $H_0 : p \leq .9$ vs $H_1 : p > .9$ with a sample size of $n = 25$. The corresponding value of $\alpha =$ maximum probability that y will belong to R if H_0 is true is then $P_{.9}\{b \leq y \leq 25\}$, and this is .072 for $b = 25$. Therefore, in using $R = \{y = 25\}$ he had decided to operate at the significance level $\alpha = .072$. Alternatively, he could have observed $y = y^*$, say, computed the value $\alpha^* = P_{.9}\{y^* \leq y \leq 25\}$, and told the company that the observed y^* *rejects* H_0 *at the α^* level of significance*, or that y^* *is significant at the α^* level.* Thus, for example, an observed value y^* of y equal to

20 would be significant at the $P_{.9}\{20 \leq y \leq 25\} = .967$ level

24 would be significant at the $P_{.9}\{24 \leq y \leq 25\} = .271$ level

25 would be significant at the $P_{.9}\{y = 25\} = .072$ level

Once this "observed significance level" of y^* is announced, the question of whether or not to reject H_0 could then be made by whoever in the company is responsible for making the final decision on offering the warranty, according to whether α^* is regarded as acceptably small or unacceptably large.

4.7 Appendix. A Small-Sample Test for Comparing Two Unknown Probabilities (the Fisher-Irwin Test)

Suppose n_1 binomial trials with an unknown single-trial success probability p_1 give y_1 successes (and $n_1 - y_1$ failures), while n_2 independent binomial trials with an unknown single-trial success probability p_2 give y_2 successes (and $n_2 - y_2$ failures). On the basis of these observations we wish to test the null hypothesis $H_0 : p_1 \geq p_2$ vs $H_1 : p_1 < p_2$.

To begin with, suppose $p_1 = p_2$. We then ask the following question: *conditional on* (that is, given) *the total number of successes* $y = y_1 + y_2$, but in ignorance of y_1 and y_2 *separately*, what is the probability distribution of the number of successes y_1 in the first group of n_1 trials? Imagine the $n_1 + n_2$ trials represented by boxes. Each box must contain an S (a success) or an F (a failure). There are y_1 S's to be put into the first group of n_1 boxes and $y_2 = y - y_1$ S's to be put into the second group of n_2 boxes; all the other $n_1 + n_2 - y$ boxes are to contain F's.

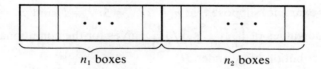

$$\underbrace{}_{n_1 \text{ boxes}} \qquad \underbrace{}_{n_2 \text{ boxes}}$$

There are $\binom{n_1}{y_1} \cdot \binom{n_2}{y - y_1}$ ways of doing this. But the total number of ways of putting the given number y of S's into any of the $n_1 + n_2$ boxes (and then filling the remaining boxes with F's) is $\binom{n_1 + n_2}{y}$, *and under the assumption that* $p_1 = p_2$ all these ways represent equally likely outcomes of the experiment. Hence if $p_1 = p_2$ the ratio

$$\frac{\binom{n_1}{y_1}\binom{n_2}{y - y_1}}{\binom{n_1 + n_2}{y}} \tag{19}$$

gives the *conditional probability of obtaining* y_1 *successes in the first* n_1 *trials, given that a total of* y *successes occurred in all* $n_1 + n_2$ *trials.* Here, for any fixed value of y, y_1 can range over the values 0, 1, ..., y. The sum of the values of (19) for $y_1 = 0, \ldots, y$ is easily shown to be 1. In fact, if we compare (19) with formula 3.37 for the hypergeometric distribution, we see that y_1 has, when $p_1 = p_2$, a hypergeometric distribution with $a = n$, $b = n_2$, $N = a + b$, and $n = y$. The *probability distribution of* y_1 *under* H_0 *does not depend on the common value* $p_1 = p_2$, about which no assumption is made.

Now, to test $H_0 : p_1 \geq p_2$ vs $H_1 : p_1 < p_2$, we observe that given the value y of the total number of successes, large values of y_1 tend to support H_0, whereas small values of y_1 tend to support H_1. *We therefore choose as critical region* **R** *the event*

$$R = \{0 \leq y_1 \leq m\} \tag{20}$$

for some integer m. When $p_1 = p_2$, the conditional probability of R, given the observed value of y, is by (19)

$$\sum_{i=0}^{m} \frac{\binom{n_1}{i} \cdot \binom{n_2}{y-i}}{\binom{n_1 + n_2}{y}} \tag{21}$$

This will be the significance level α of the test with critical region (20), since the conditional probability of (20) under any pair of probabilities $p_1 \geq p_2$ for which H_0 is true is *at most* equal to that for which $p_1 = p_2$; that is, at most equal to (21).

For example, suppose that $n_1 = 7$, $n_2 = 5$, $y_1 = 2$, and $y_2 = 4$. Computing the values of $\binom{7}{i}\binom{5}{6-i} / \binom{12}{6}$ gives for the conditional probability distribution of y_1 under H_0

y_1:	Prob.	0	$\frac{1}{132}$	$\frac{5}{44}$	$\frac{25}{66}$	$\frac{25}{66}$	$\frac{5}{44}$	$\frac{1}{132}$
	Value	0	1	2	3	4	5	6

Hence, when $p_1 = p_2$, for $n_1 = 7$ and $n_2 = 5$ trials, respectively, we have for $m = 2$

$$\alpha = P(y_1 \leq 2 | y = 6) = \frac{1}{132} + \frac{5}{44} = .0076 + .1136 = .1212$$

so the observed result $y_1 = 2$ would (conditional on $y = 6$) lead to rejection of H_0 only if $\alpha > .12$. This would usually be deemed too large, even though the point estimates of p_1 and p_2 are $2/7 = .286$ and $4/5 = .80$, respectively. However, we would reject (overwhelmingly) H_0 by this test if y_1 had been equal to 1, since for $m = 1$ the significance level is $\alpha = 1/132 = .0076$.

We summarize our results below.

A small-sample test for comparing two probabilities:

Let y_1 and y_2 be the number of successes in n_1 and n_2 independent binomial trials with respective success probabilities p_1 and p_2, and let $y = y_1 + y_2$.

Null hypothesis	Alternative hypothesis	Critical region: reject H_0 if	$\alpha =$ significance level
$H_0 : p_1 \geq p_2$	$H_1 : p_1 < p_2$	$y_1 \leq m$	$\displaystyle\sum_{i=0}^{m} \frac{\binom{n_1}{i} \cdot \binom{n_2}{y-i}}{\binom{n_1 + n_2}{y}}$
$H_0 : p_1 \leq p_2$	$H_1 : p_1 > p_2$	$y_i \geq m$	$\displaystyle\sum_{i=m}^{y} \frac{\binom{n_1}{i} \cdot \binom{n_2}{y-i}}{\binom{n_1 + n_2}{y}}$

Example 11

A random sample of $n_1 = 10$ college students aged between 18 and 25 years showed that $y_1 = 7$ favored a certain proposal, whereas a sample of $n_2 = 12$ noncollege youths aged between 18 and 25 years yielded 3 who favored the proposal. Is there enough evidence to justify claiming that $p_1 > p_2$?

Here we wish to test $H_0 : p_1 \leq p_2$ against the alternative $H_1 : p_1 > p_2$, with $n_1 = 10$, $n_2 = 12$, $y_1 = 7$, and $y_2 = 3$. With $y = 10$ and $\binom{n_1 + n_2}{y} = \binom{22}{10} = 646{,}646$, by arithmetic we get for the larger values of $y_1 = i$ in (20)

i	$\binom{10}{i}\binom{12}{10-i} / \binom{22}{10}$
10	$\dfrac{1}{646{,}646} = .00000$
9	$\dfrac{120}{646{,}646} = .00019$
8	$\dfrac{2970}{646{,}646} = .00459$
7	$\dfrac{26{,}400}{646{,}646} = .04083$
6	$\dfrac{103{,}950}{646{,}646} = .16075$

The critical region $\{y_1 \geq 7\}$ gives $\alpha = .00000 + .00019 + .00459 + .04083 = .04561 \cong .046$. Hence, at the .05 significance level we would conclude that $p_1 > p_2$, and say that the proportion favoring the proposal is greater for college students than for noncollege students in the 18–25 age group.

PROBLEMS 4.7

1. A random sample of five men and five women in a certain state are asked whether or not they are in favor of a women's rights amendment to the state constitution. If y_1 men favor the amendment and y_2 women favor the amendment, and $y_1 + y_2 = 7$, give the rejection region of the form $\{y_1 \leq m\}$ for testing the hypothesis $H_0 : p_1 \geq p_2$ against $H_1 : p_1 < p_2$, where p_1 and p_2 are the proportions of men and women in the state favoring the amendment. Use a level of significance between .05 and .10. If $y_1 = 2$ is the result, state the conclusion of the test.

2. Two random samples, each containing eight mice, are raised under identical conditions, except that group 1 is exposed to a combination of pollutants in the atmosphere and group 2 is not. After one year the mice are killed and autopsied. If y_1 mice from group 1 and y_2 mice from group 2 show evidence of damage to their lung tissue and $y_1 + y_2 = 5$, give the rejection region of the form $\{y_1 \geq m\}$ for testing the hypothesis $H_0 : p_1 \leq p_2$ versus $H_1 : p_1 > p_2$, where p_1 and p_2 are the proportions of mice showing damaged lung tissue from group 1 and group 2. Use a level of significance between .05 and .10. If $y_1 = 4$ is the result, state the conclusion of the test.

3. To test the effectiveness of a new cancer drug, a random sample of 13 osteogenic sarcoma patients treated by surgery are randomly divided into two groups. Six patients are given the standard treatment (T_1) and seven are given a new drug treatment (T_2). If one year after surgery four patients under treatment T_1 have a recurrence of the disease, while only one patient under treatment T_2 has a recurrence, does this evidence show that T_2 is better than T_1 with regard to recurrence at a level of significance between .05 and .10? Give the appropriate hypotheses and rejection region of the test.

4. To test the effect of lack of rest on performance in marksmanship, a random sample of 18 army personnel are put randomly into two groups of 8 and 10 each. Group 1 (8 persons) is allowed normal sleep over a 48-hour period, while group 2 (10 persons) is allowed only 5 hours sleep in the same period. Each group is subjected to a marksmanship test at the beginning and the end of the 48-hour period. In group 1, three persons did worse at the end of the period, while in group 2, eight people did worse. Is this sufficient evidence at a level of significance between .01 and .05 that lack of sleep has a bad effect on marksmanship? Give the appropriate hypotheses and rejection region of the test.

The Sample Mean and the Sample Variance

5 The Sample Mean and the Sample Variance

Given a random sample from some population, we estimate the mean value μ and the variance σ^2 of the population by computing the sample mean $\bar{x}$ and sample variance s^2. Sections 5.1–5.3 concern the behavior of $\bar{x}$ and s^2 in random sampling. Section 5.4 introduces the so-called normal distribution, and section 5.5 shows how this distribution governs the behavior of $\bar{x}$ in large samples from an arbitrary population.

5.1 The Sample Mean $\bar{x}$ and the Sample Variance s^2

Let x be a discrete random variable with a probability distribution

$$x: \quad \begin{array}{c|cccc} \text{Prob.} & p_1 & p_2 & \ldots & p_k \\ \hline \text{Value} & b_1 & b_2 & \ldots & b_k \end{array} \tag{1}$$

having a mean value (the "central value" of x)

$$\mu = m.v.\,(x) = \sum_{i=1}^{k} b_i p_i \tag{2}$$

and a variance (the "dispersion" of x about μ)

$$\sigma^2 = \text{var}(x) = \sum_{i=1}^{k} (b_i - \mu)^2 \cdot p_i \tag{3}$$

The numbers μ and σ^2 are called *parameters* of the distribution (1), in accordance with the following definition.

Definition 1
A parameter of a probability distribution (or "population") is a number associated with (and in some way descriptive of) that distribution.
   When the exact nature of the probability distribution (1) is unknown to us, as in problems of statistical inference, we acquire information about it by taking a random sample $\{x_1, \ldots, x_n\}$, as defined in section 3.5. Briefly, $\{x_1, \ldots, x_n\}$ is a random sample from the distribution (1) if the x's are independent random variables, each with the same distribution (1). To estimate the value of any unknown parameter of a distribution, one computes the value of some appropriately chosen *statistic* associated with the sample.

Definition 2
A statistic is some specified numerical function of the observed sample values $x_1, \ldots, x_n$.
   In particular, the two basic population parameters μ and σ^2 are estimated by the statistics

$$\bar{x} = \frac{1}{n} \sum_{i=1}^{n} x_i, \text{ the } sample\ mean, \text{ an estimator of } \mu \qquad (4)$$

$$s^2 = \frac{1}{n-1} \sum_{i=1}^{n} (x_i - \bar{x})^2, \text{ the } sample\ variance^*, \text{ an estimator of } \sigma^2 \quad (5)$$

The parameters μ and σ^2 are (usually unknown) constants associated with the probability distribution (1) according to the definitions (2) and (3). The statistics $\bar{x}$ and s^2 are (observable) random variables associated with the random sample $\{x_1, \ldots, x_n\}$. The formulas (4) and (5) are chosen because they give $\bar{x}$ and s^2 certain desirable properties which we shall now discuss.

a. The statistics $\bar{x}$ and s^2 are *unbiased estimators* of the corresponding population parameters μ and σ^2. This means that for any distribution (1), and for any value of n,

$$m.v.(\bar{x}) = \mu_{\bar{x}} = \mu, \ m.v.(s^2) = \mu_{s^2} = \sigma^2 \qquad (6)$$

b. The statistics $\bar{x}$ and s^2 are *consistent estimators* of μ and σ^2, respectively, in the sense that as the sample size n increases, the proba-

---

*The reason for dividing by $n-1$ instead of the more "natural" value n will be explained below. Note that (5) requires that $n \geq 2$.

bility that $\bar{x}$ will be close to μ, and s^2 will be close to σ^2, approaches 1. Here "close" means "within a given distance ϵ of," where ϵ is any positive constant, no matter how small, chosen in advance.

The proofs of (a) and (b) will be given below. First we give some numerical examples to show how $\bar{x}$ and s^2 are computed from a sample.

Example 1
The number x of children was recorded for each of a random sample of eight families. The observed values of x were 2, 0, 2, 3, 6, 4, 2, 1.

The corresponding sample estimates of μ and σ^2 for the population of families from which the sample of 8 was taken are therefore

$$\bar{x} = \frac{2+0+\ldots+1}{8} = 2.5 \quad \text{and}$$

$$s^2 = \frac{(2-2.5)^2 + (0-2.5)^2 + \ldots + (1-2.5)^2}{7} = \frac{24}{7} = 3.429$$

In general, to compute $\bar{x}$ and s^2 we can arrange the sample values $\{x_1, \ldots, x_n\}$ in a vertical column and compute the sums.

i	x_i	$x_i - \bar{x}$	$(x_i - \bar{x})^2$
1	x_1	$x_1 - \bar{x}$	$(x_1 - \bar{x})^2$
2	x_2	$x_2 - \bar{x}$	$(x_2 - \bar{x})^2$
$\vdots$	$\vdots$	$\vdots$	$\vdots$
n	x_n	$x_n - \bar{x}$	$(x_n - \bar{x})^2$
Sums	$\sum\limits_{i=1}^{n} x_i$	0	$\sum\limits_{i=1}^{n} (x_i - \bar{x})^2$

The value $\bar{x}$ is obtained by dividing the sum of column 2 by n, whereas s^2 is obtained by dividing the sum of column 4 by $n-1$.

Example 2
In a random sample of 10 measurements (to the nearest 1/100 inch) the observed values were

1.78   3.20   2.54   2.71   3.07   2.63   2.16   2.41   3.74   2.86

To find $\bar{x}$ and s^2 we compute the entries in the table at the top of the facing page. From this table we obtain

$$\bar{x} = 27.10/10 = 2.71, \text{ and } s^2 = 2.7458/9 = .305.$$

i	x_i	$x_i - \bar{x}$	$(x_i - \bar{x})^2$
1	1.78	−.93	.8649
2	3.20	.49	.2401
3	2.54	−.17	.0289
4	2.71	0	.0000
5	3.07	.36	.1296
6	2.63	−.08	.0064
7	2.16	−.55	.3025
8	2.41	−.30	.0900
9	3.74	1.03	1.0690
10	2.86	.15	.0225
Sums	27.10	0	2.7458

In using a desk calculator the value of s^2 is often easier to compute by using the *alternative formula for s^2*:

$$s^2 = \frac{n\left(\sum_{i=1}^{n} x_i^2\right) - \left(\sum_{i=1}^{n} x_i\right)^2}{n(n-1)} \tag{7}$$

That (5) and (7) are equivalent follows from the identity

$$\sum_{i=1}^{n} (x_i - \bar{x})^2 = \sum_{i=1}^{n} (x_i^2 - 2\bar{x}\, x_i + \bar{x}^2) \tag{8}$$

$$= \sum_{i=1}^{n} x_i^2 - 2\bar{x} \cdot \sum_{i=1}^{n} x_i + n\bar{x}^2$$

$$= \sum_{i=1}^{n} x_i^2 - 2\bar{x} \cdot n\bar{x} + n\bar{x}^2$$

$$= \sum_{i=1}^{n} x_i^2 - n\bar{x}^2$$

Dividing both sides of (8) by $n - 1$ gives (7).

To compute s^2 using (7) we form the sums

i	x_i	x_i^2
1	x_1	x_1^2
2	x_2	x_2^2
⋮	⋮	⋮
n	x_n	x_n^2
Sums	$\sum_{i=1}^{n} x_1$	$\sum_{i=1}^{n} x_i^2$

Using (4) and (7) we then obtain $\bar{x}$ and s^2 from the two column-sums of this table.

Example 3

A true-false test with 100 questions was given to 15 students. The resulting scores were

Student i	x_i	x_i^2
1	96	9216
2	84	7056
3	72	5184
4	78	6084
5	64	4096
6	53	2809
7	76	5776
8	81	6561
9	59	3481
10	74	5476
11	70	4900
12	83	6889
13	86	7396
14	91	8281
15	76	5776
Sums	1143	88981

$$\bar{x} = \frac{1143}{15} = 76.2,$$

$$s^2 = \frac{15(88981) - (1143)^2}{(15)(14)}$$

$$= \frac{1334715 - 1306449}{210}$$

$$= \frac{28266}{210} = 134.6$$

PROBLEMS 5.1

1. Explain briefly each of the following terms.

   a. parameter   **c.** sample mean
   b. population   **d.** sample standard deviation

2. In problem 1, which of the quantities (a) to (d) are statistics?

3. The daily low temperatures on January 1 for the last 10 years were: $-2°$, $10°$, $5°$, $-3°$, $15°$, $8°$, $23°$, $7°$, $31°$, $9°$. Find the sample mean, sample variance, and sample standard deviation for these data.

4. A random sample of 15 stocks on the N.Y. Stock Exchange on Dec. 15, 1974, showed closing prices (to the nearest dollar): 42, 31, 187, 12, 4, 71, 31, 18, 23, 12, 37, 28, 97, 63, 40. Find $\bar{x}$, s^2, and s for these data.

5. A random sample of 20 entering university freshmen showed the following results on an IQ test: 107, 128, 124, 113, 141, 120, 133, 161, 117, 112, 118, 123, 119, 130, 126, 115, 140, 132, 115, 126. Find $\bar{x}$, s^2, and s for these data.

6. A random sample of 26 persons who applied for marriage licenses at a county clerk's office showed ages of: 22, 18, 32, 43, 23, 20, 24, 31, 19, 20, 35, 56, 18, 29, 22, 30, 60, 25, 37, 22, 21, 26, 24, 27, 35, 23. Find $\bar{x}$, s^2, and s for these data.

5.2 Properties of $\bar{x}$ and s^2 in Random Sampling

5.2.1 Properties of $\bar{x}$ in Random Sampling

The sample mean $\bar{x}$ is a random variable with a probability distribution of its own. An explicit computation of this distribution for $n \geq 2$ is usually difficult. Fortunately, there are simple formulas that give at once the mean value and variance of $\bar{x}$ in terms of the mean value and variance of the "parent" distribution (1) from which the sample is taken. These formulas are based on the following theorem.

Theorem 1 If $x_1, \ldots, x_n$ are any random variables and if $y = x_1 + \ldots + x_n$ is their sum then

$$\text{m.v.}(y) = \mu_y = \mu_{x_1} + \ldots + \mu_{x_n} \tag{9}$$

Moreover, if the x_i are *mutually independent* then

$$\text{var}(y) = \sigma_y^2 = \sigma_{x_1}^2 + \ldots + \sigma_{x_n}^2 \tag{10}$$

Thus, for independent random variables, the mean value of a sum is the sum of the mean values, and the variance of a sum is the sum of the variances. We omit the proof.

From (9) and (10) we obtain for the sample mean $\bar{x} = y/n$ of a random sample $\{x_1, \ldots, x_n\}$

$$\text{m.v.}(\bar{x}) = \mu_{\bar{x}} = \frac{1}{n}\mu_y = \frac{1}{n}(\mu + \ldots + \mu) = \mu \tag{11}$$

$$\text{var}(\bar{x}) = \sigma_{\bar{x}}^2 = \frac{1}{n^2}\mu_y = \frac{1}{n^2}(\sigma^2 + \ldots + \sigma^2) = \frac{\sigma^2}{n} \tag{12}$$

where μ and σ^2 are the mean value and variance of the distribution from which the random sample $\{x_1, \ldots, x_n\}$ was taken (the "parent" distribution or population).

Thus, while the mean value of $\bar{x}$ equals the mean value μ of the parent distribution, the variance of $\bar{x}$ is equal to the variance σ^2 of the parent distribution *divided by the sample size n.* This fact is of great importance in statistical inference.

From (11) we see that $\bar{x}$ is an *unbiased* estimator of μ. To show that it is a *consistent* estimator of μ (this is a "large-sample" property) we may use (11) and (12) together with Chebyshev's inequality to obtain for any constant $c > 0$ the probability inequality

$$P\left\{|\bar{x} - \mu| \geq \frac{c\sigma}{\sqrt{n}}\right\} \leq \frac{1}{c^2} \tag{13}$$

or, putting $\epsilon = c\sigma/\sqrt{n}$, the equivalent inequality

$$P\{|\bar{x} - \mu| \geq \epsilon\} \leq \frac{\sigma^2}{n\epsilon^2} \tag{14}$$

valid for any constant $\epsilon > 0$. When μ, σ^2, and ϵ are fixed, the right-hand side of (14) tends to 0 as n increases, proving the consistency of $\bar{x}$ as an estimator of the population mean μ. This fact is called the *Law of Large Numbers*: for large n the sample mean $\bar{x}$ will usually be close to the population mean μ.

5.2.2 Properties of s^2 in Random Sampling

The sample variance s^2 is also a random variable having a distribution of its own, which is in general very difficult to compute explicitly. We shall first show that s^2 is an *unbiased estimator* of the population variance σ^2; in other words that

$$m.v.(s^2) = \mu_{s^2} = \sigma^2 \tag{15}$$

To prove this we use the identity

$$\sum_{i=1}^{n} (x_i - \bar{x})^2 = \sum_{i=1}^{n} [(x_i - \mu) + (\mu - \bar{x})]^2 \tag{16}$$

$$= \sum_{i=1}^{n} (x_i - \mu)^2 + 2(\mu - \bar{x}) \sum_{i=1}^{n} (x_i - \mu) + n(\mu - \bar{x})^2$$

$$= \sum_{i=1}^{n} (x_i - \mu)^2 + 2(\mu - \bar{x})n(\bar{x} - \mu) + n(\mu - \bar{x})^2$$

$$= \sum_{i=1}^{n} (x_i - \mu)^2 - n(\bar{x} - \mu)^2$$

from which, since m.v. $[(\bar{x} - \mu)^2] = \text{var}(\bar{x}) = \sigma^2/n$ by (11) and (12),

$$m.v.\left(\sum_{i=1}^{n} (x_i - \bar{x})^2\right) = \sum_{i=1}^{n} \sigma^2 - n\sigma_{\bar{x}}^2 = n\sigma^2 - n\frac{\sigma^2}{n} = (n-1)\sigma^2$$

Dividing both sides by $n - 1$ gives (15).*

---

*We divide by $n - 1$ instead of n in the definition (5) of s^2 precisely in order to make (15) hold.

We now show that s^2 is a *consistent estimator* of σ^2. From (16) we have the relation

$$s^2 = \frac{n}{n-1}\left[\frac{1}{n}\sum_{i=1}^{n}(x_i - \mu)^2 - (\bar{x} - \mu)^2\right] \tag{17}$$

a. By the Law of Large Numbers applied to $\{(x_1 - \mu)^2, (x_2 - \mu)^2, \ldots, (x_n - \mu)^2\}$, a random sample from a probability distribution with mean value $m.v.[(x - \mu)^2] = \mathrm{var}(x) = \sigma^2$, we see that $\frac{1}{n}\sum_{i=1}^{n}(x_i - \mu)^2$ is a consistent estimator of σ^2; that is, that $\frac{1}{n}\sum_{i=1}^{n}(x_i - \mu)^2$ will be close to σ^2 with probability near 1 when n is large.

b. We already know that $\bar{x}$ is a consistent estimator of μ, so $\bar{x} - \mu$ will be close to 0 with probability near 1 when n is large, and therefore the same will be true of $(x - \mu)^2$.

From (a) and (b) it follows that the quantity within the square bracket in (17) will be close to σ^2 with probability near 1 when n is large. Since the factor $n/(n - 1)$ is also close to 1 for a large n, it follows that s^2 will be close to σ^2 with probability near 1 when n is large, thus establishing the consistency of s^2 as an estimator of σ^2.

We have incidentally established that $\frac{1}{n}\sum_{i=1}^{n}(x_i - \mu)^2$ is also an unbiased and consistent estimator of σ^2. However, this quantity is not a *statistic*, since it is not a function of the sample values $\{x_1, \ldots, x_n\}$ alone, and hence is not computable entirely from the observed values x_i in the sample. Of course, if μ is *known*, we can and should use $\frac{1}{n}\sum_{i=1}^{n}(x_i - \mu)^2$ to estimate an unknown σ^2, since it is usually somewhat closer to σ^2 than the statistic s^2.

PROBLEMS 5.2

1. A die is labeled with two faces showing a 1, two faces showing a 2, and two faces showing a 3. The die is tossed twice, and $x_1 = $ the number on the top of the die on the first toss, $x_2 = $ the number on the top of the die on the second toss.

 a. Find μ_{x_1} and μ_{x_2}
 b. Find the distribution of $y = x_1 + x_2$, and compute μ_y
 c. Using (a) and (b), does $\mu_{x_1 + x_2} = \mu_{x_1} + \mu_{x_2}$? (See (9).)
 d. Find the distribution of $y = x_1 \cdot x_2$
 e. Using (a) and (d), does $\mu_{x_1 \cdot x_2} = \mu_{x_1} \cdot \mu_{x_2}$? Are x_1 and x_2 independent?

2. A game of chance consists of choosing a card at random from a deck; one wins $1, $2, or $3 depending on whether the card is a heart, a spade, or a diamond. If the card is a club, the player loses $2. The game is played twice, each time with a newly shuffled deck. Let x_1 and x_2 be the amounts won (−$2 in the case of a club) on the first and second plays of the game.

 a. Find μ_{x_1} and μ_{x_2}
 b. Find the distribution of $y = x_1 + x_2$, and compute μ_y
 c. Using (a) and (b), does $\mu_{x_1 + x_2} = \mu_{x_1} + \mu_{x_2}$? (See (9).)
 d. Find the distribution of $y = x_1 \cdot x_2$
 e. Using (a) and (d), does $\mu_{x_1 \cdot x_2} = \mu_{x_1} \cdot \mu_{x_2}$? Are x_1 and x_2 independent?

3. In problem 1, suppose one loses $5x_1$ cents for the first toss and wins $5x_2$ cents for the second toss.

 a. Find the expected amount won in the two tosses, using (9).
 b. Find the variance of the amount won in the two tosses, using (10).

4. In problem 2, suppose one modifies the game so that the amount won on the first game is doubled and the amount won on the second game is multiplied by −3.

 a. Find the expected amount won in the two modified games, using (9).
 b. Find the variance of the amount won in the two games, using (10).

5. Let x_1, x_2, x_3, x_4 be a random sample of size 4 from a distribution with mean 3 and variance 2. Find the mean and variance of each of the following random variables:

 a. $x_1 + 2x_2 + 3x_3 + 4x_4$
 b. $x_1 + x_2 + x_3 + x_4$
 c. $\bar{x} = (x_1 + x_2 + x_3 + x_4)/4$

6. Let x_1, x_2, x_3 be a random sample of size 3 from a distribution with mean −5 and variance 3. Find the mean and the variance of the following random variables:

 a. $x_1 - x_2 + 2x_3$
 b. $x_1 + x_2 + x_3$
 c. $\bar{x} = (x_1 + x_2 + x_3)/3$

7. Suppose that a random sample $x_1, \ldots, x_n$ of new light bulbs are tested to check their lifetimes. The distribution of lifetimes has

mean 230 hours and variance 40 hours. Let $\bar{x} = \frac{1}{n}\sum_{i=1}^{n} x_i$. Find the mean, variance, and standard deviation of $\bar{x}$ if: (a) $n = 10$; (b) $n = 100$; and (c) $n = 400$.

8. A random sample $x_1, \ldots, x_n$ of n army recruits are given a one-mile running test. If the running time for recruits has a mean of 7.10 minutes with a variance of 1.21 minutes, find the mean, variance, and standard deviation of $\bar{x} = \frac{1}{n}\sum_{i=1}^{n} x_i$ if: (a) $n = 10$; (b) $n = 100$; and (c) $n = 900$.

9. A fair coin is tossed n times. Find the mean, variance, and standard deviation of $y =$ the number of heads in the n tosses, for $n = 100$, 400, and 900.

10. Suppose that 20 percent of the people in the United States contract flu in a nationwide epidemic. Find the mean, variance, and standard deviation of $y =$ the number of persons in a random sample of n people who become ill in this way, for $n = 100$, 400, and 900.

11. Let x_1, x_2, x_3 be a random sample of size 3 from the distribution

$$x: \frac{\text{Prob.}}{\text{Value}} \left\| \begin{array}{c|c|c} \frac{1}{3} & \frac{1}{3} & \frac{1}{3} \\ \hline 0 & 1 & 2 \end{array} \right.$$

a. Find the mean μ and variance σ^2 of this distribution.
b. Find the distribution of $\bar{x} = (x_1 + x_2 + x_3)/3$.
c. Using (a) and (b), verify that $\bar{x}$ is an unbiased estimator of μ_x; that is, show that $\mu_{\bar{x}} = \mu$.
d. Find the distribution of $s^2 = \frac{1}{2}\sum_{i=1}^{3}(x_i - \bar{x})^2$.
e. Using (a) and (d), verify that s^2 is an unbiased estimator of σ_x^2; that is, show that $\mu_{s^2} = \sigma^2$.

12. Let x_1, x_2, x_3, x_4 be a random sample of size 4 from the distribution

$$x: \frac{\text{Prob.}}{\text{Value}} \left\| \begin{array}{c|c} \frac{1}{2} & \frac{1}{2} \\ \hline -1 & 1 \end{array} \right.$$

a. Find the mean μ and the variance σ^2 of this distribution.
b. Find the distribution of $\bar{x} = (x_1 + x_2 + x_3 + x_4)/4$.
c. Using (a) and (b), verify that $\mu_{\bar{x}} = \mu$.
d. Find the distribution of $s^2 = \frac{1}{3}\sum_{i=1}^{4}(x_i - \bar{x})^2$.
e. Using (a) and (d) verify that $\mu_{s^2} = \sigma^2$.

13. Let $\{x_1, \ldots, x_n\}$ be a random sample of size n from the distribution of a random variable x with mean μ and variance σ^2.

  a. Suppose that the population has mean $\mu = 0$ and variance $\sigma^2 = 5$. Use the result (14) to find upper bounds for $P(|\bar{x}| \geq 1)$ if $n = 10, 100, 1000$. As n gets larger, what do these results suggest?

  b. Use the result (14) to justify the statement that $P(|\bar{x} - \mu| \geq \epsilon)$ approaches 0 as the sample size n becomes larger. What does this say about the statistic $\bar{x}$ as an estimator of the unknown parameter μ for larger and larger sample sizes?

5.3 The Mean Value and Variance of $\bar{x}$ in Sampling Without Replacement from a Finite Population

In random sampling from a probability distribution the sample values $\{x_1, x_2, \ldots, x_n\}$ are assumed to be independent, each with the given distribution. This remains true in *sampling with replacement* from a finite population. In *sampling without replacement* from a finite population, the successive sample values $x_1, x_2, \ldots$, are no longer completely independent, since the population changes as each element of the sample is removed. The sample mean $\bar{x} = \dfrac{1}{n} \sum\limits_{i=1}^{n} x_i$ is still an unbiased estimator of the population mean μ in sampling without replacement, since it can be shown that $\mu_{x_i} = \mu$ for each $i = 1, 2, \ldots$ and hence that

$$m.v. \ (\bar{x}) = \mu_{\bar{x}} = \frac{1}{n}(\mu + \ldots + \mu) = \mu \tag{18}$$

However, it can be shown that in sampling without replacement (12) no longer holds. Instead,

$$\text{var}(\bar{x}) = \sigma_{\bar{x}}^2 = \frac{\sigma^2}{n} \cdot \frac{N - n}{N - 1} \tag{19}$$

where N is the size of the population. The factor $(N - n)/(N - 1)$ is called the *finite population correction* for the variance of $\bar{x}$ in sampling without replacement. It is always ≤ 1, so that $\bar{x}$ is more concentrated about its mean value μ in sampling without replacement than in sampling with replacement. (This is obvious in the extreme case in which $n = N$ so that the sample is always the same—the entire population—and hence $\bar{x}$ is equal to the constant μ and has variance 0, in agreement with (19) for $n = N$.)

When the population size N is large and the sample size n small compared to N, the factor $(N - n)/(N - 1)$ in (19) is close to 1 and can safely be ignored. In the sequel we shall use formula 12, even in sampling from a finite population without replacement, whenever $n \leq .05\,N$. For example, for $N = 100$ and $n = 5$,

$$\frac{N - n}{N - 1} = \frac{95}{99} \cong .96$$

while for $N = 50{,}000$ and $n = 1000$

$$\frac{N - n}{N - 1} = \frac{49{,}000}{49{,}999} \cong .98$$

One way of obtaining a random sample of size n without replacement from a finite population of N members is to use a table of "random numbers," such as appendix table 3. For example, in sampling from a group of, say, $N = 8342$ students, the students could be listed alphabetically and assigned numbers from 1 to 8342, the first student being 1, and so on. We then begin at some point in the table of random numbers and read down. If the last four digits of the first number are, say, 1811, then student 1811 becomes the first sampled student. If the last four digits of the first number are > 8342, we go to the next number in the table, and continue in this way until the first sampled student is determined. This process is continued until n different students have been chosen.

In random sampling from a finite population, with or without replacement, the sample mean $\bar{x}$ is always an unbiased estimator of the population mean value μ and its variance does not exceed σ^2/n, where σ^2 is the variance of the population, *no matter how large or how small the population from which the sample is drawn*. This is why rather small samples, say, one or two thousand, usually suffice for public opinion polling, where $\sigma^2 = pq \leq 1/4$, provided that the samples are truly random and drawn from the population of interest. This is very hard to achieve in practice owing to bias in selection, self-selection, nonresponses, and so forth.

PROBLEMS 5.3

1. A group of 1000 students are numbered from 000 to 999 inclusive. Use appendix table 3 to draw a sample of size 20 from this population. Write down the 20 numbers you obtain.

2. Draw a random sample of size 10 without replacement of the pages in this book by using appendix table 3. List the 10 pages of your sample.

3. A statistics class of 80 students has mean score 74 on a midterm examination with standard deviation 12. If an instructor samples 25 examinations and computes the sample mean $\bar{x}$, what is the mean, variance, and standard deviation of $\bar{x}$?

4. Suppose that the 100 senators in the U.S. Senate have a mean age of 56 years with standard deviation 9.8 years. Find the mean, variance, and standard deviation of the mean of a random sample of 30 senators.

5. A random sample of $n = 100$ students is taken from a population of N students with a mean IQ of 120 and variance 80.
   a. Find the mean value and variance of the sample mean $\bar{x}$ if $N = 200$, $N = 400$, $N = 1000$, and $N = 5000$.
   b. As N becomes larger, what happens to the mean value and variance of $\bar{x}$?

6. A random sample of $n = 30$ bolts is taken without replacement from a box containing 100 bolts, of which 10 are defective. If y = number of defective bolts in the sample, find the mean value and variance of y.

5.4 The Normal Distribution

In section 3.1 we discussed briefly the concept of a *continuous* random variable x. To get an intuitive feeling for this concept we may imagine the x-axis to be a straight wire of varying density and with total mass 1. The *probability* that x will lie in any interval $\{a \leq x \leq b\}$ is then identified with the *mass* of this segment of the wire. It is convenient to represent the mass or probability geometrically by drawing a curve above the x-axis such that the mass or probability of any segment $\{a \leq x \leq b\}$ is equal to the *area under the curve* from a to b. (This is done by making the *height* of the curve above the x-axis at any point x equal to the *density* $f(x)$ of mass or probability at that point. See figure 5.1.) We then have

$$P\{a \leq x \leq b\} = \text{area under the curve } y = f(x) \text{ from } a \text{ to } b \quad \textbf{(20)}$$

With the probability interpretation, $f(x)$ is called the *probability density function* of the random variable x. For any constant c and any small positive number ϵ, the probability that the random variable x will lie in the interval from $c - \epsilon/2$ to $c + \epsilon/2$ is approximately $\epsilon \cdot f(c)$. From (20) the total area under the curve $y = f(x)$ over the whole x-axis is necessarily equal to 1, the probability of the certain event.

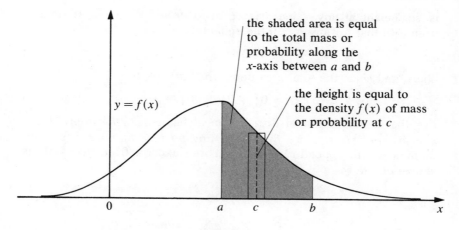

FIGURE 5.1

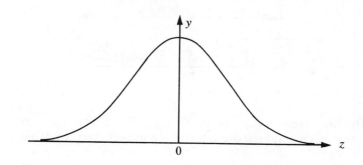

FIGURE 5.2
The standard normal random variable x

Since the area above any *single point* $x = c$ is 0 no matter what the height of the curve, it follows that for any continuous random variable x with a probability density function $f(x)$

$$P\{x = c\} = 0 \tag{21}$$

Hence for any two constants $a < b$

$$P\{a \le x \le b\} = P\{a < x \le b\} = P\{a \le x < b\} = P\{a < x < b\} \tag{22}$$

Among all continuous random variables, the one of greatest importance in statistics is the "standard normal," denoted by z, with probability density function given by the bell-shaped curve of figure 5.2. This curve is symmetrical about the vertical axis through $z = 0$; that is, its height at any value z is equal to its height at $-z$. It follows from (20) that for any $b > 0$ the equality

$$P\{-b \leq z \leq 0\} = P\{0 \leq z \leq b\} \tag{23}$$

holds, and since the total area under the curve is 1

$$P\{z \leq 0\} = P\{z \geq 0\} = .5 \tag{24}$$

For the standard normal distribution of figure 5.2, *the area* $P\{0 \leq z \leq b\}$ *under the curve from* 0 *to any positive number* b *is given numerically in appendix table 6.* A brief excerpt from that table is shown below.

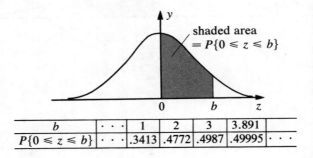

b	$\cdots$	1	2	3	3.891	
$P\{0 \leq z \leq b\}$	$\cdots$	.3413	.4772	.4987	.49995	$\cdots$

By the symmetry property (23) it follows that the probability that z will lie in a symmetric interval about 0 is given by table 5.1.

TABLE 5.1

$P\{-b \leq z \leq b\}$, z **Standard Normal**

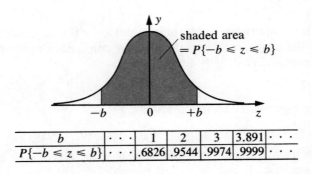

b	$\cdots$	1	2	3	3.891	$\cdots$
$P\{-b \leq z \leq b\}$	$\cdots$	.6826	.9544	.9974	.9999	$\cdots$

The same thing is shown geometrically in figure 5.3.

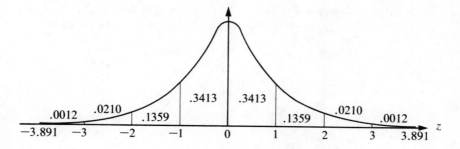

FIGURE 5.3
Probabilities of areas for the standard normal distribution

Probabilities of the form $P\{z \leq b\}$ or $P\{a \leq z \leq b\}$ are computed by using equations (23) and (24) in conjunction with appendix table 6. We give some examples.

a. $P\{z \leq 1.6\} = P\{z \leq 0\} + P\{0 < z \leq 1.6\}$
$\qquad = .5 + .4452 = .9452$

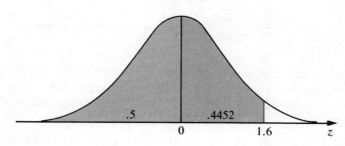

b. $P\{.52 \leq z \leq 2.28\} = P\{0 < z \leq 2.28\} - P\{0 < z \leq .52\}$
$\qquad = .4887 - .1985 = .2902$

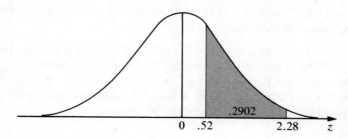

c. $P\{z \leq -.86\} = P\{z \leq 0\} - P\{-.86 \leq z \leq 0\}$
$$= .5 - P\{0 \leq z \leq .86\} = .5 - .3051 = .1949$$

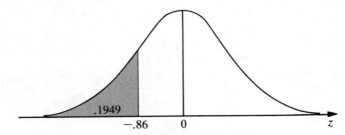

d. $P\{-1.10 \leq z \leq .22\} = P\{-1.10 \leq z \leq 0\} + P\{0 \leq z \leq .22\}$
$$= P\{0 \leq z \leq 1.10\} + P\{0 \leq z \leq .22\}$$
$$= .3643 + .0871 = .4514$$

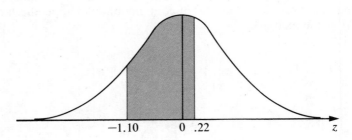

The behavior of any *continuous* random variable (such as the standard normal z) can be approximated by a properly constructed *discrete* random variable. We may carry out this approximation in two steps.

1. We first choose some large positive number B and replace any value of z that is $< -B$ by $-B$, and any value of z that is $>B$ by B. This is called *truncation* of z at the values $-B$, B.
2. We then subdivide the interval from $-B$ to B into some large number k of equal subintervals, each of the length $2B/k$, and re-place the values of z that lie in each of these subintervals by the *midpoint* of the subinterval.

The discrete random variable, call it z', obtained by this process from z, will have only a *finite* number k of values, call them $b_1, b_2, \ldots, b_k$, taken on with probabilities $p_1, p_2, \ldots, p_k$ adding up to 1. Moreover, if k is so large for a given B that $2B/k$ is very small, then z' will be almost indistinguishable from z in its behavior.

By this process of approximation we can assign a mean value and a variance to the continuous z. These values are computed by taking a sequence of approximations with B larger and larger, and $2B/k$ smaller and smaller, and finding the limiting values to which the mean value and variance of the approximating discrete z' tend. For the standard normal z it can be shown that these limiting values are respectively 0 and 1. Thus we say that *the standard normal z has mean value 0 and variance 1.*

To "standardize" an arbitrary random variable x with mean value μ and variance σ^2, we form the new random variable

$$z_x = \frac{x - \mu}{\sigma} \tag{25}$$

which is just x referred to its own mean value μ as origin and with its own standard deviation σ as unit. The mean value and variance of z_x, the *standardized x*, are 0 and 1, respectively, since

$$m.v. \ (z_x) = \frac{1}{\sigma}(m.v. \ (x) - \mu) = \frac{1}{\sigma}(\mu - \mu) = 0$$

$$var. \ (z_x) = \frac{1}{\sigma^2}(var \ (x) - 0) = \frac{\sigma^2}{\sigma^2} = 1$$

Often a random variable x arising in applications will be distributed in such a manner that the corresponding standardized random variable z_x given by (25) has (approximately) the standard normal distribution of the z of figure 5.3. We then say that x is normal with mean μ and variance σ^2. The probability that such a random variable x will lie between any two constants $a < b$ is found as follows:

$$P\{a \le x \le b\} = P\left\{\frac{a - \mu}{\sigma} \le \frac{x - \mu}{\sigma} \le \frac{b - \mu}{\sigma}\right\}$$

$$\cong P\left\{\frac{a - \mu}{\sigma} \le z \le \frac{b - \mu}{\sigma}\right\}$$

where the last probability is obtained by regarding z as standard normal, as in (a) − (d) above. For example, if x is approximately normal with mean value 7 and variance 4, then

$$P\{3 \le x \le 11\} = P\left\{\frac{3 - 7}{2} \le \frac{x - 7}{2} \le \frac{11 - 7}{2}\right\} \cong P\{-2 \le z \le 2\}$$

$$= 2P\{0 \le z \le 2\} = .9544 \text{ by table 5.1.}$$

The probability that a normally distributed random variable x will lie within $c = 1, 2,$ or 3 standard deviations σ from its mean value μ is shown in figure 5.4.

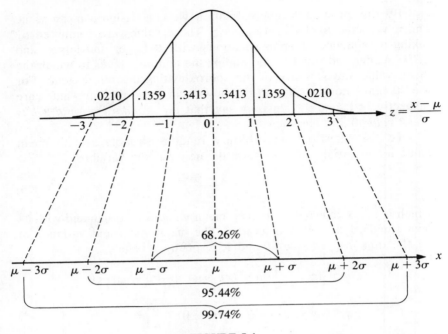

FIGURE 5.4

The probabilities of lying within $c = 1, 2,$ or 3 standard deviations of its value for a general normal random variable

PROBLEMS 5.4

In problems 1–8, use appendix table 6.

1. If z is a standard normal random variable, find the probability that
   a. $0 \leq z < 1$ **d.** $-1 < z \leq 0$
   b. $0 \leq z < 2$ **e.** $-2 < z \leq 0$
   c. $0 \leq z < 1.5$ **f.** $-1.5 < z \leq 0$

2. If z is a standard normal random variable, find the probability that
   a. $0 \leq z < 2.33$ **d.** $-2.33 < z \leq 0$
   b. $0 \leq z < 0.5$ **e.** $-0.5 \ < z \leq 0$
   c. $0 \leq z < 1.96$ **f.** $-1.96 < z \leq 0$

3. If z is a standard normal random variable, find the probability that
   a. $-1 < z < 1$ **d.** $-1 < z < 3$
   b. $-2 < z < 2$ **e.** $-1.5 < z < 2.5$
   c. $-3 < z < 3$ **f.** $-2.3 < z < 1.28$

4. If z is a standard normal random variable, find the probability that:

   a. $-1.65 < z < 1.65$ d. $-2 < z < .5$
   b. $-1.96 < z < 1.96$ e. $-1.6 < z < 2.83$
   c. $-2.58 < z < 2.58$ f. $-1.72 < z < 1.62$

5. If z is a standard normal random variable, find the probability of the following events. Draw a picture of the area under the normal curve in each case.

   a. $-1.06 < z < 1.28$
   b. $z > -1.29$
   c. $z < -1.5$ or $z > 1.5$
   d. $|z| > 2.0$
   e. $(-2.21 < z < -1.1)$ or $(.7 < z < 1.39)$
   f. $(z < -1.61)$ or $(z > 1.49)$

6. If z is a standard normal random variable, find the probability of the following events. Draw a picture of the area under the normal curve in each case.

   a. $z < -.78$ or $z > 1.42$ d. $z < .42$ or $1.00 < z < 2.71$
   b. $|z| < 2.33$ e. $z < -1.28$ or $z > 0$
   c. $|z| > .72$ f. $1.21 < |z| < 2.58$

7. If x has a general normal distribution with mean 24 and standard deviation 4, find the probability that

   a. $x > 24$ d. $28 < x < 31$
   b. $x < 24$ e. $18.4 < x < 27.2$
   c. $20 < x < 30$ f. $|x - 24| < 8$

8. If x has a general normal distribution with mean 102 and standard deviation 20, find the probability that

   a. $x > 102$ d. $62.8 < x < 141.2$
   b. $x < 82$ e. $|x - 102| < 46.6$
   c. $72 < x < 132$ f. $[(x > 122)$ or $(x < 82)]$

9. Suppose that the population of students at a university have weights given by a normal distribution with mean 148 lbs and standard deviation 29 lbs. If a student is chosen at random from this population, find the probability that the student chosen

   a. weighs between 120 and 170 lbs.
   b. weighs more than 200 lbs.
   c. weighs less than 150 lbs.
   d. weighs between 100 and 200 lbs.

10. Suppose the yearly income of a population of workers is normally distributed with mean $9820 and standard deviation $3450. If a

worker is chosen at random from this population, find the probability that the worker chosen

a. earns between $7000 and $11,000 per year.
b. earns more than $15,000 per year.
c. earns less than $10,000 per year.
d. earns more than $18,000 per year.

11. If z is a standard normal random variable, find the value c such that

a. $P(0 \leq z < c) = .2823$ **d.** $P(|z| < c) = .9500$
b. $P(z > c) = .1230$ **e.** $P(|z| > c) = .02$
c. $P(-c < z < c) = .8664$ **f.** $P(z < c) = .7703$

12. If z is a standard normal random variable, find the value c such that

a. $P(0 \leq z < c) = .4686$ **d.** $P(|z| < c) = .9000$
b. $P(z > c) = .1539$ **e.** $P(|z| > c) = .0020$
c. $P(-c < z < c) = .7286$ **f.** $P(z < c) = .3974$

13. A psychologist uses a test to measure "degree of authoritarianism"; the test is standardized with mean 100 and standard deviation 30. If the scores on such a test have a normal distribution, find the score c such that

a. 20 percent of the population is above c.
b. 10 percent of the population is below c.
c. 50 percent of the population is between $100 - c$ and $100 + c$.

14. The physical education department of a university has established that incoming freshmen women have a mean running time for the mile of 7.6 minutes, with standard deviation 1.1 minutes. If this measurement is normally distributed, find the value c for which

a. 75 percent of the women freshmen record a time between 7.6 $-c$ and 7.6 $+ c$ minutes.
b. 10 percent of the women freshmen record a time of more than c minutes.
c. 5 percent of the women freshmen record a time of less than c minutes.

5.5 The Central Limit Theorem

In the preceding section we remarked that many random variables arising in applications are found to be approximately normally distributed. The most important case is that of the sample mean $\bar{x} =$

$\dfrac{1}{n} \displaystyle\sum_{i=1}^{n} x_i$ of a random sample $\{x_1, \ldots, x_n\}$ from an *arbitrary* distribution (1) with any mean value μ and variance σ^2. The statistic $\bar{x}$ has been seen in (11) and (12) to have mean value and variance

$$\mu_{\bar{x}} = \mu \qquad \sigma_{\bar{x}}^2 = \frac{\sigma^2}{n}$$

so that the standardized version of $\bar{x}$ is

$$z_n = \frac{\bar{x} - \mu}{\dfrac{\sigma}{\sqrt{n}}}$$

The random variable z_n, with mean value 0 and variance 1 for every $n = 1, 2, \ldots$, tends to have more and more nearly the standard normal distribution as the sample size n increases. The formal statement of this fact is called, because of its importance, *The Central Limit Theorem:*

For any constants $a < b$ the approximation

$$P\left\{a \leq \frac{\bar{x} - \mu}{\dfrac{\sigma}{\sqrt{n}}} \leq b\right\} \cong P\{a \leq z \leq b\} \qquad (26)$$

is more and more accurate as n increases, where z is standard normal.
    We omit the proof of this fundamental theorem.

Example 7
Suppose that the IQ test score x for a population of college students has a distribution with mean value 121 and standard deviation 11. If 100 students are chosen at random from this population, find the probability that the sample mean $\bar{x}$ will lie between 119 and 123. By (26)

$$P\{119 < \bar{x} < 123\} = P\left\{\frac{119 - 121}{11/\sqrt{100}} < \frac{\bar{x} - 121}{11/\sqrt{100}} < \frac{123 - 121}{11/\sqrt{100}}\right\}$$
$$\cong P(-1.82 < z < 1.82)$$
$$= 2P(0 \leq z < 1.82) = .9312$$

Example 8
Suppose that the mean income of full-time workers in the United States is \$6165, with a standard deviation of 2550. In a random sample of 400 such workers, what is the probability that the sample mean income $\bar{x}$ will lie within the interval $5830 \leq \bar{x} \leq 6500$?
    Using (26) we have

$$P\{5830 \leq \bar{x} \leq 6500\} = P\left\{\frac{5830 - 6165}{\frac{2550}{\sqrt{400}}} \leq \frac{\bar{x} - 6165}{\frac{2550}{\sqrt{400}}} \leq \frac{6500 - 6165}{\frac{2550}{\sqrt{400}}}\right\}$$

$$= P\left\{-2.63 \leq \frac{\bar{x} - 6165}{\frac{2550}{\sqrt{400}}} \leq 2.63\right\}$$

$$\cong P\{-2.63 \leq z \leq 2.63\} = 2P\{0 < z \leq 2.63\} = .9914$$

We remark that the distribution of income x in an actual population is usually far from normal, but for a sample of $n = 400$ the use of (26) to find $P\{c \leq \bar{x} \leq d\}$ should be quite accurate.

An important special case of (26) is that in which the distribution (1) of the sample values is the 2-valued distribution

$$x: \quad \frac{\text{Prob.}}{\text{Value}} \begin{array}{c|c} p & q \\ \hline 1 & 0 \end{array} \qquad (q = 1 - p)$$

In this case the sum

$$y = x_1 + \ldots + x_n$$

has a *binomial* distribution with n trials and success probability p for each trial, and

$$\bar{x} = y/n = \hat{p}$$

is the *relative frequency of success* in the n trials. Since

$$\mu_x = 1 \cdot p + 0 \cdot q = p$$

$$\sigma_x^2 = \mu_{x^2} - (\mu_x)^2 = 1^2 \cdot p + 0^2 \cdot q - p^2 = p - p^2 = p(1 - p) = pq$$

we have

$$\frac{\bar{x} - \mu_x}{\frac{\sigma_x}{\sqrt{n}}} = \frac{\hat{p} - p}{\sqrt{\frac{pq}{n}}}$$

and hence by (26)

$$P\left\{a \leq \frac{\hat{p} - p}{\sqrt{\frac{pq}{n}}} \leq b\right\} \cong P\{a \leq z \leq b\}$$

for large n, where z is standard normal. In particular,

$$P\left\{-2 \leq \frac{\hat{p} - p}{\sqrt{\frac{pq}{n}}} \leq 2\right\} \cong P\{-2 \leq z \leq 2\} = .9544, \text{ or, equivalently,}$$

$$P\left\{p - 2\sqrt{\frac{pq}{n}} \leq \hat{p} \leq p + 2\sqrt{\frac{pq}{n}}\right\} \cong .9544$$

when n is large. When $p = .5$ this becomes

$$P\left\{.5 - \frac{1}{\sqrt{n}} \leq \hat{p} \leq .5 + \frac{1}{\sqrt{n}}\right\} \cong .9544$$

so that in 10,000 tosses of a fair coin the result $.49 \leq \hat{p} \leq .51$ will occur about 95 percent of the time, with $\hat{p} < .49$ and $\hat{p} > .51$ each occurring about 2.5 percent of the time.

The standard normal distribution can be used to obtain good approximations to the individual probabilities

$$P\{y = i\} = \binom{n}{i}p^i q^{n-i} \qquad (i = 0, 1, \ldots, n)$$

of the binomial distribution by first making a "continuity correction" in passing from the discrete y to the continuous standard normal z. This gives the approximation

$$P\{y = i\} = P\{i - .5 \leq y \leq i + .5\} \qquad \text{(continuity correction)} \qquad (27)$$

$$= P\left\{\frac{i - .5 - np}{\sqrt{npq}} \leq \frac{y - np}{\sqrt{npq}} \leq \frac{i + .5 - np}{\sqrt{npq}}\right\}$$

$$\cong P\left\{\frac{i - .5 - np}{\sqrt{npq}} \leq z \leq \frac{i + .5 - np}{\sqrt{npq}}\right\} \qquad \begin{array}{l}\text{(normal}\\\text{approximation)}\end{array}$$

Example 9

We toss a fair coin some even number $2m$ of times. What is the probability that exactly m of the tosses are heads? Let $y =$ number of heads in $2m$ tosses, a binomial random variable with $p = .5$ and $n = 2m$.

a. $n = 10$. Direct computation gives

$$P\{y = 5\} = \binom{10}{5}\frac{1}{2^5} \cdot \frac{1}{2^5} = \frac{10 \cdot 9 \cdot 8 \cdot 7 \cdot 6}{1 \cdot 2 \cdot 3 \cdot 4 \cdot 5} \cdot \frac{1}{2^{10}}$$

$$= \frac{63}{256} = .246 \ldots$$

The normal approximation (27), with $n = 10$, $i = 5$, $p = .5$, and $\sqrt{npq} = \sqrt{2.5} = 1.58$, gives

$$P\{y = 10\} \cong P\left\{-\frac{.5}{1.58} \leq z \leq \frac{.5}{1.58}\right\} = P\{-.32 \leq z \leq .32\}$$

$$= 2P\{0 \leq z \leq .32\} = .251$$

by appendix table 6. Thus for $n = 10$ the normal approximation is in error by about .005.

b. $n = 20$. By appendix table 4

$$P\{y = 10\} = P\{y \le 10\} - P\{y \le 9\}$$
$$= .588 - .412 = .176$$

The normal approximation (27), with $n = 20$, $i = 10$, $p = .5$, and $\sqrt{npq} = \sqrt{5} = 2.24$, gives

$$P\{y = 5\} \cong P\left\{\frac{-.5}{2.24} \le z \le \frac{.5}{2.24}\right\} = 2P\{0 \le z \le .22\} = .1742$$

an error of about .002.

c. $n = 30$. Here $P\{y = 15\} = .144$, while the normal approximation gives .1428, an error of about .001.

In these examples we found the approximate probability that y will have a *single* specified value i. By summing (27) over i we find an approximation to the probability that y will lie within a specified *interval* of values. Thus for any two integers $0 \le c \le d \le n$ we have by (27)

$$P\{c \le y \le d\} = \sum_{i=c}^{d} P\{y = i\} \tag{28}$$

$$\cong \sum_{i=c}^{d} P\left\{\frac{i - .5 - np}{\sqrt{npq}} \le z \le \frac{i + .5 - np}{\sqrt{npq}}\right\}$$

$$= P\left\{\frac{c - .5 - np}{\sqrt{npq}} \le z \le \frac{d + .5 - np}{\sqrt{npq}}\right\}$$

The approximation (28) involving the continuity correction $\pm.5$ is somewhat more accurate than the direct use of the Central Limit Theorem (26), which would give

$$P\{c \le y \le d\} = P\left\{\frac{c - np}{\sqrt{npq}} \le \frac{y - np}{\sqrt{npq}} \le \frac{d - np}{\sqrt{npq}}\right\}$$

$$\cong P\left\{\frac{c - np}{\sqrt{npq}} \le z \le \frac{d - np}{\sqrt{npq}}\right\}$$

although for large n the difference between the right-hand side of this expression and that of (28) becomes negligible.

Example 10
For $n = 300$ and $p = .25$, find approximately $P\{y \ge 95\}$ and $P\{60 \le y \le 90\}$.

a. Since $P\{y \geq 95\} = 1 - P\{y \leq 94\}$ we use (28) with $c = 0$ and $d = 94$, obtaining

$$P\{y \leq 94\} \cong P\left\{\frac{-75.5}{7.5} \leq z \leq \frac{19.5}{7.5}\right\}$$
$$= P\{-10.07 \leq z \leq 2.60\} = .5 + P\{0 \leq z \leq 2.60\}$$
$$= .5 + .4953 = .9953$$

Hence

$$P\{y \geq 95\} \cong 1 - .9953 = .0047$$

(The exact value is .0055.)

b. $P\{60 \leq y \leq 90\} = P\left\{\dfrac{59.5 - 75}{7.5} \leq z \leq \dfrac{90.5 - 75}{7.5}\right\}$
$$= P\{-2.07 \leq z \leq 2.07\} = 2P\{0 \leq z \leq 2.07\}$$
$$= .9616$$

(The exact value is .9615.)

The standard normal approximation can also be used for the approximate evaluation of probabilities in sampling *without replacement* from a finite population. We give an example to illustrate this.

Example 11 (optional)
In an election, candidate A received $a = 15,100$ votes and candidate B received $b = 14,900$ votes. The losing candidate B challenged the result, claiming that about $n = 3600$ of the $N = a + b = 30,000$ votes were illegally cast, and that if n votes were to be removed *at random* from the total there would be an appreciable chance of a reversal of the result. How likely is this?

Suppose, for any values of $a > b$, $N = a + b$, and n, that of n votes removed at random (without replacement) from the N votes, y are for candidate A and $n - y$ for candidate B. A "reversal" will occur if

$$a - y \leq b - (n - y); \text{ i.e. } y \geq (n + a - b)/2$$

The random variable y here is of the form

$$y = x_1 + \ldots + x_n = n\bar{x}$$

where $\{x_1, \ldots, x_n\}$ represents a random sample of n taken *without replacement* from a bowl containing N chips, of which a are numbered with a 1 and $N - a = b$ are numbered with a 0. For this population

$$\mu = \frac{a}{N} \qquad \sigma^2 = \frac{a}{N} \cdot \frac{b}{N}$$

since for a single chip the probability of getting a 1 is $p = a/N$, with

$$q = 1 - p = 1 - \frac{a}{N} = \frac{N - a}{N} = \frac{b}{N} \qquad \text{(one-trial binomial)}$$

Hence by (18) and (19)

$$\mu_y = n\mu_{\bar{x}} = \frac{na}{N}, \; \sigma_y^2 = n^2\sigma_{\bar{x}}^2 = \sigma^2 \cdot \frac{(N - n)n}{N - 1} = \frac{ab(N - n)n}{N^2(N - 1)}$$

Denote by z_n the *standardized* value of y,

$$z_n = \frac{y - \mu_y}{\sigma_y} = \frac{y - \dfrac{na}{N}}{\sqrt{\dfrac{ab(N - n)n}{N^2(N - 1)}}}$$

We saw that a reversal will occur only if $y \geq (n + a - b)/2$; that is,

$$z_n \geq \frac{\dfrac{(n + a - b)}{2} - \dfrac{na}{N}}{\sqrt{\dfrac{ab(N - n)n}{N^2(N - 1)}}}$$

But

$$\frac{(n + a - b)}{2} - \frac{na}{N} = \frac{N(n + a - b) - 2na}{2N} = \frac{(N - n)(a - b)}{2N}$$

so a reversal will occur only if

$$z_n \geq \frac{(N - n)(a - b)}{2N\sqrt{\dfrac{ab(N - n)n}{N^2(N - 1)}}} = \frac{(a - b)\sqrt{N - n}}{2\sqrt{\dfrac{abn}{N - 1}}}$$

$$\cong \frac{(a - b)\sqrt{N - n}}{2\sqrt{\dfrac{abn}{N}}} \qquad \text{for large } N$$

Now, since $a + b = N$

$$ab = a(N - a) = -(a^2 - Na)$$

$$= -\left(a^2 - Na + \frac{N^2}{4}\right) + \frac{N^2}{4} = \frac{N^2}{4} - \left(a - \frac{N}{2}\right)^2 \leq \frac{N^2}{4}$$

(with approximate equality when $a \cong N/2$; i.e., when $a \cong b$). Hence a reversal will occur only if

$$z_n \geq \frac{(a - b)\sqrt{N - n}}{2\sqrt{\dfrac{n}{N} \cdot \dfrac{N}{4}}} = \frac{(a - b)\sqrt{N - n}}{\sqrt{Nn}} = (a - b)\sqrt{\frac{1}{n} - \frac{1}{N}}$$

and by Chebyshev's inequality

$$P\left\{z_n \geq (a - b)\sqrt{\frac{1}{n} - \frac{1}{N}}\right\} \leq P\left\{|z_n| \geq (a - b)\sqrt{\frac{1}{n} - \frac{1}{N}}\right\}$$

$$\leq \frac{1}{(a - b)^2 \cdot \left(\dfrac{1}{n} - \dfrac{1}{N}\right)}$$

In fact, when N is large and n is small compared with N, the standardized "hypergeometric" random variable z_n, like the standardized binomial, can be shown to be approximately standard normal. Hence

$$P(\text{reversal}) \cong P\left[z \geq (a - b)\sqrt{\frac{1}{n} - \frac{1}{N}}\right] \tag{29}$$

which can be computed from the normal distribution table.

In the example with $a = 15,100$, $b = 14,900$, $N = 30,000$, $n = 3600$

$$(a - b)\sqrt{\frac{1}{n} - \frac{1}{N}} = 200\sqrt{\frac{1}{3600} - \frac{1}{30,000}} \cong 3.3$$

and $P(z \geq 3.3) = .005$ for a standard normal z. Thus, even a margin of victory as small as 200 in an election with a total of 30,000 votes is highly unlikely to be reversed by the random nullification of 3600 votes.

PROBLEMS 5.5

1. A random sample is taken of the weights of 400 college men. If the population of college men from which the sample is taken has a mean weight $\mu = 152$ lbs with a standard deviation of 23, find the probability that the sample mean $\bar{x}$ is: (a) between 150 and 154; (b) less than 149; and (c) more than 153.

2. A random sample of 100 flashlight batteries are tested until the electrical output is below a specified level. The "effective" lifetimes for the batteries are then recorded. If the batteries have mean effective lifetime of 50.8 hours with a standard deviation of 10.2 hours, find the probability that the sample mean $\bar{x}$ of effective lifetimes is: (a) less than 49 hours; (b) greater than 52 hours; and (c) between 48.6 and 53.0 hours.

3. A manufacturer of cigarettes claims an average of 18.5 milligrams of tar per cigarette.

   a. Assuming that the standard deviation is 4.2 milligrams per cigarette, find the probability that in a random sample of 400 cigarettes, the sample mean $\bar{x}$ of milligrams of tar per cigarette is greater than 19.

b. What might one conclude if $\bar{x} = 19.2$?

4. The fish caught in Shell lake have a mean length of 15.2 inches, with a standard deviation of 4.8 inches. A random sample of 100 fish caught after a new processing plant was constructed on the shoreline resulted in $\bar{x} = 14$ inches.

   a. Assuming that no change has taken place, compute the probability that $\bar{x} \leq 14$.

   b. With the results of the sample and the computation in (a), what might one suspect has happened to the fish population since the construction of the processing plant?

5. An automobile insurance company, studying its settlement costs per claim, randomly sampled 100 claims paid within the last year.

   a. If these claims are distributed with mean $\mu = \$478$ and standard deviation $\$136$, find the probability that the insurance company will miss the true value of $\$478$ by more than $\$30$ if they use $\bar{x}$, the sample mean, to estimate μ. (Hint: Find $P\{(\bar{x} < 478 - 30) \text{ or } (\bar{x} > 478 + 30)\}$.)

   b. Do the same for $P\{|\bar{x} - \mu| > 40\}$.

6. An entomologist wishes to estimate the mean wing length of a species of butterfly from a sample of $n = 50$ fully grown specimens.

   a. If the species has a mean wing length of $\mu = 5.3$ centimeters with standard deviation .5 centimeters, find the probability that the entomologist will miss the true value of 5.3 centimeters by more than 0.1 centimeters. (Hint: Find $P\{(\bar{x} < 5.1)$ or $(\bar{x} > 5.5)\}$.)

   b. Repeat for $P\{|\bar{x} - \mu| > .2\}$.

7. A fair die is tossed $n = 30$ times, and $y =$ the sum of the faces of the 30 tosses. Use the Central Limit Theorem to compute (a) $P(95 \leq y \leq 115)$; (b) $P(y \leq 120)$; and (c) $P(y < 85)$.

8. A box contains three nickels, two dimes, and one quarter. A coin is chosen at random from the box, the amount is recorded, and the coin replaced. If this experiment is repeated 25 times, and $y =$ the sum of all the coins chosen in the 25 experiments, use the Central Limit Theorem to compute (a) $P(2.00 \leq y \leq 3.00)$; (b) $P(y > 3.50)$; and (c) $P(y > 1.50)$.

9. Let y have a binomial distribution with $n = 15$ and $p = .3$. Find each of the probabilities below both by the exact method using appendix table 4 and by the normal approximation.

   a. $P(y = 5)$ **c.** $P(3 \leq y \leq 7)$
   b. $P(y = 6)$ **d.** $P(y > 4)$

10. Let y have a binomial distribution with $n = 20$ and $p = .6$. Find each of the probabilities below both by the exact method using appendix table 4 and by the normal approximation (28).

    a. $P(y = 12)$ **c.** $P(y \leq 6)$
    b. $P(10 \leq y \leq 15)$ **d.** $P(y > 15)$

11. A fair coin is tossed 100 times. Find the probability of the following events, using the normal approximation (28) to the binomial distribution.

    a. The number of heads in the 100 tosses is between 40 and 60, including 40 and 60.
    b. More than 65 heads occur in the 100 tosses.
    c. Exactly 50 heads occur in the 100 tosses.

12. A fair die is tossed 180 times. Find the probability of the following events, using the normal approximation (28) to the binomial distribution.

    a. The number of times a 6 appears in the 180 tosses is between 24 and 36, including 24 and 36.
    b. The number of times a 6 appears in the 180 tosses is more than 45.
    c. The number of times a 6 appears in the 180 tosses is at least 20.

13. Sixty percent of pigs irradiated at a high level of rads show a precancerous skin condition.

    a. What is the probability that less than half of 100 pigs so irradiated will show this condition?
    b. What is the probability that between 50 and 70 of the 100 pigs will show this condition?

14. Suppose that 54 percent of the voters in New York State intend to vote for a certain candidate for governor at the time a poll is taken. If a random sample of 1000 such voters is taken, find the probability that in this sample

    a. less than half intend to vote for this candidate.
    b. between 510 and 570 of the voters intend to vote for this candidate.

15. Five years ago, 20 percent of U.S. men used a certain brand of razor. The manufacturer of this razor takes a random sample of 1000 men and finds that now y of these men use his brand of razor. What value y_0 will give $P(y \geq y_0) = .05$ if the razor manufacturer still has 20 percent of the market? If he observes that $y = 233$ use his razor, should be conclude that the 20 percent figure is no longer correct?

16. In 1960, 30 percent of the women over 18 in a certain city held full-time jobs outside the home. In a 1973 random sample of $n = 500$ women over 18 in this city, y of these women held full-time jobs outside the home. What value y_0 will give $P(y \geq y_0) = .01$ if the 30 percent figure still holds in 1973? What might be concluded if $y = 187$ for the sample of 500 women in 1973?

17. A random sample of 100 students is taken without replacement from a college class of 800 students; 480 students in this class are men and 320 are women. Let $y =$ number of men in the sample. Using the normal approximation to

$$z_n = \frac{y - \mu_y}{\sigma_y}, \quad \text{find}$$

a. $P(y \geq 60)$ **b.** $P(40 \leq y \leq 70)$ **c.** $P(y \leq 35)$

18. A random sample of 200 voters is taken without replacement from a population of 1000 voters, of which 550 favor candidate A and 450 favor candidate B. Let $y =$ the number of voters in the sample favoring candidate A. Using the normal approximation to

$$z_n = \frac{y - \mu_y}{\sigma_y}, \quad \text{find}$$

a. $P(y > 100)$ **b.** $P(100 \leq y \leq 120)$ **c.** $P(y < 100)$

Based on the result in (a), if one claims that candidate A is the preferred candidate in this situation, what is the probability of being wrong?

Statistical Inference for Means: Large-Sample Theory

6 Statistical Inference for Means: Large-Sample Theory

This chapter is devoted to statistical inference concerning unknown population mean values when sample sizes are large. The procedures are based on the Central Limit Theorem, according to which the sample mean $\bar{x} = \dfrac{1}{n} \sum\limits_{i=1}^{n} x_i$ of a random sample $\{x_1, \ldots, x_n\}$ from any population will be approximately *normally distributed* when the sample size is sufficiently large, with $\mu_{\bar{x}} = \mu$ and $\sigma_{\bar{x}}^2 = \sigma^2/n$, where μ and σ^2 are the mean value and variance of the population from which the sample is drawn.

Example 1
To estimate the mean value μ of the age at which women marry in a large urban county, a random sample of 400 marriage records is drawn from the records of the last two years at the county clerk's office. Suppose the sample mean age for women is $\bar{x} = 23.4$ years. How good an estimate of μ is this?

Example 2
A manufacturer of light bulbs wants to estimate the amount of improvement in product lifetime when a new type of filament is used. A sample of 50 old bulbs yields a mean lifetime of 1271 hours, while a sample of 60 new bulbs yields a mean lifetime of 1416 hours. How well does the observed difference, $1271 - 1416 = -145$, estimate the true but unknown difference in population mean lifetimes of the new and old bulbs?

Example 3

An oncologist wants to determine whether a certain chemical alters the growth of cancer tumors in mice. Tumors are implanted in a sample of 60 mice. 30 of these mice, randomly chosen, are given the chemical for four weeks. The other 30 mice, a control group, are kept under the same conditions for four weeks but are not given the chemical. The treated mice show an average tumor weight of 1.28 grams after four weeks, whereas the control mice show an average tumor weight of 1.43 grams. Should the oncologist assert that the chemical affects tumor growth?

These examples are problems of statistical inference concerning unknown population mean values. In example 1 we want to estimate μ, the unknown mean age of marriage for the population of all women in the county who married during the last two years. In example 2 we want to estimate the difference, $\mu_1 - \mu_2$, between the mean lifetimes of bulbs with old and new filaments. In example 3 we want to test the null hypothesis $H_0 : \mu_1 = \mu_2$, where μ_1 and μ_2 represent the the mean tumor sizes in control and treated mice.

In this chapter we show how to obtain *confidence interval estimates* and *tests of hypotheses* for problems involving the mean value of a single population or the difference between the mean values of two populations. These methods, based on the Central Limit Theorem, are valid *when the sample sizes are large.*

The examples above gave only the *sample means* and *sample sizes*. This information is *not* enough for valid statistical inference concerning population mean values. The *population variances*, or at least *sample estimates of them*, are also needed. This will become clear when we describe the inference procedures.

6.1 Confidence Interval Estimation of the Mean Value of a Single Population

In example 1 we want to estimate the population mean value μ of the age of women at marriage. The data available are a sample of $n = 400$ observations, for which the sample mean is $\bar{x} = 23.4$ years. This provides only a *point estimate* of μ, which is unlikely to be exactly correct. It is much more useful to construct a *confidence interval* with lower and upper confidence limits μ_L and μ_U, in such a way that the probability that the interval (μ_L, μ_U) will contain μ is high.

Let $\{x_1, \ldots, x_n\}$ be a random sample from a population with an unknown mean value μ. Suppose first that the population variance

σ^2 is known. If $\bar{x}$ denotes the sample mean, then $\mu_{\bar{x}} = \mu$ and $\sigma_{\bar{x}}^2 = \sigma^2/n$. The Central Limit Theorem of section 5.6 states that when n is large the standardized random variable

$$z_n = \frac{\bar{x} - \mu}{\sigma/\sqrt{n}}$$

(for which $\mu_{z_n} = 0$ and $\sigma_{z_n}^2 = 1$) has approximately a standard normal distribution, so that $P\{-b < z_n < b\} \cong P\{-b < z < b\}$, where z is standard normal. If we take $b = z_{\alpha/2} > 0$, where $z_{\alpha/2}$ is by definition the number such that $P\{z > z_{\alpha/2}\} = \alpha/2$, then

$$P\{-z_{\alpha/2} < z_n < z_{\alpha/2}\} \cong P\{-z_{\alpha/2} < z < z_{\alpha/2}\} = 1 - \alpha \qquad (1)$$

(See figure 6.1 below.)

We now observe that *the following two events are equivalent:*

$$\{-z_{\alpha/2} < z_n < z_{\alpha/2}\} \qquad \left\{\bar{x} - z_{\alpha/2} \cdot \frac{\sigma}{\sqrt{n}} < \mu < \bar{x} + z_{\alpha/2} \cdot \frac{\sigma}{\sqrt{n}}\right\}$$

In fact, the first event occurs if and only if $\bar{x}$ and μ differ from one another by no more than $z_{\alpha/2} \cdot \sigma/\sqrt{n}$, and exactly the same is true of the second event. We therefore obtain from the probability approximation (1)

A 100 $(1 - \alpha)$% confidence interval for μ (σ^2 known, n large): With probability approximately $1 - \alpha$

$$\mu_L = \bar{x} - z_{\alpha/2} \cdot \frac{\sigma}{\sqrt{n}} < \mu < \bar{x} + z_{\alpha/2} \cdot \frac{\sigma}{\sqrt{n}} = \mu_U \qquad (2)$$

$1 - \alpha$ is called the *confidence coefficient* of the confidence interval (μ_L, μ_U) given by (2).

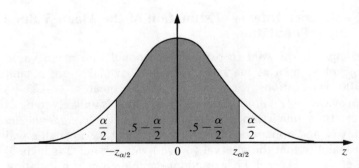

FIGURE 6.1

$$P\{-z_{\alpha/2} \le z \le z_{\alpha/2}\} = 1 - \alpha$$

Example 1 (continued)

Suppose that we know (or are willing to assume from data obtained from other studies of age at marriage) that the standard deviation of age at marriage for the population in question is $\sigma = 6.2$ years. To construct a 95% confidence interval for μ we compute the upper and lower confidence limits μ_L and μ_U of (2), with $z_{\alpha/2} = 1.96$, $n = 400$, $\sigma = 6.2$, and $\bar{x} = 23.4$. The resulting interval is

$$\mu_L = 22.79 < \mu < 24.01 = \mu_U$$

with a confidence coefficient of approximately 95%. Although we do not (and may never) know whether this *particular* statement about μ is true, we do know that if we follow the procedure above repeatedly, and construct each time the confidence interval $\bar{x} \pm 1.96 \ \sigma/\sqrt{n}$, then about 95% of the time this randomly varying interval will in fact contain the value μ.

About 95% of the time the confidence interval (μ_L, μ_U) will contain μ, about 2.5% of the time it will lie entirely to the left of μ, and about 2.5% of the time entirely to the right. If we do not know μ, we do not know in any given case which of these three situations is the true one, but if we make it a rule to assert that the confidence interval contains μ, we shall be right about 95% of the time.

In practice, the variance σ^2 of the population is usually unknown. But in section 5.3 we showed that for a large n the unbiased sample estimator of σ^2 given by

$$s^2 = \frac{1}{n-1} \sum_{i=1}^{n} (x_i - \bar{x})^2$$

will be nearly equal to σ^2 with high probability. This fact allows us to replace σ by s in (2) without much error when n is large*, and thereby obtain

---

*An *exact* result, valid even for a *small* n when the underlying population itself is normal, is obtained in chapter 7.

A 100 (1 − α)% confidence interval for μ (σ² unknown, n large):
With probability approximately $1 - \alpha$

$$\mu_L = \bar{x} - z_{\alpha/2} \cdot \frac{s}{\sqrt{n}} < \mu < \bar{x} + z_{\alpha/2} \cdot \frac{s}{\sqrt{n}} = \mu_U \qquad (3)$$

Example 4

The closing prices of a random sample of 150 stocks on the New York Stock Exchange are recorded. Using the sample values of $\bar{x}$ and s^2, we wish to construct a 90% confidence interval for μ, the average closing price of all stocks for the day in question. Since for $\alpha = .10$, $z_{\alpha/2} = 1.65$, the interval (3) for μ is

$$\bar{x} \pm 1.65 \frac{s}{\sqrt{n}} \qquad (4)$$

If the sample values are, for example, $\bar{x} = 52.7$ and $s = 23.8$, then since

$$1.65 \frac{s}{\sqrt{n}} = \frac{(1.65)(23.8)}{\sqrt{150}} \cong 3.2$$

the 90% confidence interval (4) in this case becomes

$$\mu_L = 49.5 < \mu < 55.9 = \mu_U$$

We are therefore "90% confident" that $49.5 < \mu < 55.9$; that is, that 90% of the time a random sample of 150 stocks will result in an interval (4) that does contain μ.

Example 5

A random sample of 1832 army inductees (ages 18–25) gave an average chest girth of $\bar{x} = 37.7$ inches, with $s = 3.6$. From these data, the army wishes to estimate μ, the mean population chest girth of its inductees, by a 98% confidence interval. Here $\alpha = .02$, $z_{\alpha/2} = 2.33$, and since

$$z_{\alpha/2} \cdot \frac{s}{\sqrt{n}} = \frac{(2.33)(3.6)}{\sqrt{1832}} \cong .2$$

the 98% confidence interval (3) for μ is $37.7 \pm .2$; that is, $\mu_L = 37.5$ to $\mu_U = 37.9$ inches.

PROBLEMS 6.1

1. State whether each of the following statements is true or false.

    a. A confidence interval has random variables for its upper and lower limits.

b. A confidence interval for the mean μ is a statement about a certain random interval containing μ.

c. A 95% confidence interval will have a higher probability of coverage as the sample size increases.

d. A 95% confidence interval will cover the population mean 95 out of 100 times.

e. A 98% confidence interval calculated by (3) will always be shorter than a 99% confidence interval for the same sample.

2. Define and explain each of the following in your own words.

   a. A confidence interval.
   b. The upper and lower limits of a confidence interval.
   c. The meaning of (3).

3. Find a 95% confidence interval for the mean height of a population of males if $\bar{x} = 70.3$ inches in a sample of 100 such males. Assume that $\sigma = 5$ inches.

4. Find a 98% confidence interval for the mean monthly rental of one-bedroom apartments, based on a random sample of 150 such apartments with $\bar{x} = \$162$. Assume that $\sigma = \$25$.

5. A random sample of 400 families of four in a certain state revealed that the food bill for a given month had a sample mean $212 and a sample standard deviation $49. Construct a 99% confidence interval for the mean food bill for a family of four in this state for the given month.

6. A random sample of 49 household TV sets in a certain city on a given day resulted in a sample mean viewing time of 5.3 hours, with a sample standard deviation of 1.4 hours. Construct a 95% confidence interval for the mean viewing time per TV household in this city for the specified day.

6.2 A Confidence Interval for p (continued)

In section 5.2, we saw that for a binomial random variable $y = x_1 + \ldots + x_n$, the probability is about $1 - \alpha$ that for large n

$$\hat{p} - \frac{z_{\alpha/2}}{\sqrt{n}} \sqrt{\hat{p}(1 - \hat{p})} < p < \hat{p} + \frac{z_{\alpha/2}}{\sqrt{n}} \sqrt{\hat{p}(1 - \hat{p})} \tag{5}$$

where $\hat{p} = y/n$.

This is just a slightly modified special case of the general confidence interval (3). For a sample $\{x_1, \ldots, x_n\}$, where $x_i = 0$ or 1 depending on whether the ith trial is a failure or success, $x_i^2 = x_i$, since $0^2 = 0$ and $1^2 - 1$. Therefore the sample estimator of $\sigma^2 = p(1 - p)$ is by (5.7)

$$s^2 = \frac{n \sum_{i=1}^{n} x_i^2 - \left(\sum_{i=1}^{n} x_i \right)^2}{n(n-1)} = \frac{ny - y^2}{n(n-1)} = \frac{y(n-y)}{n(n-1)}$$

$$= \frac{y}{n}\left(\frac{n}{n-1} - \frac{y}{n-1} \right) \cong \hat{p}(1 - \hat{p})$$

for a large n. Substitution of this approximation into (3) yields (5), since here $\bar{x} = \hat{p}$, and the population mean value μ is $p \cdot 1 + (1 - p) \cdot 0 = p$. Thus the binomial confidence interval (5) for p is essentially a special case of the general confidence interval (3) for an arbitrary population mean value μ.

PROBLEMS 6.2

1. If 280 out of 900 cars randomly sampled in a certain state are in violation of the state's mandatory antismog law, find a 95% confidence interval for the proportion of cars in the state in violation of the law.

2. If 1200 out of 1600 randomly sampled adults in the United States think that inflation is out of hand, find a 98% confidence interval for the proportion of adults in the U.S. who agree with this view.

6.3 On Choosing the Sample Size When Estimating μ or p

Example 6
In studying "attitude toward authority" for a large group of students, a nationally standardized test is used that purports to measure such attitudes; the lower the score on the test, the more negative the attitude toward authority. To estimate μ, the group's mean score on the test, with an error of at most 2 and with a 95% confidence level, how large a sample must be used? Assume that $\sigma = 20$ for the test.

To solve this problem, consider the confidence interval (2). This interval contains μ whenever the distance between μ and the center, $\bar{x}$, of the interval is $\leq D = z_{\alpha/2} \cdot \sigma/\sqrt{n}$. Hence the *required sample size to guarantee a given bound D on the error in estimating μ by $\bar{x}$ is*

$$n = \left(\frac{z_{\alpha/2} \cdot \sigma}{D} \right)^2 \tag{6}$$

We can now determine the sample size required for, say, a 95% confidence interval with an error of at most 2; setting $D = 2$, $\sigma = 20$, and $z_{\alpha/2} = z_{.025} = 1.96$, the required sample size is seen by (6) to be

$$n = \left[\frac{(1.96)(20)}{2}\right]^2 = 384.16$$

One can therefore estimate μ by $\bar{x}$ with an error of at most 2 and with 95% confidence, provided that the sample of students is of size $n \geq 385$. Note that (6) can be used only when σ is known (perhaps from earlier similar studies), or when at least an upper bound for σ is known.

Example 7
A physiologist, investigating the lung capacity of males (ages 18–30) who exercise regularly, wishes to form a 98% confidence interval for μ, the population mean lung capacity in liters. Based on previous studies, it is known that $\sigma \leq .3$. What sample size n will guarantee that the error in estimating μ by $\bar{x}$ will be $\leq .05$? Replacing σ by .3 in (6) yields

$$n = \left[\frac{(2.33)(.3)}{.05}\right]^2 = (13.98)^2 = 195.44$$

so that a sample size of $n \geq 196$ will guarantee that with probability 98%, μ will be within .05 of $\bar{x}$.

A similar formula can be obtained for the sample size in estimating a binomial parameter p. In (5) the error $|\hat{p} - p|$ is at most equal to

$$D = \frac{z_{\alpha/2}}{\sqrt{n}} \sqrt{\hat{p}(1 - \hat{p})} \tag{7}$$

where $\hat{p} = $ the observed proportion of successes. Now, for all $0 \leq t \leq 1$, it is true that $t(1 - t) \leq 1/4$, as shown in figure 6.2.

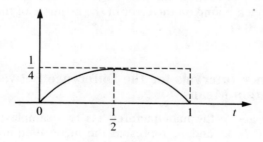

FIGURE 6.2
The graph of $y = t(1 - t)$

Equality holds only for $t = 1/2$, and hence *the right-hand side of* (7) *is largest when* $\hat{p} = 1/2$. From (7) with $\hat{p} = 1/2$ it follows that a sample size

$$n \geq \frac{1}{4}\left(\frac{z_{\alpha/2}}{D}\right)^2 \tag{8}$$

will ensure that the error in estimating p by $\hat{p}$ will be $\leq D$ at least 100 $(1 - \alpha)\%$ of the time.

Example 8
A pollster wishes to estimate p, the proportion of voters favoring the Democratic candidate in an approaching election, to within $D = .03$ (3 percentage points). The required sample size by (8) for a 95% confidence interval ($z_{\alpha/2} = 1.96$) is

$$n = \frac{1}{4}\left(\frac{1.96}{.03}\right)^2 \cong 1067$$

With a sample size of 1067, the sample proportion $\hat{p}$ will be within .03 of p at least 95% of the time. (Note: this sample size does *not* depend on the size of the population from which the sample is taken.)

PROBLEMS 6.3

1. In problem 3 of section 6.1, how large a random sample must be taken so that the bound on the error of the estimate is .2 inches?

2. In problem 4 of section 6.1, how large a random sample must be taken so that the bound on the error of the estimate is $2?

3. In problem 2 of section 6.2, how large a random sample is needed to guarantee a bound on the error of the estimate of the proportion of at most .02?

4. In problem 1 of section 6.2, how large a random sample is needed to guarantee a bound on the error of the estimate of the proportion of at most .03?

6.4 Confidence Intervals for the Difference Between Two Population Means

In example 2 above the manufacturer has two samples: 50 old and 70 new bulbs. If μ_1 and μ_2 represent the mean lifetimes (in hours) for the old and new populations, respectively, then the manufacturer wishes to estimate $\mu_1 - \mu_2$. This illustrates the following problem. Let $\{x_{11}, \ldots, x_{1n_1}\}$ and $\{x_{21}, \ldots, x_{2n_2}\}$ be two samples, of sizes n_1 and

n_2, respectively. (Note the use of two subscripts on the observations. The first subscript, $i = 1$ or 2, represents which population the observation is drawn from; the second subscript represents which sample observation it is. Thus, x_{12} is the second observation in sample 1, x_{25} the fifth observation in sample 2, and so forth.)

The samples are assumed to be independent of each other*; that is, the observations in the first sample are independent of those in the second. Let $\bar{x}_i$ and s_i^2 be the sample estimates of μ_i and σ_i^2 for the ith sample; $i = 1,2$:

$$\bar{x}_i = \frac{1}{n_i} \sum_{j=1}^{n_i} x_{ij} \qquad s_i^2 = \frac{1}{n_i - 1} \sum_{j=1}^{n_i} (x_{ij} - \bar{x}_i)^2$$

We shall use the observed values $\bar{x}_1$, $\bar{x}_2$, s_1^2, s_2^2 from the two samples to construct a confidence interval for the unknown difference $\mu_1 - \mu_2$ of population means.

The difference $\bar{x}_1 - \bar{x}_2$ of the sample means is an unbiased point estimator of $\mu_1 - \mu_2$, with

$$\mu_{\bar{x}_1 - \bar{x}_2} = \mu_1 - \mu_2 \tag{9}$$

and

$$\sigma_{\bar{x}_1 - \bar{x}_2}^2 = \sigma_{\bar{x}_1}^2 + \sigma_{\bar{x}_2}^2 = \frac{\sigma_1^2}{n_1} + \frac{\sigma_2^2}{n_2} \tag{10}$$

Moreover, the standardized random variable,

$$\frac{(\bar{x}_1 - \bar{x}_2) - (\mu_1 - \mu_2)}{\sqrt{\dfrac{\sigma_1^2}{n_1} + \dfrac{\sigma_2^2}{n_2}}} \tag{11}$$

with mean value zero and variance 1, has an approximately standard normal distribution when n_1 and n_2 are both large. To see this, we first recall that by the Central Limit Theorem $\bar{x}_1$ and $\bar{x}_2$ individually have approximately normal distributions. We now invoke the following theorem concerning the normal distribution, the proof of which is omitted here.

Theorem 1
Let $x_1, \ldots, x_k$ be any mutually independent and normally distributed random variables. *Then any linear combination* $y = c_1 x_1 + \ldots + c_k x_k$ *of the x's is also normally distributed.*

---

*For example, they are not "before and after" responses to some treatment of the same $n = n_1 = n_2$ subjects.

Using theorem 1 for $k = 2$, since $\bar{x}_1$ and $\bar{x}_2$ are approximately normal, we see that $\bar{x}_1 - \bar{x}_2$ is also approximately normal. The mean value of $\bar{x}_1 - \bar{x}_2$ is given by (9), and its variance by (10). Therefore (11) is approximately *standard normal* if n_1 and n_2 are large, and hence for any constant b, the probability that (11) will fall between $-b$ and b is $\cong P\{-b < z < b\}$, where the standard normal distribution of z is given in appendix table 6. If we take $b = z_{\alpha/2}$ we obtain the approximation

$$P\left\{-z_{\alpha/2} < \frac{(\bar{x}_1 - \bar{x}_2) - (\mu_1 - \mu_2)}{\sqrt{\dfrac{\sigma_1^2}{n_1} + \dfrac{\sigma_2^2}{n_2}}} < z_{\alpha/2}\right\} \cong 1 - \alpha$$

and by the same argument as that which led to (3) this yields

A 100(1 − α)% confidence interval for $\mu_1 - \mu_2$ (large samples): With probability approximately $1 - \alpha$

$$\bar{x}_1 - \bar{x}_2 - z_{\alpha/2} \cdot c < \mu_1 - \mu_2 < \bar{x}_1 - \bar{x}_2 + z_{\alpha/2} \cdot c \tag{12}$$

where by definition

$$c = \sqrt{\frac{\sigma_1^2}{n_1} + \frac{\sigma_2^2}{n_2}} \qquad \text{(when } \sigma_1 \text{ and } \sigma_2 \text{ are known)} \tag{13}$$

If σ_1^2 and σ_2^2 are unknown, the c in (12) is replaced by

$$c = \sqrt{\frac{s_1^2}{n_1} + \frac{s_2^2}{n_2}} \tag{14}$$

The justification for this is that s_1^2 and s_2^2 are approximately equal to σ_1^2 and σ_2^2 with high probability when n_1 and n_2 are sufficiently large.

If σ_1^2 and σ_2^2 are unknown but *we are willing to assume that they are equal*, we replace the c of (14) by the somewhat more accurate estimator of $\sigma_{\bar{x}_1 - \bar{x}_2}$ given by

$$c = s\sqrt{\frac{1}{n_1} + \frac{1}{n_2}} \tag{15}$$

where by definition

$$s^2 = \frac{(n_1 - 1)s_1^2 + (n_2 - 1)s_2^2}{n_1 + n_2 - 2} \tag{16}$$

is the *pooled variance* of the two samples. It is an unbiased, consistent estimator of σ^2 when $\sigma_1^2 = \sigma_2^2 = \sigma^2$. The unbiasedness follows by noting that $\mu_{s_1^2} = \sigma_1^2$, $\mu_{s_2^2} = \sigma_2^2$, so that when $\sigma_1^2 = \sigma_2^2 = \sigma^2$

$$\mu_{s^2} = \frac{(n_1 - 1)\sigma_1^2 + (n_2 - 1)\sigma_2^2}{n_1 + n_2 - 2} = \frac{(n_1 + n_2 - 2)\sigma^2}{n_1 + n_2 - 2} = \sigma^2$$

In example 2, suppose the samples give (in hours): bulbs with old type filament: $\bar{x}_1 = 1271$, $x_1 = 148$, $n_1 = 50$; bulbs with new type filament: $\bar{x}_2 = 1416$, $s_2 = 261$, $n_2 = 70$.

To construct a 95% confidence interval for $\mu_1 - \mu_2$ we compute $\bar{x}_1 - \bar{x}_2 = 1271 - 1416 = -145$, and since there is no strong reason here to assume that $\sigma_1^2 = \sigma_2^2$, we use (14) to obtain

$$c = \sqrt{\frac{s_1^2}{n_1} + \frac{s_2^2}{n_2}} = \sqrt{\frac{(148)^2}{50} + \frac{(261)^2}{70}} = 37.57$$

The lower and upper confidence limits in (12) with $z_{\alpha/2} = z_{.025} = 1.96$ ($\alpha = .05$) are then: lower confidence limit $= -145 - (1.96)(37.57) = -145 - 73.6 = -218.6$; upper confidence limit $= -145 + 73.6 = -71.4$.

The manufacturer can thus be 95% confident that the new filament *increases* the mean lifetime of the bulbs by something between 71.4 and 218.6 hours, since in repeated sampling the procedure used will give a true statement 95% of the time.

In the example that follows the assumption that $\sigma_1^2 = \sigma_2^2$ is made.

Example 9
To estimate the effect of fertilizer on the yield of corn, an agronomist planted $n_2 = 50$ experimental plots with fertilizer and $n_1 = 40$ plots without fertilizer. The plots receiving fertilizer were randomly chosen from 90 similar plots. The yields in bushels per plot were:

$$\text{unfertilized plots: } n_1 = 40, \ \bar{x}_1 = 6.1, \ s_1^2 = 3.9$$
$$\text{fertilized plots: } n_2 = 50, \ \bar{x}_2 = 7.3, \ s_2^2 = 4.4$$

Based on past experience, the agronomist is willing to assume that $\sigma_1^2 = \sigma_2^2 = \sigma^2$, with σ^2 unknown. The pooled estimate of σ^2 from (16) is

$$s^2 = \frac{(n_1 - 1)s_1^2 + (n_2 - 1)s_2^2}{n_1 + n_2 - 2} = \frac{(39)(3.9) + (49)(4.4)}{88} = 4.18$$

so that $s = \sqrt{4.18} = 2.04$. To construct a 95% confidence interval for $\mu_1 - \mu_2$, the population mean difference in yield per plot due to fertilizer, the agronomist uses (12) with the c given by (15)

$$c = s\sqrt{\frac{1}{n_1} + \frac{1}{n_2}} = 2.04\sqrt{\frac{1}{50} + \frac{1}{40}} = 2.04\sqrt{.045} = (2.04)(.212) = .433$$

The corresponding confidence limits for $\mu_1 - \mu_2$ are
lower confidence limit $= (\bar{x}_1 - \bar{x}_2) - (1.96)(.433) = (6.1 - 7.3) - .85$
$$= -1.2 - .85 = -2.05$$
upper confidence limit $= -1.2 + .85 = -.35$
and the agronomist can thus say with 95% confidence that

$$-2.05 < \mu_1 - \mu_2 < -.35$$

That is, there is a gain in yield because of the fertilizer of between .35 and 2.05 bushels per plot.

PROBLEMS 6.4

1. A random sample of eight women students and ten men students is taken from the population of students at a large university. The population of women students has a mean weight of 120 lbs, with standard deviation 18 lbs; the population of men students has a mean weight of 155 lbs and a standard deviation of 23 lbs. Assuming that the samples are independent of each other, find the mean, variance, and standard deviation of $\bar{x}_1 - \bar{x}_2$, where $\bar{x}_1$ and $\bar{x}_2$ are the sample means for the women and men, respectively. (You may assume that the two populations of men and women students are large enough that the sampling can be assumed, without error, to be with replacement.)

2. Two independent random samples of $n_1 = 10$ and $n_B = 12$ mice are fed diet A and diet B for two weeks. Let $\bar{x}_A$ and $\bar{x}_B$ be the sample means of the weight gains recorded for the samples fed on the two diets. Find the mean, variance, and standard deviation of $\bar{x}_A - \bar{x}_B$ if $\mu_A = .5$ grams and $\mu_B = .4$ grams are the means of mice fed on diets A and B, and $\sigma_A = .1$ grams and $\sigma_B = .12$ grams are the standard deviations.

3. In problem 1, assuming that both men's and women's weights are normally distributed, use the normality of $\bar{x}_1 - \bar{x}_2$ to find
   a. $P(\bar{x}_1 \leq \bar{x}_2)$ **b.** $P(-50 \leq \bar{x}_1 - \bar{x}_2 \leq -15)$

4. In problem 2, assuming that the populations of mice weight gains under the two diets are normally distributed, use the normality of $\bar{x}_A - \bar{x}_B$ to find
   a. $P(\bar{x}_A \geq \bar{x}_B)$ **b.** $P(-.1 \leq \bar{x}_A - \bar{x}_B \leq .21)$

5. A random sample of 90 students in a high school language class is divided into two groups of $n_1 = 50$ and $n_2 = 40$. Group 2 is taught by a traditional method and group 1 is taught by a new method using laboratories in which students listen to language tapes. If the 50 students in group 1 have a sample mean of $\bar{x}_1 = 84$ on a final examination and the 40 students in group 2 have $\bar{x}_2 = 76$, find a 95% confidence interval for the difference of the population means $\mu_1 - \mu_2$ for the two groups, assuming that:
   a. $\sigma_1 = 8$, $\sigma_2 = 9$, the respective population standard deviations, are known.

b. $s_1 = 7.8$, $s_2 = 9.1$ are the respective sample standard deviations, and σ_1 and σ_2 are unknown.

6. A manufacturer of automobile tires places in $n_1 = 35$ tires nylon threads compressed in the rubber of the tire; in $n_2 = 45$ tires, he does not. The tires are then run 20,000 miles each on a machine. The wear is given by the following table.

Tire type	Sample size	Sample mean	Sample standard deviation
Without nylon	$n_1 = 35$	$\bar{x}_1 = 1.8$ cm.	$s_1 = .42$ cm.
With nylon	$n_2 = 45$	$\bar{x}_2 = 1.5$ cm.	$s_2 = .36$ cm.

a. Find a 98% confidence interval for $\mu_1 - \mu_2$, the difference in means between the tire wear in 20.000 miles.

b. If $\sigma_1 = .45$ and $\sigma_2 = .35$ are known, find a 98% confidence interval for $\mu_1 - \mu_2$.

7. Solve problem 5b assuming that $\sigma_1 = \sigma_2$.

8. Solve problem 6a assuming that $\sigma_1 = \sigma_2$.

9. **a.** Construct a 95% confidence interval for the difference in means $\mu_1 - \mu_2$, based on the following two independent random samples of incomes of elementary school teachers in two different cities.

City	Sample size	Sample mean	Sample standard deviation
1	$n_1 = 100$	$\bar{x}_1 = \$10,928$	$s_1 = 1620$
2	$n_2 = 150$	$\bar{x}_2 = \$10,150$	$s_2 = 1540$

b. If it is assumed $\sigma_1 = \sigma_2$, find the confidence interval in (a).

10. **a.** Construct a 99% confidence interval for the difference in mean ages $\mu_1 - \mu_2$, based on the following two independent random samples of persons in two different states.

State	Sample size	Sample mean	Sample standard deviation
1	230	$\bar{x}_1 = 30.8$	$s_1 = 14.7$
2	420	$\bar{x}_2 = 35.2$	$s_2 = 15.3$

b. If it is assumed $\sigma_1 = \sigma_2$, find the confidence interval in (a).

6.5 Confidence Intervals for the Difference Between Two Probabilities

Example 10

A legislatòr wishes to estimate the difference in preference for a proposed law between high-income (over $20,000 per year) and low-income (under $5000 per year) voters. In a random sample of $n_1 = 400$ low-income voters, $y_1 = 164$ favored the proposed law, while in a random sample of $n_2 = 200$ high-income voters, $y_2 = 126$ favored the law. What can the legislator infer from these figures?

Let p_1 and p_2 represent the unknown population proportions of low- and high-income voters favoring the law. The problem is one of estimating $p_1 - p_2$, the difference of two binomial parameters, based on two binomial random variables y_1 and y_2, where y_i is a binomial random variable with n_i trials and parameter p_i, $i = 1,2$. Now $\hat{p}_i = y_i/n_i = (x_{i1} + \ldots + x_{in_i})/n_i$ is the sample mean of n_i one-trial random variables with mean value p_i and variance $p_i q_i$. Thus, for this special case, in which

$$\mu_i = p_i \text{ and } \sigma_i^2 = p_i q_i \qquad (q_i = 1 - p_i) \tag{17}$$

we have

$$\mu_{\hat{p}_1 - \hat{p}_2} = p_1 - p_2 \tag{18}$$

$$\sigma^2_{\hat{p}_1 - \hat{p}_2} = \frac{p_1 q_1}{n_1} + \frac{p_2 q_2}{n_2}$$

Replacing p_1 and p_2 in (18) by their respective point estimators $\hat{p}_1$ and $\hat{p}_2$ we obtain

A $100(1 - \sigma)\%$ confidence interval for the difference between two probabilities (large samples). Let p_1, p_2 be the unknown probabilities of "success" in two populations. With probability approximately $1 - \alpha$

$$\hat{p}_1 - \hat{p}_2 - z_{\alpha/2} \cdot c < p_1 - p_2 < \hat{p}_1 - \hat{p}_2 + z_{\alpha/2} \cdot c \tag{19}$$

where by definition

$$c = \sqrt{\frac{\hat{p}_1 \hat{q}_1}{n_1} + \frac{\hat{p}_2 \hat{q}_2}{n_2}} \tag{20}$$

and $\hat{p}_i =$ the relative frequency of "success" in population i, $\hat{q}_i = 1 - \hat{p}_i$, for $i = 1,2$

The reasoning here involves standardizing $\hat{p}_1 - \hat{p}_2$ to obtain

$$\frac{(\hat{p}_1 - \hat{p}_2) - (p_1 - p_2)}{\sqrt{\frac{p_1 q_1}{n_1} + \frac{p_2 q_2}{n_2}}}$$

with mean value 0 and variance 1, and appealing to the Central Limit Theorem and theorem 1 to obtain (19), as was done in the previous section.

$$\text{In example 10, } \hat{p}_1 - \hat{p}_2 = \frac{164}{400} - \frac{126}{200} = .41 - .63 = -.22$$

$$c = \sqrt{\frac{\hat{p}_1 \hat{q}_1}{n_1} + \frac{\hat{p}_2 \hat{q}_2}{n_2}} = \sqrt{\frac{(.41)(.59)}{400} + \frac{(.63)(.37)}{200}}$$

$$= \frac{1}{10} \sqrt{\frac{.2419}{4} + \frac{.2331}{2}} = \frac{1}{10} \sqrt{.1770} = .042$$

so the 95% confidence limits (19) for $\alpha = .05$, $z_{\alpha/2} = 1.96$ are $-.22 \pm (1.96)(.042)$, or $-.22 \pm .082$. Thus with 95% confidence the legislator can assert that $-.302 < p_1 - p_2 < -.138$.

PROBLEMS 6.5

1. Suppose two independent random samples of $n_1 = 2000$ voters in New York and $n_2 = 1000$ voters in Wisconsin show, respectively, $y_1 = 1140$ and $y_2 = 610$ voters favoring a certain proposed constitutional amendment. Find a 98% confidence interval for $p_1 - p_2$, where p_1 and p_2 are the proportion of voters favoring the amendment in New York and Wisconsin.

2. Suppose two independent random samples of patients are treated with two types of decongestant tablets for 24 hours with the following results.

Brand	Sample size	Number of patients who obtain relief
1	$n_1 = 80$	$y_1 = 56$
2	$n_2 = 100$	$y_2 = 58$

Find a 95% confidence interval for $p_1 - p_2$, the difference between the proportion of all patients who would obtain relief with brand 1 and brand 2.

6.6 One-Sided Hypothesis Tests for μ (Large Samples)

Example 11

Suppose that it has been well established by previous studies that the response time for a randomly chosen driver to react to a sight stimulus has the mean value 1.4 seconds, with standard deviation .24. A new tranquilizing drug is made available to the public, and a safety council wishes to determine if the drug slows driver response time appreciably. It is agreed that if the population mean response time μ under the influence of the drug is 1.5 seconds or less, then no warning should be issued. How does the council decide whether to issue a warning?

In terms of hypothesis testing, suppose the council assumes that σ is still .24 when the drug is used and decides to test the one-sided hypothesis $H_0 : \mu \leq 1.5$ against the alternative $H_1 : \mu > 1.5$. In so doing it will control the type I error, here equal to *the probability of issuing a warning when none is warranted*.

In the general one-sided hypothesis testing situation, let $\{x_1, \ldots, x_n\}$ be a random sample from a population with the *unknown* mean value μ and the *known* variance σ^2. We wish to test for a given value μ_0

$$H_0 : \mu \leq \mu_0 \text{ vs } H_1 : \mu > \mu_0$$

Since $\bar{x}$ will be close to μ with high probability when n is large, $\bar{x}$ will tend to be larger when H_1 is true than when H_0 is true. The event $\{\bar{x} > c\}$, for some constant c, is thus a reasonable critical region R for the test. To specify c, as in the binomial case in chapter 5, we look at the *power function of the test*, defined as the *probability of rejecting H_0 when the true value of the mean is μ,*

$$P_\mu(\text{reject } H_0) = P_\mu\{\bar{x} > c\}$$

For a given value of c this is a function of μ.

We first standardize the sample mean $\bar{x}$, which has mean value μ and variance σ^2/n, obtaining the standardized random variable

$$z_n = \frac{\bar{x} - \mu}{\sigma/\sqrt{n}}$$

with mean value 0 and variance 1. The critical region is therefore

$$\{\bar{x} > c\} = \{z_n > d\}, \text{ with } d = \frac{c - \mu}{\sigma/\sqrt{n}}$$

Now, by the Central Limit Theorem, for any fixed d and large n,

$$P_\mu\{z_n > d\} > P\{z \geq d\} \tag{21}$$

where z is a standard normal random variable. The graph of this function of μ is shown in figure 6.3. It increases from 0 to 1 as μ goes from $-\infty$ to $+\infty$. The maximum probability of rejecting H_0 for all those values $\mu \leq \mu_0$ for which H_0 is true occurs at μ_0, and has a value α approximately given by

$$\alpha = P\{z > d_0\} \text{ where } d_0 = \frac{c - \mu_0}{\sigma/\sqrt{n}} \tag{22}$$

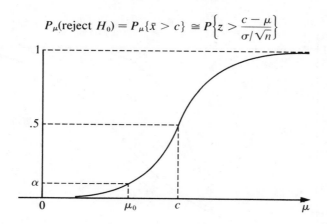

$$P_\mu(\text{reject } H_0) = P_\mu\{\bar{x} > c\} \cong P\left\{z > \frac{c - \mu}{\sigma/\sqrt{n}}\right\}$$

FIGURE 6.3
The power function of the test with critical region $\{\bar{x} > c\}$

*The value α is called the level of significance of the test: if H_0 is true
(that is, if $\mu \leq \mu_0$), then the probability of rejecting H_0 is at most α.*
To specify c for the test the experimenter may choose any desired
level of significance α, usually between .01 and .1, and solve equations
(22) for d_0 and then for c.

In example 11, suppose the council wishes α to be .05 and decides on a sample size of $n = 100$. Then $d_0 = 1.65$, and

$$1.65 = d_0 = \frac{c - \mu_0}{\sigma/\sqrt{n}} = \frac{c - 1.5}{.024}$$

so $c = 1.5 + (.024)(1.65) = 1.5 + .04 = 1.54$. The test thus becomes:
Reject H_0 in favor of H_1 if $\bar{x} > 1.54$.

This test has the desired level $\alpha = .05$, since (approximately)

$$P_{1.5}\{\bar{x} > 1.54\} = .05$$

so the chance of making a type I error (rejecting H_0 when it is true) is
at most .05, this value being attained when $\mu = 1.5$.

The graph of the power function for this test is given by the solid
line in figure 6.4. For example, the power at $\mu = 1.56$ is by (21) equal to

$$P_{1.56}\{\bar{x} > 1.54\} \cong P\left\{z > \frac{1.54 - 1.56}{.024}\right\} = P\{z > -.83\}$$

$$= .5000 + P\{0 \leq z < .83\} = .5000 + .2967 = .7967$$

In chapter 4 we saw that the probability of a type II error (*failing*

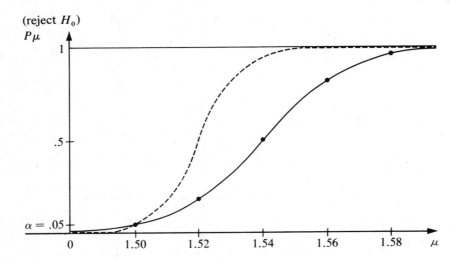

FIGURE 6.4

The power function of the test of example 10

to reject H_0 when it is *false*) can be calculated from the power function: if $\beta(\mu) = $ the probability of a type II error for $\mu > \mu_0$, then

$$\beta(\mu) = 1 - P_\mu(\text{reject } H_0) \tag{23}$$

In the present example, for $\mu = 1.56$

$$\beta(1.56) = 1 - P_{1.56}\{\bar{x} > 1.54\} = 1 - .7967 = .2033$$

Now, if this high a probability of type II error when in fact $\mu = 1.56$ is unacceptable, then one must either (a) *increase the level α of the test*, or (b) *increase the sample size n*. By adjusting α and the sample size n, a satisfactory test can usually be obtained. For example, take $n = 400$, rather than $n = 100$, and maintain the level at $\alpha = .05$. Then

$$c = \mu_0 + (1.65)\frac{\sigma}{\sqrt{n}} = 1.5 + \frac{(1.65)(.24)}{20} = 1.52$$

and the probability of a type II error at $\mu = 1.56$ is now

$$\beta(1.56) = 1 - P_{1.56}\{\bar{x} > 1.52\} = 1 - P\left\{z_n > \frac{1.52 - 1.56}{.24/20}\right\}$$

$$\cong 1 - P\{z > -3.33\} = .5000 - P\{0 \le z < 3.33\}$$

$$= .500 - .4998 = .0002$$

The probability of a type II error at $\mu = 1.56$ thus decreases from .2033 to .0002 when we increase the sample size from 100 to 400. The power function for this test, which rejects H_0 if $\bar{x} > 1.52$ with $n = 400$ and also has level $\alpha = .05$, is shown by the dotted line in figure 6.4. It is clearly superior compared to the test with $n = 100$, but requires a sample size four times as large.

A one-sided test for $H_0 : \mu \geq \mu_0$ vs $H_1 : \mu < \mu_0$ can be constructed in a similar manner. The critical region for such a test is $\{\bar{x} < c\}$, and the procedure, based on reasoning similar to that above, is stated in table 6.1 below.

Tests of the type just discussed require a knowledge of σ^2. If σ^2 is unknown and n is large we replace σ^2 by its sample estimate s^2.

If $\{x_1 , \ldots , x_n\}$ is a sample from a single-trial binomial distribution with parameter $p = P\{x_i = 1\}$, and $q = 1 - p = P\{x_i = 0\}$, then $\mu = p$ and $\bar{x} = y/n = \hat{p}$, where $y = x_1 + \ldots + x_n$ is a binomial random variable with n trials and a success probability p. In this case the variance of x_i when $p = p_0$ is $\sigma^2 = p_0(1 - p_0)$. The test given below for the binomial case was discussed briefly in section 4.3. We summarize these tests in the following table.

TABLE 6.1
One-Sided Level α Hypothesis Tests for μ (or p) When n Is Large

Let $\{x_1 , \ldots , x_n\}$ be a random sample from a distribution with mean value μ and variance σ^2 [$\mu = p$ and $\sigma^2 = p(1 - p)$ in the binomial case]. Assume that n is large (as a rule of thumb, $n \geq 30$). Let α be the desired level of the test, and let z_α be defined by $\alpha = P\{z > z_\alpha\}$, where z is standard normal.

H_0	H_1	Critical region: reject H_0 if	Power function at μ (or p)
$\mu \leq \mu_0$	$\mu > \mu_0$	$\bar{x} < c = \mu_0 + z_\alpha \cdot \dfrac{\sigma}{\sqrt{n}}$ (use s if σ is unknown)	$P_\mu\{\bar{x} > c\} = P\{z > d\}$, where $d = \dfrac{c - \mu}{\sigma/\sqrt{n}}$
$\mu \geq \mu_0$	$\mu < \mu_0$	$\bar{x} < c = \mu_0 - z_\alpha \cdot \dfrac{\sigma}{\sqrt{n}}$ (use s if σ is unknown)	$P_\mu\{\bar{x} < c\} = P\{z < d\}$ where $d = \dfrac{c - \mu}{\sigma/\sqrt{n}}$
$p \leq p_0$	$p > p_0$	$\hat{p} < c = p_0 + z_\alpha \sqrt{\dfrac{p_0(1 - p_0)}{n}}$	$P_p\{\hat{p} > c\} = P\{z > d\}$ where $d = \dfrac{c - p}{\sqrt{p(1 - p)/n}}$
$p \geq p_0$	$p < p_0$	$\hat{p} < c = p_0 - z_\alpha \sqrt{\dfrac{p_0(1 - p_0)}{n}}$	$P_p\{\hat{p} < c\} = P\{z < d\}$ where $d = \dfrac{c - p}{\sqrt{p(1 - p)/n}}$

It is hard to say just how large n must be in these tests to ensure that the type I error probability is close to the desired level α. A more accurate method is given in chapter 7 for cases where σ^2 is unknown and estimated by s^2 and the sample size is small.

Example 12

An insurance company is considering settling small claims by mail rather than by the personal attention of agents, hoping thereby to reduce the time of settling such claims. Under the old system claims were settled with a mean time μ of 33.2 days. The company decides that the new system is worth adopting if it will reduce the mean time μ to less than 30 days. The company handles a random sample of 900 small claims by the new system and finds that for this sample $\bar{x} = 28.3$ days, with $s = 8.2$. Should the company adopt the new system (that is, decide that $\mu < 30$) if it is willing to take no more than a .05 chance of error in adopting the new system when in fact it is no better than the old?

$$\text{Hypotheses: } H_0 : \mu \geq 30 \text{ vs } H_1 : \mu < 30$$

$$\text{Critical region: Reject } H_0 \text{ if } \bar{x} < c, \text{ where}$$

$$c = \mu_0 - z_\alpha \cdot \frac{s}{\sqrt{n}} = 30 - \frac{(1.65)(8.2)}{30} = 30 - .45 = 29.55$$

Since $\bar{x} = 28.33 < 29.55$, the company rejects H_0 in favor of H_1 and adopts the new system.

Example 13

Incumbent political candidate A must decide whether to debate candidate B in a two-way race. A's manager feels that A should debate (risky for an incumbent) only if B's current vote proportion p is greater than .5. Should A debate if a poll of 400 voters shows that 211 favor B? A's manager wants the probability of debating when $p \leq .5$ to be at most .01.

$$\text{Hypotheses: } H_0 : p \leq .5 \text{ vs } H_1 : p > .5$$

$$\text{Critical region: Reject } H_0 \text{ if } \hat{p} > c, \text{ where}$$

$$c = p_0 + z_\alpha \sqrt{\frac{p_0(1 - p_0)}{n}} = .5 + 2.33 \sqrt{\frac{(.5)(.5)}{400}} = .5 + .058 = .558$$

Since $\hat{p} = 211/400 = .53$ is not in the critical region, A does not debate.

In so doing, A does not make a type I error, but does risk making a type II error. What is the probability of a type II error if, say, $p = .6$?

To calculate this, we observe that

$$\beta(p) = \beta(.6) = 1 - P_{.6}(\hat{p} > .558)$$

But

$$P_{.6}(\hat{p} > .558) \cong P(z \geq d)$$

where

$$d = \frac{.558 - .6}{\sqrt{\frac{(.6)(.4)}{400}}} = \frac{-.042}{\frac{\sqrt{6}}{100}} = -.7 \sqrt{6} = -1.71$$

$$P(z \geq -1.71) = .5 + P\ 0 \leq z < 1.71) = .5 + .4564 = .9564$$

The probability of a type II error (not debating) when $p = .6$ is therefore

$$\beta(.6) \cong 1 - P(z \geq -1.71) = 1 - .9564 = .0436$$

PROBLEMS 6.6

1. A consumers agency samples 50 cans of soup to see if there are 11 ounces of soup per can, as the label states. The agency wishes to test $H_0 : \mu \geq 11$ vs $H_1 : \mu < 11$.

   a. Give the critical region for a test with the level of significance $\alpha = .05$ based on a mean of $\bar{x}$ ounces in the 50 sampled cans. Assume that $\sigma = .5$ ounces.

   b. Repeat (a) if σ is unknown and $s = .6$ ounces.

   c. State your conclusion in (a) and (b) if $\bar{x} = 10.8$ ounces.

   d. What type of error might you be making in your conclusions in (c)?

2. A gasoline company uses an additive in its fuel in the hope that it will increase mileage. Without the additive, the mileage per gallon for a certain type of car is 13.2. A random sample of 36 runs with the additive yielded a sample mean of $\bar{x}$ miles per gallon. The manufacturer wishes to test $H_0 : \mu \leq 13.2$ vs $H_1 : \mu > 13.2$.

   a. Assuming $\sigma = 3$ mpg is known and $\alpha = .02$ is the desired level of significance, give the critical region of the test in terms of $\bar{x}$.

   b. Repeat (a) if σ is unknown and $s = 2.8$ mpg.

   c. State your conclusions in (a) and (b) if $\bar{x} = 13.8$.

   d. What type of error might you be making in your conclusions in (c)?

3. In problem 1a, compute the power of the test at the alternative $\mu = 10.8$. In 1b, compute the probability of a type II error at the alternative $\mu = 10.7$.

4. In problem 2a, compute the probability of a type II error at the alternative $\mu = 15$. In 2b, compute the power of the test at the alternative $\mu = 15.5$.

5. In the past an appliance manufacturer had 10 percent of all toasters sold returned with defects in six months. Unhappy with this, he does a pilot study on a new process of assembly which, although more expensive, will be worthwhile if it reduces the percentage of returned toasters to 5 percent or less. Of 4000 toasters produced by the new process, 168 are returned with defects in six months.

   a. State the appropriate null and alternative hypotheses for this testing problem.
   b. Give the critical region of a test at level of significance $\alpha = .05$.
   c. Does the data confirm that the new process has achieved a defect rate of less than 5 percent at level of significance $\alpha = .05$?

6. Suppose that 42 percent of all adults in the United States were smokers 10 years ago. If a current random sample of 1500 adults shows that 613 are smokers, test whether or not the smoking rate has decreased in 10 years.

   a. State the appropriate null and alternative hypotheses.
   b. Give the critical region of the test at level of significance $\alpha = .05$.
   c. At this level does the data support the claim that there has been a decrease in the last 10 years?

6.7 Two-Sided Hypothesis Tests for μ (Large Samples)

To test the two-sided hypothesis $H_0 : \mu = \mu_0$ vs $H_1 : \mu \neq \mu_0$ (or, in the binomial case, $H_0 : p = p_0$ vs $H_1 : p \neq p_0$) we compute the statistic

$$z = \frac{\bar{x} - \mu_0}{\sigma/\sqrt{n}}$$

where σ^2 is the population variance and n is the sample size.

This is approximately standard normal when H_0 is true. Since large positive or negative values of z tend to cast doubt on H_0 ($\bar{x} - \mu_0$ will usually be close to $\mu - \mu_0$ for n large), a reasonable procedure is to reject H_0 if either $z > b$ or $z < -b$. By the symmetry of the standard normal random variable z under H_0, we take $b = z_{\alpha/2}$ for a test of level α, since then $P\{z > z_{\alpha/2} \text{ or } z < -z_{\alpha/2}\} = \alpha$ under H_0. (By taking $\mu_0 = p_0$ and $\sigma = \sqrt{p_0(1 - p_0)}$ we get the corresponding two-sided test in the binomial case.) The results are summarized in table 6.2.

TABLE 6.2
Two-Sided Level α Hypothesis Test for μ (or p) When n Is Large

H_0	H_1	Critical region: reject H_0 if
$H_0 : \mu = \mu_0$	$H_1 : \mu \neq \mu_0$	$\dfrac{\bar{x} - \mu_0}{\sigma/\sqrt{n}} > z_{\alpha/2}$ (and say $\mu > \mu_0$) or $\dfrac{\bar{x} - \mu_0}{\sigma/\sqrt{n}} < -z_{\alpha/2}$ (and say $\mu < \mu_0$) (Use s if σ is unknown)
$H_0 : p = p_0$	$H_1 : p \neq p_0$	$\dfrac{\hat{p} - p_0}{\sqrt{\dfrac{p_0(1 - p_0)}{n}}} > z_{\alpha/2}$ (and say $p > p_0$) or $\dfrac{\hat{p} - p_0}{\sqrt{\dfrac{p_0(1 - p_0)}{n}}} < -z_{\alpha/2}$ (and say $p < p_0$)

The probability of wrongly rejecting H_0 when $\mu = \mu_0$ is α, while the probability of wrongly stating that $\mu > \mu_0$ ($\mu < \mu_0$) when in fact $\mu < \mu_0$ ($\mu > \mu_0$) is at most $\alpha/2$. (See the discussion after example 15.)

In the binomial case when $p_0 = .5$, this test is the same as that introduced in (4.15).

Example 14

A college entrance examination in verbal ability is known to have a national mean score of 130 (on a scale from 40 to 200), with a standard deviation of 28. In a sample of 49 applicants for Kent State University, the sample mean score is $\bar{x}$. Test with $\alpha = .05$ whether the population of applicants for Kent State University has the same mean as the national mean. (Assume that σ for the population of applicants for Kent State is also 28.) Here, $\sigma = 28$, $n = 49$, and $z_{\alpha/2} = z_{.025} = 1.96$. To test

$$H_0 : \mu = 130 \text{ vs } H_1 : \mu \neq 130$$

we therefore use the critical region

$$\text{Reject } H_0 \text{ if } z = \frac{\bar{x} - 130}{28/\sqrt{49}} = \frac{\bar{x} - 130}{4} > 1.96 \text{ or } < -1.96$$

that is, reject H_0 if $\bar{x} > 137.84$ or $\bar{x} < 122.16$

Suppose the sample gives $\bar{x} = 126.4$. Then at the .05 level there is not enough evidence to assert that the mean score of applicants for Kent State University is different from the national mean of 130.

Example 15

In previous years, a department store has found that 15 percent of items sold were exchanged or returned. Based on a current random sample of 260 items sold, the management wishes to see whether the proportion has changed this year. Let $y =$ the number of items exchanged or returned in the sample. Suppose the management is willing to take a 10 percent chance of making an error and asserting a change when in fact $p = .15$ this year. Here $\bar{x} = \hat{p} = y/n$, with the null hypothesis $H_0 : p = .15$; the alternative hypothesis $H_1 : p \neq .15$.

Critical region: Reject H_0 if

$$z = \frac{\hat{p} - p_0}{\sqrt{\dfrac{p_0(1 - p_0)}{n}}} = \frac{\hat{p} - .15}{\sqrt{\dfrac{(.15)(.85)}{260}}} = \frac{\hat{p} - .15}{.022} > 1.65 \text{ or } < -1.65$$

or, equivalently, if $\hat{p} > .15 + .036 = .186$ or $\hat{p} < .15 - .036 = .114$. If the observed value of $\hat{p}$ is $52/260 = .2$, the test rejects H_0 and asserts that $p \neq .15$.

In fact, since $\hat{p} = .2 > .186$, it appears that there has been an *increase* in the proportion of items exchanged or returned. This is why we use the "three action procedure":

a. If $\hat{p} > .186$, assert that $p > .15$.
b. If $\hat{p} < .114$, assert that $p < .15$.
c. If $.114 \leq \hat{p} \leq .186$ reserve judgement about p (that is, do not reject $H_0 : p = .15$).

Since the values .114 and .186 were determined so that when $p = .15$, $P\{\hat{p} > .186\} = P \{\hat{p} < .114\} \cong .05$, it follows that

$$\text{when } p \leq .15, P \text{ (assert that } p > .15) \leq .05$$

$$\text{when } p \geq .15, P \text{ (assert that } p < .15) \leq .05$$

Thus if we do not regard reserving judgment about p as an error then *the "error" probability of this procedure is* $\leq .05$, (not .10) *no matter what the true value of p*, provided that it is not *precisely* .15. On the other hand, the probability of reserving judgment about p will be close to .90 if p is sufficiently near the value .15, and the probability of rejecting H_0 when it is precisely true is .10, since we reject H_0 when either $\hat{p} > .186$ or $\hat{p} < .114$.

PROBLEMS 6.7

1. Last year, the mean IQ of entering freshmen at a university was 118. A random sample of 60 entering freshmen this year shows a mean IQ of $\bar{x} = 119.7$, with $s = 13.3$. It is desired to see whether or not the mean IQ of entering freshmen has increased.

   a. State the appropriate null and alternative hypotheses.
   b. Give the critical region of the test at the level of significance $\alpha = .05$.
   c. At this level does the data provide sufficient evidence to claim that the IQ of entering freshmen has increased?

2. An automobile company claims that a certain model gives a mileage of at least 18.5 miles per gallon. A random sample of 50 of these cars is taken, and each car is driven for 100 miles, with a sample mean $\bar{x} = 18.8$ mpg and a sample standard deviation $s = 2.1$ mpg. It is desired to test whether or not the claim is correct.

   a. State the appropriate null and alternative hypotheses.
   b. Give the critical region of the test at the level of significance $\alpha = .10$.
   c. Do the data support the company's claim at the above level?

3. The Department of Commerce released a report which showed that hourly employees in the brewery industry earned an average of $3.30 per hour. A state survey of 100 such employees had mean $\bar{x}$ and standard deviation s.

   a. State the null and alternative hypotheses for testing whether or not income in this state is the same as the national average.
   b. State the critical region of your test at the level of significance $\alpha = .05$.
   c. What conclusion would be made if $\bar{x} = \$3.16$ and $s = 1.05$?
   d. What type of error, if any, could be made in (c)?

4. Suppose that five years ago in Wisconsin the mean age of a woman at the birth of her first child was 21.7. A recent random sample of 80 first births had a sample mean age $\bar{x}$ and a sample standard deviation $s = 2.6$.

   a. State the null and alternative hypotheses for testing whether or not the mean age of a woman at the birth of her first child has changed.
   b. State the critical region of your test at the level of significance $\alpha = .02$.
   c. What conclusion would be made if $\bar{x} = 22.5$?
   d. What type of error, if any, could be made in (c)?

5. Suppose a coin is tossed 50 times and we want to test whether or not the coin is fair.

    a. State the null and alternative hypotheses for the test.

    b. Give the critical region of the test at level $\alpha = .05$.

    c. State your conclusion if you get 34 heads in 50 tosses.

6. One year ago a news-magazine publisher had 35 percent of all news-magazine sales. The publisher took a random sample of 900 such sales last month to see whether or not this percentage had changed.

    a. State the null and alternative hypotheses for the test.

    b. Give the critical region of the test at level $\alpha = .02$.

    c. State the conclusion of the test if the sample showed that 304 of the 900 sales were of this publisher's magazine.

7. In problem 3: (a) find the power of the test at the alternative $\mu = \$3.00$; (b) find the probability of a type II error at the alternative $\mu = \$3.40$; (c) recompute (b) for the test one would get in problem 3 if the sample size were increased to 500 and $\sigma = \$1.05$ (that is, assume σ is the same as the s for $n = 100$).

8. In problem 4: (a) find the power of the test at the alternative $\mu = 24$; (b) find the power of the test one would get in problem 4 at $\mu = 24$ if the sample size were increased to 300 and $\sigma = 2.6$ (that is, assume σ is the same as the s for $n = 80$); (c) repeat (a) and (b) for the alternative $\mu = 24.3$.

9. In problem 5, let $p = $ probability of heads in one toss of the coin.

    a. Compute the power of the test given in (b) of problem 5 at $p = .2, .3, .4, .5, .6, .7,$ and $.8$. Sketch the power curve of the test based on these calculations.

    b. Compute the power of the test one would get in (b) of problem 5 if $n = 100$ at $p = .2, .3, .4, .5, .6, .7,$ and $.8$. Sketch this power curve and compare it with that given in (a).

    c. Repeat (b) for $n = 400$.

    d. Based on the power curves in (a), (b), and (c), discuss what happens to the test of part (b) of problem 5 as the sample size increases.

6.8 Testing the Equality of Two Population Mean Values

Let $\{x_{11}, \ldots, x_{1n_1}\}$ and $\{x_{21}, \ldots, x_{2n_2}\}$ be two random samples, independent of each other, the first of size n_1 from a population with unknown mean value μ_1 and variance σ_1^2, and the second of size

n_2 from a population with unknown mean value μ_2 and variance σ_2^2. Let $\bar{x}_i$ and s_i^2 be the sample estimates of μ_i and σ_i^2 for $i = 1,2$.

Table 6.3 gives a large sample two-sided test for $H_0 : \mu_1 = \mu_2$ against the alternative $H_1 : \mu_1 \neq \mu_2$, as well as the associated one-sided tests.

TABLE 6.3
One and Two-Sided Level α Tests for the Difference Between Two Means (independent large samples)

H_1	H_0	Critical region: reject H_0 if
$H_0 : \mu_1 = \mu_2$	$H_1 : \mu_1 \neq \mu_2$	$\bar{x}_1 - \bar{x}_2 > Cz_{\alpha/2}$ (and say $\mu_1 > \mu_2$), or $\bar{x}_1 - \bar{x}_2 < -Cz_{\alpha/2}$ (and say $\mu_1 < \mu_2$)
$H_0 : \mu_1 \leq \mu_2$	$H_1 : \mu_1 > \mu_2$	$\bar{x}_1 - \bar{x}_2 > Cz_\alpha$
$H_1 : \mu_1 \geq \mu_2$	$H_1 : \mu_1 < \mu_2$	$\bar{x}_1 - \bar{x}_2 < -Cz_\alpha$

where C is an estimate of the standard deviation of $\bar{x}_1 - \bar{x}_2$. Thus

$$C = \sqrt{\frac{s_1^2}{n_1} + \frac{s_2^2}{n_2}} \quad \text{(if } \sigma_1^2 \text{ may be different from } \sigma_2^2\text{)} \qquad (24)$$

or

$$C = s\sqrt{\frac{1}{n_1} + \frac{1}{n_2}} \quad \text{(if } \sigma_1^2 = \sigma_2^2\text{)} \qquad (25)$$

where

$$s^2 = \frac{(n_1 - 1)s_1^2 + (n_2 - 1)s_2^2}{n_1 + n_2 - 2} \qquad (26)$$

is the "pooled" estimate of the assumed common population variance σ^2.

The reasoning behind this test is that when $\mu_1 = \mu_2$, $(\bar{x}_1 - \bar{x}_2)/C$ has approximately a standard normal distribution. The critical regions in each case are taken as the normal tail probabilities that are suitable in each situation.

In example 3 above, based on independent samples of $n_1 = 30$ and $n_2 = 30$ mice, the investigator wishes to test $H_0 : \mu_1 = \mu_2$ vs $H_1 : \mu_1 \neq \mu_2$, where μ_1, μ_2 represent the population mean tumor weights after four weeks for experimental and control mice, respectively. To test this hypothesis, table 6.3 is used with C as in (24) or (25). (These are equal when $n_1 = n_2$.) Suppose the sample results are

$$\bar{x}_1 = 1.28, \; s_1 = .31, \; n_1 = 30$$
$$\bar{x}_2 = 1.53, \; s_2 = .38, \; n_2 = 30$$

For $\alpha = .05$

$$C_{z\alpha/2} = 1.96 \sqrt{\frac{.0961}{30} + \frac{.1440}{30}} = (1.96)(.09) = .176$$

The resulting test at the .05 level is: Reject H_0 if $\bar{x}_1 - \bar{x}_2 > .176$ or $< -.176$.

Since $\bar{x}_1 - \bar{x}_2 = 1.28 - 1.53 = -.25 < -.176$, the investigator concludes that the drug *does* affect tumor growth. Moreover, since $\bar{x}_1 - \bar{x}_2 = -.25$, the sample results indicate that tumor growth is retarded by the drug. In fact, the probability that $\bar{x}_1 - \bar{x}_2 < -.176$ when in fact $\mu_1 \geq \mu_2$ is at most equal to .025, attained when $\mu_1 = \mu_2$. Hence if we agree to assert that

$$\mu_1 < \mu_2 \text{ whenever } \bar{x}_1 - \bar{x}_2 < -1.96 \; C$$
$$\mu_1 > \mu_2 \text{ whenever } \bar{x}_1 - \bar{x}_2 > 1.96 \; C$$

and otherwise to reserve judgment, then the probability of making an assertion that is wrong is at most .025 (not .05), except in the case when μ_1 is precisely equal to μ_2.

If in this example we had been interested only in finding compounds that retard growth, the hypotheses of interest would be $H_0 : \mu_1 \geq \mu_2$ versus $H_1 : \mu_1 < \mu_2$. Table 6.3 gives the one-sided test:

Reject H_0 if $\bar{x}_1 - \bar{x}_2 < -Cz_\alpha = z_\alpha \sqrt{\dfrac{s_1^2}{n_1} + \dfrac{s_2^2}{n_2}} = (1.65)(.09) = .15$

Since $\bar{x}_1 - \bar{x}_2 = -.25 < -.15 = C$, we would assert that the compound in question does retard tumor growth.

PROBLEMS 6.8

1. A study of two random samples of adult men in two income groups showed the following sample results for calorie intake for a week (in units of 1000 calories):

Group	Sample size	Sample mean	Sample standard deviation
Low income	$n_1 = 80$	$\bar{x}_1 = 22.5$	$s_1 = 4.7$
High income	$n_2 = 50$	$\bar{x}_2 = 20.7$	$s_2 = 4.9$

a. State the null and alternative hypotheses for testing whether or not these two income groups have the same mean caloric intake for a week.

   b. State the critical region of the test for the level of significance $\alpha = .05$. Assume that $\sigma_1 = \sigma_2$.

   c. Apply the test in (b) to the data above and state your conclusion.

   d. Do (b) and (c), without assuming that $\sigma_1 = \sigma_2$.

2. Two random samples of men and women students at Temple University gave the following grade point averages (GPA):

Group	Sample size	Sample mean	Sample standard deviation
Women	$n_1 = 35$	$\bar{x}_1 = 2.70$	$s_1 = .63$
Men	$n_2 = 45$	$\bar{x}_2 = 2.78$	$s_2 = .55$

   a. State the null and alternative hypotheses for testing whether or not there is a difference in mean GPA between men and women students at this university.

   b. State the critical region of the test at the level of significance $\alpha = .02$. Assume that $\sigma_1 = \sigma_2$.

   c. Apply the test in (b) to the data above and state your conclusion.

   d. Do (b) and (c), without assuming that $\sigma_1 = \sigma_2$.

3. Suppose that in problem 1, $s_1 = 5.8$ and $s_2 = 3.8$. Solve parts (b), (c), and (d) as in problem 1. Do you think one should assume that $\sigma_1 = \sigma_2$ in this case?

4. Suppose that in problem 2, $s_1 = .72$, $s_2 = .46$, $\bar{x}_1 = 2.64$, and $\bar{x}_2 = 2.95$. Solve parts (b), (c), and (d) as in problem 2. Do you think one should assume that $\sigma_1 = \sigma_2$ in this case?

6.9 Hypothesis Tests for the Equality of Two Proportions

If the independent samples $\{x_{11}, \ldots, x_{1n_1}\}$ and $\{x_{21}, \ldots, x_{2n_2}\}$ of the previous section came from single-trial binomial distributions with parameters p_1 and p_2 respectively, then

$$\hat{p}_1 = \bar{x}_1 = \frac{y_1}{n_1} \quad \text{and} \quad \hat{p}_2 = \bar{x}_2 = \frac{y_2}{n_2}$$

where $y_1 = x_{11} + \ldots + x_{1n_1}$ and $y_2 = x_{21} + \ldots + x_{2n_2}$ are binomial random variables with parameters p_1 and p_2 and sample sizes n_1 and n_2. To test $H_0 : p_1 = p_2$ vs $H_1 : p_1 \neq p_2$ we use

$$\hat{p} = \frac{y_1 + y_2}{n_1 + n_2}$$

as a pooled estimate of the common value $p = p_1 = p_2$ under H_0, and use

$$s = \sqrt{\hat{p}\hat{q}} \quad (\hat{q} = 1 - \hat{p})$$

in (25) ($\sigma_1 = \sqrt{pq} = \sigma_2$ under H_0) as the pooled estimate of $\sigma = \sqrt{pq}$. This test is given below in table 6.4, along with the appropriate one-sided tests.

TABLE 6.4

One and Two-Sided Level α Tests for Differences Between Two Probabilities (independent large samples)

H_0	H_1	Critical region: reject H_0 if
$H_0 : p_1 = p_2$	$H_1 : p_1 \neq p_2$	$\hat{p}_1 - \hat{p}_2 > Cz_{\alpha/2}$ (and say $p_1 > p_2$), or $\hat{p}_1 - \hat{p}_2 < -Cz_{\alpha/2}$ (and say $p_1 < p_2$)
$H_0 : p_1 \leq p_2$	$H_1 : p_1 > p_2$	$\hat{p}_1 - \hat{p}_2 > Cz_\alpha$
$H_0 : p_1 \geq p_2$	$H_1 : p_1 < p_2$	$\hat{p}_1 - \hat{p}_2 < -Cz_\alpha$

where

$$C = \sqrt{\hat{p}\hat{q}\left(\frac{1}{n_1} + \frac{1}{n_2}\right)}, \hat{p} = \frac{y_1 + y_2}{n_1 + n_2}, \hat{q} = 1 - \hat{p}$$

If we had followed the analogy of (24), we would have obtained the following test of $H_0 : p_1 = p_2$ vs $H_1 : p_1 \neq p_2$: Reject H_0 (accept H_1) if

$$\hat{p}_1 - \hat{p}_2 > C' z_{\alpha/2} \text{ or } \hat{p}_1 - \hat{p}_2 < -C' z_{\alpha/2}$$

where

$$C' = \sqrt{\frac{\hat{p}_1\hat{q}_1}{n_1} + \frac{\hat{p}_2\hat{q}_2}{n_2}} \quad \hat{p}_i = \frac{y_i}{n_i}, q_i = 1 - \hat{p}_i$$

When $n_1 = n_2$ there is little difference between C and C', but if $n_1 \neq n_2$ the two tests may differ considerably, neither being clearly preferred in all cases.

Example 15

A manufacturer of robots develops two new models, but for production economy wishes to market only one of them. He chooses at random 400 users and randomly divides them into two groups of 200 each

$(n_1 = n_2 = 200)$. Each group uses one model for a week and then responds to the question "Would you prefer this robot to the one you now use?" The results are:

TABLE 6.5
User Preference for Two Groups

Robot	Yes	No	Total
Model 1	$68(y_1)$	$132(n - y_1)$	$200(n = n_1)$
Model 2	$52(y_2)$	$148(n - y_2)$	$200(n = n_2)$
Total	$120(y_1 + y_2)$	$280(2n - y_1 - y_2)$	$400(n_1 + n_2)$

Here, $\hat{p} = \dfrac{y_1 + y_2}{n_1 + n_2} = \dfrac{120}{280} = .43$, $\sqrt{\hat{p}\hat{q}} = \sqrt{.24} = .49$

and $\sqrt{\dfrac{1}{n_1} + \dfrac{1}{n_2}} = \sqrt{\dfrac{2}{200}} = .1$

The test using table 6.4 at level $\alpha = .05$ becomes: Reject $H_0 : p_1 = p_2$ if $\hat{p}_1 - \hat{p}_2 > 1.96C$ or $< -1.96C$, where

$$1.96C = 1.96 \cdot \sqrt{\hat{p}\hat{q}\left(\dfrac{1}{n_1} + \dfrac{1}{n_2}\right)} = (1.96)(.49)(.1) = .10$$

The sample results of table 6.3 yield

$$\hat{p}_1 - \hat{p}_2 = \dfrac{68}{200} - \dfrac{52}{200} = .34 - .26 = .08$$

which is not sufficient to reject H_0 at the .05 level. The manufacturer might therefore decide to act as though $p_1 = p_2$ and choose which to market on some other basis, to take a larger sample, or to develop other models which might be preferred to either of the above.

If in this example the sample results had been such that $\hat{p}_1 - \hat{p}_2 > .10$, then the manufacturer should not merely reject H_0 but assert that $p_1 > p_2$. In so doing he would be running the risk of asserting that $p_1 > p_2$, when in fact $p_1 \leq p_2$, with probability at most .025, the latter value being attained when $p_1 = p_2$.

Cautionary remark: Suppose the manufacturer had taken a sample of only 200 persons and asked them to try each of the models for a week in random order and answer the same question. Suppose he obtains the same numerical results as before:

TABLE 6.6
User Preference, One Group

Robot	Yes	No	Total
Model 1	68	132	200
Model 2	52	148	200
Total	120	280	400

Can the manufacturer use the same test as before? No; these random variables y_1 and y_2 are *not* independent, since both depend on the same n respondents (each respondent is doubly represented in this table).

Let us examine the situation further. Suppose that of the 200 respondents, 35 said Yes to both, $68 - 35 = 33$ said Yes to model 1 and No to model 2, and $52 - 35 = 17$ said No to both models. (These facts are not shown in table 6.6.) Since the $35 + 115 = 150$ users responding both Yes or both No are neutral in preference, they may be ignored in deciding which model to market. We therefore form the reduced table showing only those who have declared opposite opinions regarding models 1 and 2.

Model 1 (Yes) Model 2 (No)	33
Model 1 (No) Model 2 (Yes)	17

Let $y =$ the number saying Yes to model 1 among the 50 users who are not neutral. Then y is a binomial random variable with $n = 50 = 33 + 17$ trials and $p =$ the probability that a nonneutral user will say Yes to model 1 and No to model 2. The manufacturer can now test $H_0 : p = .5$ vs $H_1 : p \neq .5$ to see if the two models are equally preferred. An $\alpha = .05$ level test for this hypothesis is given by table 6.2.

Setting $\hat{p} = y/50$ and $n = 50$ we agree to assert that $p > .5$ if $\hat{p} > c$, to assert that $p < .5$ if $\hat{p} < b$, and to reserve judgment otherwise, where

$$c = p_0 + 1.96 \sqrt{\frac{p_0(1 - p_0)}{50}} = .5 + \frac{1.96}{\sqrt{200}}$$

$$= .5 + (1.96)(.071) = .5 + .139 = .639$$

and

$$b = .5 - .139 = .361.$$

In the sample above $\hat{p} = 33/50 = .66 > c$, so the manufacturer concludes that $p > .5$, and markets model 1. (This conclusion would not have been reached if the manufacturer had used the inappropriate test for two groups given by table 6.5.) His probability of asserting that $p > .5$ if in fact $p \le .5$, or that $p < .5$ if in fact $p \ge .5$, is at most 0.25. (The probability α of rejecting H_0 when $p = .5$ is equal to .05).

Although tables 6.5 and 6.6 look alike, only table 6.5 represents two independent samples of size $n_1 = n_2 = 200$ each, for which the test given by table 6.4 is valid. It is *not* valid when one sample of $n = 200$ is used to obtain two dependent binomial random variables y_1 and y_2. In such cases the test given above should be used.

PROBLEMS 6.9

1. Suppose that patients coming into a clinic are randomly assigned to one of two treatments for a certain disease. Treatment T_1 results in 41 cures among 100 patients within a week, and treatment T_2 results in 59 cures among 100 patients within a week. It is desired to test whether or not there is a difference in the probability of cure between the two treatments.

   a. State the null and alternative hypotheses for the desired test.
   b. State the rejection region of the test for $\alpha = .05$.
   c. Based on the data given above, what conclusion can be drawn from the test in (b)?

2. Two random samples of voters are taken in the south and in the north, with the following results regarding a certain bill pending before Congress:

Voters	Sample size	Number of voters favoring the bill
North	$n_1 = 2000$	$y_1 = 890$
South	$n_2 = 1600$	$y_2 = 730$

   a. State the null and alternative hypotheses for testing equality between the proportions of voters in the north and south favoring the bill.
   b. State the rejection region of the test for $\alpha = .02$.
   c. Based on the data given above, what conclusion can be drawn from the test in (b)?

Statistical Inference for Normal Populations (Small or Large Samples)

7 Statistical Inference for Normal Populations (Small or Large Samples)

In chapter 6 the Central Limit Theorem was used for large samples to obtain approximately valid confidence coefficients and levels of significance for estimating and testing hypotheses about population means. Often, however, because of the cost, time, or physical limitations of sampling, one is not able to obtain large samples. In this chapter we discuss methods of inference that are valid even for small samples, *if these samples are from underlying normal (or approximately normal) populations.*

The assumption of normality for many kinds of continuous measurements—heights, weights, reaction times, body temperatures, test scores, and so on—is very convenient mathematically. Moreover, empirical evidence shows that such observations are often approximately normally distributed. There are some theoretical reasons for this. For example, if we observe the height x of an adult chosen at random from a more or less homogeneous population, we may think of that height as being composed of some constant μ, the mean value for the population, plus a number of independent random increments that alter the height. Thus a person's height x can be thought of as

$x = \mu + \sum_{i=1}^{k} u_i$, where μ is the mean population height and the u_i's

are small random increments arising from a variety of sources. For example, u_1 might be the effect due to a person's particular genetic makeup, u_2 the effect of the mother's prenatal diet, u_3 the effect of the person's own diet during the first year, u_4 the effect of diet during years 2 to 12, u_5 the effect of diet during adolescence, u_6 the effect of exercise during youth, u_7 the effect of childhood diseases. Viewed in this way, an adult's height x is composed of μ plus a rather large number of random additive effects u_i. If these effects are independent, a general Central Limit Theorem for a large number k of individual effects will account for x being approximately normally distributed. The theoretical model of a measurement x as composed of a constant μ plus numerous small independent (or nearly so) random effects u_i is reasonable in many physical situations, and helps to explain why many continuous variables in the real world are found to be approximately normally distributed.

Under the assumption, then, of sampling from a nearly normal distribution, we will discuss in this chapter methods of constructing confidence intervals and testing hypotheses for various population parameters when the sample sizes are small. The questions at issue will concern the mean μ of a single population, the difference $\mu_1 - \mu_2$ between two such means, the variance σ^2 of a single population, and the ratio σ_1^2/σ_2^2 of the variances of two populations. Before discussing the inference procedures, we state some results from probability theory concerning random samples from a normal distribution.

7.1 The Distribution of the Sample Sum and Sample Mean in Samples from a Normal Distribution.

We ask first how the *sample sum* and the *sample mean* are distributed in sampling from a normal distribution. The following theorem answers this question.

Theorem 1

Let $\{x_1, \ldots, x_n\}$ be a random sample of size n from a normal population with mean value μ and variance σ^2. Then (a) the *sample sum* $y = x_1 + \ldots + x_n$ is normally distributed (with mean value $\mu_y = n\mu$ and variance $\sigma_y^2 = n\sigma^2$) and (b) the *sample mean* $\bar{x} = \frac{1}{n}(x_1 + \ldots + x_n) = y/n$ is normally distributed (with mean value $\mu_{\bar{x}} = \mu$ and variance $\sigma_{\bar{x}}^2 = \sigma^2/n$).

Example 1

Suppose that x, the height of an adult male (18 or over) chosen at random from a certain population, has mean value $\mu = 67.4$ inches and standard deviation $\sigma = 5.1$ inches. Assume that x is normally distributed (an assumption approximating reality). A random sample of nine persons is chosen from this population. Find the probability that

a. the *sum* of the heights in the sample will exceed 600 inches.
b. the *mean* height of the sample will fall between 66 and 72 inches.

a. By theorem 1, $y = x_1 + \ldots + x_9$ is normally distributed with mean value $\mu_y = 9\mu = 9(67.4) = 606.6$ and standard deviation $\sigma_y = \sqrt{9}\,\sigma = 3(5.1) = 15.3$. Therefore, letting z denote a standard normal random variable

$$P\{y > 600\} = P\left\{\frac{y - 606.6}{15.3} > \frac{600 - 606.6}{15.3}\right\}$$

$$= P\{z > -.43\} = .500 + P\{0 < z < .43\} = .6664$$

b. By theorem 1, the sample mean $\bar{x} = (x_1 + \ldots + x_9)/9$ is normally distributed with mean value $\mu_{\bar{x}} = \mu = 67.4$ and standard deviation $\sigma_{\bar{x}} = \sigma/\sqrt{n} = 5.1/\sqrt{9} = 1.7$. Therefore

$$P\{66 < \bar{x} < 72\} = P\left\{\frac{66 - 67.4}{1.7} < \frac{\bar{x} - 67.4}{1.7} < \frac{72 - 67.4}{1.7}\right\}$$

$$= P\{-.82 < z < 2.71\}$$
$$= P\{0 \le z < .82\} + P\{0 \le z < 2.71\}$$
$$= .2939 + .4966 = .7905$$

PROBLEMS 7.1

1. Suppose that $x = $ IQ has a mean value $\mu = 115$, standard deviation $\sigma = 10$, and is normally distributed. Find the probability that in a random sample of 16 persons

   a. the total IQ of all persons in the sample exceeds 2000.
   b. the mean IQ of the sample is between 110 and 120.

2. Suppose that $x = $ ounces of soda put into a bottle by a filling machine in a typical (random) trial is normally distributed with mean value $\mu = 12.1$ and standard deviation $\sigma = .2$. A random sample of 10 bottles is taken. Find the probability that

   a. the total content in the 10 bottles is less than 122 ounces.
   b. the mean content per bottle in the sample is greater than 12 ounces.

7.2 The Distribution of s^2 in Samples from a Normal Distribution

When a sample $\{x_1, \ldots, x_n\}$ is from a normal population, the sample variance

$$s^2 = \frac{1}{n-1} \sum_{i=1}^{n} (x_i - \bar{x})^2,$$

introduced in section 5.2 as an unbiased estimator of σ^2, is also a random variable. In repeated samples $\{x_1, \ldots, x_n\}$ of size n we shall obtain different values of s^2, as well as of $\bar{x}$. Since s^2 is a random variable, it has a probability distribution. What is this distribution when the sample is from a normal population with mean value μ and variance σ^2? (In section 5.2, we saw only that $\mu_{s^2} = \sigma^2$, so that s^2 is an "unbiased" point estimator of σ^2. This is true even if the sample is not from a normal population.) We begin by making the following definition.

Definition 1

Let $y_1, y_2, \ldots, y_\nu$ be *independent standard normal* random variables (with means 0 and variances 1). Then the probability distribution of the positive-valued random variable

$$\chi^2 = y_1^2 + \ldots + y_\nu^2$$

is said to be *chi-squared with ν "degrees of freedom"* (d.f.).

A graph of the distribution of χ^2 for various values of ν is shown in figure 7.1. Since $\mu_{y_i} = 0$, $\mu_{y_i^2} = \sigma_{y_i}^2 = 1$. Hence $\mu_{\chi^2} = 1 + \ldots + 1 = \nu$,

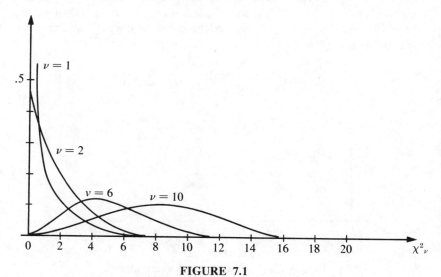

FIGURE 7.1

The χ^2 distribution for various values of ν = d.f.

so the distribution of χ^2 with ν d.f. is "centered" at ν. The variance of χ^2 can be shown to be 2ν. Thus as ν increases, the distribution of χ^2 moves to the right with increasing mean ν and variance 2ν.

The values $\chi^2_{\alpha,\nu}$ for which $P(\chi^2 > \chi^2_{\alpha,\nu}) = \alpha$ are given in appendix table 8 for various choices of ν and α. The tail areas α in the table are those shown in figure 7.2.

Now let $\{x_1, \ldots, x_n\}$ be a random sample from a normal population with mean value μ and variance σ^2. If for $i = 1, \ldots, n$ we put

$$y_i = \frac{x_i - \mu}{\sigma}$$

then the y_i are independent *standard* normal random variables. Hence the sum of the squared deviations of the x_i from their *population mean* μ, all divided by σ^2.

$$\frac{1}{\sigma^2} \cdot \sum_{i=1}^{n} (x_i - \mu)^2 = y_1^2 + \ldots + y_n^2$$

is distributed as chi-squared with n d.f.

Consider now the sum of the squared deviations of the x_i from their *sample mean* $\bar{x}$, all divided by σ^2. This sum is related to the statistic s^2 by

$$\frac{1}{\sigma^2} \cdot \sum_{i=1}^{n} (x_i - \bar{x})^2 = \frac{(n-1)s^2}{\sigma^2} \qquad (1)$$

Since $\mu_{s^2} = \sigma^2$, the mean value of (1) is $n - 1$, and in fact it may be shown that *the random variable (1) has precisely a chi-squared distribution with $\nu = n - 1$ d.f.*; that is, it is distributed exactly like the sum of the squares of $n - 1$ independent standard normal random variables. Thus both

$$\frac{1}{\sigma^2} \cdot \sum_{i=1}^{n} (x_i - \mu)^2 \qquad \text{and} \qquad \frac{1}{\sigma^2} \cdot \sum_{i=1}^{n} (x_i - \bar{x})^2$$

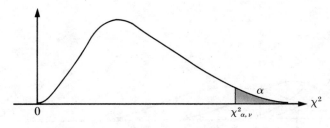

FIGURE 7.2
Tail areas of the chi-squared distribution

have chi-squared distributions; the former with n d.f. and the latter with $n - 1$, one d.f. having been "lost" by taking the squared deviations of the x's from their own sample mean $\bar{x}$ rather than from the population mean value μ. (This loss is due to the fact that while the n values $x_i - \mu$ are completely free to vary arbitrarily, the values $x_i - \bar{x}$ always satisfy the linear relation $\sum\limits_{i=1}^{n} (x_i - \bar{x}) = 0$, so only $n - 1$ of the $x_i - \bar{x}$ are "free" to vary independently.) We state this as

Theorem 2

Let $\{x_1, \ldots, x_n\}$ be a random sample from a normal population with mean value μ and variance σ^2. Then the random variable

$$\frac{(n - 1)s^2}{\sigma^2}$$

has a chi-squared distribution with $\nu = n - 1$ d.f.

Since, as stated above, the chi-squared distribution with ν d.f. has mean value ν and variance 2ν, the statistic

$$s^2 = \frac{1}{n - 1} \sum_{i=1}^{n} (x_i - \bar{x})^2 = \frac{(n - 1)s^2}{\sigma^2} \cdot \frac{\sigma^2}{n - 1}$$

for which $\mu_{s^2} = \sigma^2$, has a variance $2(n - 1) \cdot \sigma^4/(n - 1)^2 = 2\sigma^4/(n - 1)$. Thus the ratio s^2/σ^2 has mean value 1 and variance $2/(n - 1)$, which tends to 0 as n becomes large. *Hence, for large* n, *the ratio* s²/σ² *of the sample variance* s² *to the population variance* σ² *is close to 1 with high probability.*

Example 2

A certain drug is known not to alter the mean body temperature but is suspected of affecting its variability. A random sample of $n = 10$ persons are given the drug, and body temperatures are taken after the drug has had time to take effect. If body temperature (Fahrenheit) has $\mu = 98.6$ and $\sigma = .3$ under standard conditions, what number c would yield a probability of .01 that $s > c$? If the sample results in $s = .53$, what might one conclude about the drug?

By theorem 2 we see that under standard conditions the random variable

$$\frac{(n - 1)s^2}{\sigma^2} = \frac{9 s^2}{(.3)^2} = \frac{9}{.09}s^2 = 100 s^2$$

has a chi-squared distribution with $\nu = n - 1 = 9$ degrees of freedom, so that

$$P\{s > c\} = P\{s^2 > c^2\} = P\{100s^2 > 100c^2\} = P\{\chi^2 > 100c^2\}$$

From appendix table 8 we find that with $\nu = n - 1 = 9$

$$P\{\chi^2 > 21.666\} = .01$$

Hence, for $21.666 = 100\,c^2$, or $c = \sqrt{21.666/100} = .465$, it will be true that $P\{s > .465\} = .01$. With the sample result $s = .53$, we would therefore be justified in suspecting strongly that the drug does increase the variability of body temperature.

In closing this section we state an important fact about the chi-squared distribution; it follows at once from definition 1.

Theorem 3

If χ_1^2 and χ_2^2 are independent chi-squared random variables with ν_1 and ν_2 degrees of freedom, respectively, then their sum

$$\chi^2 = \chi_1^2 + \chi_2^2$$

has itself a chi-squared distribution, with $\nu = \nu_1 + \nu_2$ degrees of freedom.

PROBLEMS 7.2

1. Let χ^2 have a chi-squared distribution with ν degrees of freedom. Find
   a. c, if $\nu = 5$ and $P(\chi^2 > c) = .05$.
   b. $P(\chi^2 \le 2.70039)$, if $\nu = 9$.
   c. c, if $\nu = 18$ and $P(\chi^2 < c) = .01$.
   d. $P(1.63539 \le \chi^2 \le 18.5476)$, if $\nu = 6$.

2. Let χ^2 have a chi-squared distribution with ν degrees of freedom. Find
   a. c, if $\nu = 20$ and $P(\chi^2 > c) = .05$
   b. $P(\chi^2 \ge 23.6848)$, if $\nu = 14$.
   c. c, if $\nu = 23$ and $P(\chi^2 < c) = .05$.
   d. c_1 and c_2, if $\nu = 12$ and $P(\chi^2 < c_1) = P(\chi^2 > c_2) = .025$.

3. A machine produces normally distributed screws with standard deviation .01 inches. The machine is said to be in alignment if $\sigma = .01$. (a) If the machine is in alignment, and a random sample of $n = 20$ screws is taken, with s the standard deviation of the sample, what number c would yield $P(s > c) = .05$? (b) If the sample result is $s = .15$, what might one conclude about the machine?

4. A brand of Vitamin C tablet is supposed to have a mean content of 500 mg. and a standard deviation of 20 mg. The milligram content per tablet is assumed to follow a normal distribution. The manufacturer takes a sample of 25 tablets produced and computes s, the sample standard deviation.

a. Find the value c such that $P(s \leq c) = .01$.

b. If $s = 13$, might the manufacturer of the tablets reasonably conclude that $\sigma < 20$?

7.3 The t Distribution

A second important distribution that arises in random sampling from a normal population is the t distribution. In chapter 6 the standard normal random variable

$$z = \frac{\bar{x} - \mu}{\sigma/\sqrt{n}}$$

was used in constructing confidence intervals and tests for a population mean value μ when σ was known. When σ was unknown it was replaced by s in forming z, and the distribution of z was still approximately standard normal for a large n, since then s is approximately equal to σ with high probability. However, what if n is small? By "small" we mean, say, $n < 100$.

Definition 2
The random variable defined by

$$t = \frac{\bar{x} - \mu}{s/\sqrt{n}} \tag{2}$$

is called the t *statistic* of the sample $\{x_1, \ldots, x_n\}$.

In samples from a normal population this random variable has a specific distribution, called Student's* t distribution, $\nu = n - 1$ with degrees of freedom (d.f.).

Definition 3
Let $\{x_1, \ldots, x_n\}$ be a random sample of size n from a normal population with mean value μ and standard deviation σ. Then the random variable t defined by (2) has a t *distribution with* $\nu = n - 1$ *degrees of freedom*. This distribution does not depend on the values of μ and σ.

The random variable t (for $\nu = n - 1 \geq 1$) can take on any value between $-\infty$ and $+\infty$, and has a mean value 0. The t distribution is symmetric about 0, as is the standard normal distribution. However, a

---

*"Student" was the pen name of the statistician W.S. Gosset.

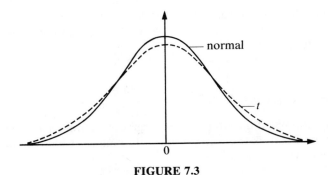

FIGURE 7.3
A comparison of the *t* and standard normal distributions

graph of the *t* distribution shows that it is more spread out than the standard normal distribution. Figure 7.3 illustrates this fact. As the sample size *n* becomes larger and larger, the graph of the *t* distribution approaches that of the standard normal distribution, until for $v \geq 100$ there is no appreciable difference between the *t* and the normal distribution. This reflects the fact mentioned above that with high probability, for a large *n* the ratio $s/\sigma \cong 1$, so that

$$t = \frac{\bar{x} - \mu}{s/\sqrt{n}} \cong \frac{\bar{x} - \mu}{\sigma/\sqrt{n}} = z \tag{3}$$

where z has an *exact* standard normal distribution by theorem 1, since we are assumed to be sampling from a normal population. The rate of approach of the *t* distribution to normality as *n* increases can be seen by comparing appendix tables 6 and 7.

Appendix table 7 gives tail probabilities for the *t* distribution for various values of $v = n - 1$ d.f. The value $t_{\alpha, v}$ such that $P\{t > t_{\alpha, v}\} = \alpha$ is given in the row labeled $v = n - 1$ and the column labeled α. (See figure 7.4.) By the symmetry of the *t* distribution about 0

$$P\{t < -t_{\alpha, v}\} = P\{t > t_{\alpha, v}\} = \alpha$$

Example 3
A psychologist, studying the difference in IQ scores for couples, measures the variable $x = $ (husband's IQ) $-$ (wife's IQ). Assume that x has mean value zero and is normally distributed, but that its variance σ^2 is unknown. A random sample of 16 couples is taken, from which $\bar{x}$ and s are computed. For what value c will it be true that (a) $P\{\bar{x} > cs\} = .01$; and (b) $P\{-cs \leq \bar{x} \leq cs\} = .80$?

By definition 3, when $\mu = 0$ the random variable $t = \bar{x}/(s/\sqrt{16}) = 4\bar{x}/s$ has a *t* distribution with $v = n - 1 = 15$ d.f.

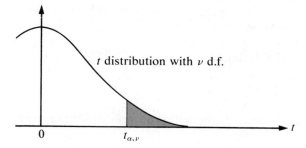

FIGURE 7.4
Tail probabilities of the t distribution

a. Here, $.01 = P\{\bar{x} > c\,s\} = P\{4\bar{x}/s > 4c\} = P\{t > 4c\}$.
   Appendix table 7 yields $t_{.01,\,15} = 2.602$ for $\nu = 15$ d.f., so $4c = 2.602$ and $c = .6505$.

b. By the symmetry of the t distribution about 0,

$$.80 = P\{-c\,s \le \bar{x} \le c\,s\} = 1 - P\left\{\left|\frac{\bar{x}}{s}\right| > c\right\}$$

$$= 1 - P\left\{\left|\frac{4\bar{x}}{s}\right| > 4c\right\} = 1 - P\{|t| > 4c\} = 1 - 2\,P\{t > 4c\}$$

Therefore, $P\{t > 4c\} = (1 - .80)/2 = .10$. Appendix table 7 yields $t_{.10,\,15} = 1.341$ for 15 d.f. Hence, $4c = 1.341$ and $c = .335$.

   In closing this section, we state a basic theorem connecting the normal, chi-squared, and t distributions.

Theorem 4
Let z be a *standard normal* random variable, and χ^2 a *chi-squared* random variable with ν degrees of freedom. If χ^2 and z are *independent*, then the random variable

$$\frac{z}{\sqrt{\chi^2/\nu}}$$

has a *t distribution* with ν degrees of freedom.
   For a sample $\{x_1, \ldots, x_n\}$ from a normal distribution it can be proved that $\bar{x}$ and s are *independent* of each other.* Now

$$t = \frac{\bar{x} - \mu}{s/\sqrt{n}} = \frac{\dfrac{\bar{x} - \mu}{\sigma/\sqrt{n}}}{\sqrt{s^2/\sigma^2}}$$

---

*This is not true in sampling from a nonnormal distribution.

where $z = (\bar{x} - \mu)/(\sigma/\sqrt{n})$ is standard normal by theorem 1, and $\chi^2 = (n - 1)s^2/(\sigma^2)$ is chi-squared with $\nu = n - 1$ d.f. by theorem 2. Since $\bar{x}$ and s are independent for a normal sample, so are z and χ^2. Theorem 4 now follows from definition 2.

PROBLEMS 7.3

1. Let t be a random variable having a t distribution with ν degrees of freedom. Find
   a. c, if $\nu = 8$ and $P(-c \le t \le c) = .90$.
   b. $P(|t| > 2.08)$, if $\nu = 21$.
   c. c, if $\nu = 18$ and $P(|t| > c) = .05$.
   d. c, if $\nu = 12$ and $P(0 \le t \le c) = .49$.

2. Let t be a random variable having a t distribution with ν degrees of freedom. Find
   a. c, if $\nu = 15$ and $P(|t| > c) = .01$.
   b. $P(-2.5 \le t \le 2.5)$, if $\nu = 23$.
   c. c, if $\nu = 11$ and $P(-c \le t \le c) = .98$.
   d. c, if $\nu = 6$ and $P(-c \le t \le 0) = .475$.

3. A random sample of $n = 9$ people is taken from a normally distributed population with mean age $\mu = 39$ years. Let $\bar{x}$ and s be the sample mean and standard deviation.
   a. Find the probability that
      (i) $P(|\bar{x} - 39| > .9653\ s)$.
      (ii) $P(39 - .4657\ s \le \bar{x} \le 39 + .4657\ s)$.
   b. Find c such that
      (i) $P(|\bar{x} - 39| < c\ s) = .95$.
      (ii) $P(\bar{x} > 39 + c\ s$ or $\bar{x} < 39 - c\ s) = .02$.

4. A random sample of $n = 15$ scores on a nationally standardized college entrance exam can be taken to be a sample of normal random variables with mean value $\mu = 100$. Let $\bar{x}$ and s be the sample mean and standard deviation.
   a. Find the probability that
      (i) $P(|\bar{x} - 100| < .6775\ s)$.
      (ii) $P(\bar{x} > 100 + .3473\ s$ or $\bar{x} < 100 - .3473\ s)$.
   b. Find c such that
      (i) $P(|\bar{x} - 100| > c\ s) = .02$.
      (ii) $P(100 - c\ s \le \bar{x} \le 100 + c\ s) = .99$.

7.4 Statistical Inference for the Mean of a Normal Distribution

Throughout this section we shall assume that a random sample $\{x_1, \ldots, x_n\}$ is from a normal distribution with mean μ, and we shall construct *exact* confidence intervals for and tests of hypotheses about μ even when n is small. Of course, the inference procedures derived here are also valid for a large n, and, in fact, agree with those of chapter 6 when n is large. The assumption of normality of the underlying population is, however, not so essential when n is large as it is when n is small.

Confidence Intervals for μ

By definition 2, the random variable $t = (\bar{x} - \mu)/(s/\sqrt{n})$ has a t distribution with $\nu = n - 1$ d.f. By the symmetry of the t distribution about 0, for any positive constant c

$$P\{-c < t < c\} = 1 - P[\{t \geq c\} \text{ or } \{t \leq -c\}]$$
$$= 1 - P\{t \geq c\} - P\{t \leq -c\}$$
$$= 1 - 2\,P\{t \geq c\}$$

In particular, taking $c = t_{\alpha/2, n-1}$, where the latter quantity is defined to be that for which

$$P\{t \geq t_{\alpha/2, n-1}\} = \frac{\alpha}{2} \tag{4}$$

and noting that by a simple manipulation of inequalities

$$\{-c < t < c\} = \left\{\bar{x} - \frac{cs}{\sqrt{n}} < \mu < \bar{x} + \frac{cs}{\sqrt{n}}\right\}$$

we get

A $100(1 - \alpha)\%$ confidence interval for μ (σ^2 unknown, sample from a normal population):

$$P\left\{\bar{x} - t_{\alpha/2, n-1} \cdot \frac{s}{\sqrt{n}} < \mu < \bar{x} + t_{\alpha/2, n-1} \cdot \frac{s}{\sqrt{n}}\right\} = 1 - \alpha \tag{5}$$

where the value $t_{\alpha/2, n-1}$ is taken from the t distribution with $\nu = n - 1$ d.f. as in (4).*

---

*Compare (5) with (6.2). There n was assumed to be large so that $t_{\alpha/2, n-1} \cong z_{\alpha/2}$, and even so the probability was only approximately $1 - \alpha$, since the sample was not assumed to come from an exactly normal distribution.

Note: If σ^2 is *known*, we can replace s by σ and $t_{\alpha/2, n-1}$ by $z_{\alpha/2}$ in (5), based on the same argument but using in place of t, $z = (\bar{x} - \mu)/(\sigma/\sqrt{n})$, which by theorem 1 has a standard normal distribution. Since σ^2 is rarely known in practice, however, (5) as given above is the more useful confidence interval.

Example 4

Assume that the price changes on the New York Stock Exchange on any given day follow a normal distribution. A sample of $n = 25$ closing prices of stocks showed changes from the previous day's close with $\bar{x} = 0.68$ (dollars) and $s = .50$. Based on these data, we wish to construct a 95% confidence interval for $\mu =$ mean stock price change for the day.

Here $\alpha = .05$ and $\nu = n - 1 = 24$, and from appendix table 7 $t_{.025, 24} = 2.064$. Hence the 95% confidence interval for μ is

$$0.474 = 0.68 - (2.064)\frac{.50}{\sqrt{25}} < \mu < 0.68 + (2.064)\frac{.50}{\sqrt{25}} = 0.886$$

Hypothesis Tests for μ

Example 5

A student association wishes to check whether the mean weekly meal expense per student has increased by more than \$1.00 over the previous semester, when it was \$21.68. Suppose that for a random sample of weekly meal expenses for 20 students, $\bar{x} = \$22.93$ and $s = \$4.12$. Assume that the population distribution of weekly student meal expenses is normal. Is this enough to justify the claim that the mean meal expense has increased by more than \$1.00? We may formulate this as a hypothesis testing problem

$$H_0 : \mu \leq 22.68 \text{ vs } H_1 : \mu > 22.68$$

In example 5 μ_0 is a given constant ($\mu_0 = 22.68$) and we wish to test the null hypothesis $H_0 : \mu \leq \mu_0$ vs the alternative hypothesis $H_1 : \mu > \mu_0$, using a sample from a normal distribution. If in fact $\mu = \mu_0$ then the random variable

$$t = \frac{\bar{x} - \mu_0}{s/\sqrt{n}}$$

has a t distribution with $\nu = n - 1$ d.f. We take as critical region R for the test the event $\{t > t_{\alpha, n-1}\}$, so that if $\mu = \mu_0$ the probability of (wrongly) rejecting H_0 is α. The power function of this test is then $P_\mu(\text{reject } H_0) =$ the probability that $t > t_{\alpha, n-1}$, when μ is the true population mean value.

This probability increases as μ increases, and therefore reaches its maximum under H_0 at $\mu = \mu_0$. Hence the maximum probability of a type I error, that is, the *significance level* of the test, is α. The test is:

Reject $H_0 : \mu \leq \mu_0$ in favor of $H_1 : \mu > \mu_0$ if $t = \dfrac{\bar{x} - \mu_0}{s/\sqrt{n}} > t_{\alpha, n-1}$ (6)

Returning to example 5, since

$$t = \frac{22.93 - 22.68}{(4.12)/\sqrt{20}} = .2914 < t_{.05, 19} = 1.729$$

we cannot reject H_0 at the .05 level of significance. The evidence is not strong enough to make the claim of a mean increase $> \$1.00$.

For a two-sided alternative, $H_0 : \mu = \mu_0$ vs $H_1 : \mu \neq \mu_0$, we split the probability α of a type I error evenly between the two tails of the t distribution.* We summarize as follows.

TABLE 7.1
Hypothesis Tests for μ with Significance Level α Based on a Random Sample from a Normal Population (σ^2 unknown)

Let $t = \dfrac{\bar{x} - \mu_0}{s/\sqrt{n}}$, and let $t_{\alpha, n-1}$ be given by appendix table 7.

H_0	H_1	Critical region: reject H_0 if
$\mu \leq \mu_0$	$\mu > \mu_0$	$t > t_{\alpha, n-1}$
$\mu \geq \mu_0$	$\mu < \mu_0$	$t < -t_{\alpha, n-1}$
$\mu = \mu_0$	$\mu \neq \mu_0$	$t > t_{\alpha/2, n-1}$ or $t < -t_{\alpha/2, n-1}$ (assert $\mu > \mu_0$) (assert $\mu < \mu_0$)

Note: If σ^2 is *known*, replace s by σ and $t_{\alpha, n-1}$ by the normal z_α in table 7.1, using $z = (\bar{x} - \mu_0)/(\sigma/\sqrt{n})$ instead of t.

Example 6
A drug manufacturer markets batches of an antibiotic in 8-ounce bottles (each batch consists of approximately 4000 bottles). Before

---

*Two-sided tests of $H_0 : \mu = \mu_0$ should be used with caution, since when n is large there will be a high probability of rejecting H_0 when $\mu - \mu_0 \neq 0$ but is so small that the difference may be of no practical consequence.

releasing a batch for distribution, the manufacturer samples 20 bottles from the batch and checks them for impurities. The standards of the industry provide that a batch may be distributed if the mean level of impurities is less than .02 ounces per 8-ounce bottle. What rule should the manufacturer use in deciding whether to release a batch? In particular, should a batch with $\bar{x} = .015$ and $s = .005$ be released?

Assuming that the amount of impurity per 8-ounce bottle in the batch is normally distributed with mean value μ and variance σ^2, the manufacturer wishes to test

$$H_0 : \mu \geq .02 \text{ vs } H_1 : \mu < .02$$

at level $\alpha = .01$; that is, he is willing to make a type I error (releasing a batch when $\mu \geq .02$) with probability at most $1 - .99 = .01$. The rule thus becomes (table 7.1): reject H_0 (that is, release the batch) if and only if

$$t = \frac{\bar{x} - .02}{s/\sqrt{20}} < -t_{.01, 19} = -2.539$$

For $\bar{x} = .015$ and $s = .005$,

$$t = \frac{.015 - .02}{.005/\sqrt{20}} = -4.47$$

so the batch would be released.

PROBLEMS 7.4

1. A random sample of 18 incomes of workers in Arizona yielded $\bar{x} = \$9227$ and $s = \$1428$. Construct the associated 95% confidence interval for the mean income μ of workers in this state. (Assume that the incomes are normally distributed.)

2. A random sample of 23 lifetimes of auto batteries had $\bar{x} = 186.4$ (in weeks) and $s = 35.2$. Assuming that such lifetimes are normally distributed, find a 98% confidence interval for the mean lifetime, μ.

3. A random sample of systolic blood pressure for 10 people on an exercise program gave

Subject	1	2	3	4	5	6	7	8	9	10
Systolic blood pressure	217	210	255	219	217	260	276	265	174	225

Assuming that such blood pressures are normally distributed, find a 90% confidence interval for the mean systolic blood pressure of people on this program.

4. A randomly chosen group of eight students at Stanford university was given a test to measure their degree of authoritarian attitude (on a 40 to 200 scale, with 200 being most authoritarian). The results were:

Student	1	2	3	4	5	6	7	8
Score	111	76	98	102	128	96	101	55

Assuming that such scores are normally distributed, find a 95% confidence interval for the mean authoritarian attitude score for this student body.

5. Six months ago, a survey showed that an average family of four in Indiana spent $78.40 on its weekly food budget. Assuming such spending to follow an (approximately) normal distribution, test at the level of significance $\alpha = .05$ the hypothesis that there has been an increase in the average weekly food budget for a family of four, based on a current random sample of 25 families with sample mean $\bar{x}$ and sample standard deviation s.

a. State the null and alternative hypotheses.
b. State the critical region of the test in terms of $\bar{x}$ and s.
c. If $\bar{x} = \$82.24$ and $s = \$9.86$, state your conclusion.

6. Last year the average score on an entrance examination was 120.8. Assuming that such scores follow a normal distribution, test at the level of significance $\alpha = .05$ the hypothesis that there has been a change in average score, based on a random sample of 20 recent scores.

a. State the null and alternative hypotheses.
b. State the critical region of the test in terms of $\bar{x}$ and s.
c. State your conclusion if $\bar{x} = 126.1$ and $s = 14.7$.

7. The following times (in seconds) were recorded in the 100 yard free-style swim for a random sample of 10 college men:

$$54.3 \quad 50.9 \quad 66.5 \quad 59.5 \quad 62.1$$
$$60.9 \quad 84.5 \quad 66.6 \quad 77.8 \quad 64.5$$

The athletic department makes the claim that the mean time for the 100 yard free-style swim for men is greater than 58 seconds. Assume the data come from an approximately normal distribution and use the level of significance $\alpha = .05$.

a. State the null and alternative hypotheses of the test.
b. State the critical region of the test in terms of $\bar{x}$ and s.
c. What conclusion would be drawn from these data?

8. The following data represent the weights (in pounds) of a random sample of 15 turkeys from a flock of 3000:

14.8	22.1	13.4	18.6	12.4
21.0	17.8	19.4	11.1	20.8
18.8	18.7	20.0	24.1	18.8

The owner of the flock wishes to claim with error probability at most .10 that the average weight of the flock is more than 17.5 pounds. Assume the weights are approximately normally distributed.

a. State the null and alternative hypotheses of the test.
b. State the critical region of the test in terms of $\bar{x}$ and s.
c. Based on these data, can the owner make the desired claim?

7.5 Inference Procedures for the Difference Between Means of Two Normal Populations with Unknown but Equal Variances (Independent Samples)

Let $\{x_{11}, \ldots, x_{1n_1}\}$ and $\{x_{21}, \ldots, x_{2n_2}\}$ be random samples of size n_1 and n_2, respectively, from normal distributions with means μ_1 and μ_2 and *equal variances* σ^2. In this section we give statistical inference procedures concerning the difference $\mu_1 - \mu_2$ of the means. For $i = 1, 2$ let the sample means and variances be

$$\bar{x}_i = \frac{1}{n_i} \sum_{j=1}^{n_i} x_{ij} \qquad s_i^2 = \frac{1}{n_i - 1} \cdot \sum_{j=1}^{n_i} (x_{ij} - \bar{x}_i)^2$$

Confidence Intervals for $\mu_1 - \mu_2$

Example 7
At Tulane University the dean of students wishes to estimate the difference (in hours) between the mean study time spent per week by freshman and seniors. A random sample of $n_1 = 12$ freshmen and $n_2 = 10$ seniors gave the data

Freshmen: $n_1 = 12$, $\bar{x}_1 = 27.8$, $s_1 = 7.2$

Seniors: $n_2 = 10$, $\bar{x}_2 = 21.3$, $s_2 = 6.9$

Find a 90% confidence interval for $\mu_1 - \mu_2$, where μ_1 and μ_2 are the mean number of hours per week spent in study by the freshman and senior populations, respectively. We solve this problem by using the following theorem.

Theorem 5
Let $\{x_{i1}, \ldots, x_{in_i}\}$, $i = 1, 2$, be independent random samples of sizes

n_i from normal distributions with means μ_i and variances σ_i^2, such that $\sigma_1^2 = \sigma_2^2$ (equality of variances). Then the statistic

$$t = \frac{(\bar{x}_1 - \bar{x}_2) - (\mu_1 - \mu_2)}{s_p \sqrt{\dfrac{1}{n_1} + \dfrac{1}{n_2}}} \tag{7}$$

where

$$s_p^2 = \frac{(n_1 - 1)s_1^2 + (n_2 - 1)s_2^2}{n_1 + n_2 - 2} \tag{8}$$

is the "pooled" estimate of the assumed common variance σ^2, has a t distribution with $v = n_1 + n_2 - 2$ degrees of freedom.

The following reasoning justifies this theorem. By theorem 1 we see that $\bar{x}_i$ is normally distributed with mean value μ_i and variance σ^2/n_i (since $\sigma_1^2 = \sigma_2^2 = \sigma^2$). Since $\bar{x}_1$ and $\bar{x}_2$ are independent, a result similar to that obtained in theorem 1 (for $n = 2$) states that $\bar{x}_1 - \bar{x}_2$ is normally distributed with mean value $\mu_1 - \mu_2$ and variance $\sigma^2\left(\dfrac{1}{n_1} + \dfrac{1}{n_2}\right)$. Hence

$$z = \frac{(\bar{x}_1 - \bar{x}_2) - (\mu_1 - \mu_2)}{\sigma \sqrt{\dfrac{1}{n_1} + \dfrac{1}{n_2}}} \tag{9}$$

has a standard normal distribution. With z as in (9), write (7) as

$$t = z \cdot \frac{\sigma}{s_p} = \frac{z}{\sqrt{\chi^2/v}}$$

where $v = n_1 + n_2 - 2$ and by definition

$$\chi^2 = \frac{(n_1 + n_2 - 2)s_p^2}{\sigma^2} \tag{10}$$

The conclusion of theorem 5, that t in (7) has a t distribution with $v = n_1 + n_2 - 2$ d.f., will now follow from theorem 4 if we can show that the χ^2 of (10) (a) has a chi-squared distribution with $v = n_1 + n_2 - 2$ d.f., and (b) is independent of z. As for (a), we observe that by theorem 2 for $i = 1,2$

$$\chi_i^2 = \frac{(n_i - 1)s_i^2}{\sigma^2}$$

has a chi-squared distribution with $v_i = n_i - 1$ d.f. Since the samples are independent, so are s_2^2 and $s_2^2 (\chi_1^2$ and $\chi_2^2)$; so theorem 3 shows that

$$\frac{(n_1 + n_2 - 2)s_p^2}{\sigma^2} = \frac{(n_1 - 1)s_1^2}{\sigma^2} + \frac{(n_2 - 1)s_2^2}{\sigma^2} = \chi_1^2 + \chi_2^2$$

has a chi-squared distribution with $\nu = \nu_1 + \nu_2 = (n_1 - 1) + (n_2 - 1) = n_1 + n_2 - 2$ d.f. From this (a) follows. Property (b) follows from the independence of the sample mean and sample variance for the normal distribution.

Theorem 5 solves the problem of obtaining exact confidence intervals for $\mu_1 - \mu_2$. By this theorem, we have with t as in (7)

$$P\{|t| < t_{\alpha/2, \nu}\} = 1 - \alpha \qquad (\nu = n_1 + n_2 - 2)$$

from which we obtain

A $100 (1 - \alpha)\%$ confidence interval for $\mu_1 - \mu_2$ (independent normal samples with unknown $\sigma_1^2 = \sigma_2^2$):

$$P[(\bar{x}_1 - \bar{x}_2) - c < \mu_1 - \mu_2 < (\bar{x}_1 - \bar{x}_2) + c] = 1 - \alpha \qquad (11)$$

where $c = t_{\alpha/2, v} \cdot s_p \sqrt{\dfrac{1}{n_1} + \dfrac{1}{n_2}}$, $s_p^2 =$ the pooled estimate of variance in (8), and $\nu = n_1 + n_2 - 2$.

Example 7 (continued)

To construct the desired 90% confidence interval we use $\alpha = .10$ in (11). Here, $n_1 + n_2 - 2 = 12 + 10 - 2 = 20$, from appendix table 7 $t_{\alpha/2, \nu} = t_{.05, 20} = 1.725$, and

$$s_p = \sqrt{\frac{11(7.2)^2 + 9(6.9)^2}{20}} = \sqrt{49.937} = 7.067$$

Thus, c of (11) becomes

$$c = (1.725)(7.067) \sqrt{\frac{1}{12} + \frac{1}{10}} = (1.725)(7.067)(.428)$$

$$= (1.725)(3.025) = 5.22$$

and the 90% confidence interval for $\mu_1 - \mu_2$, with $\bar{x}_1 - \bar{x}_2 = 27.8 - 21.3 = 6.5$, is therefore $1.28 = 6.5 - 5.22 < \mu_1 - \mu_2 < 6.5 + 5.22 = 11.72$.

At the 90% level of confidence, the dean can therefore assert that freshmen study on the average between 1.28 to 11.72 hours more per week than seniors.

Tests of Hypotheses about $\mu_1 - \mu_2$

To test hypotheses about $\mu_1 - \mu_2$ we again use theorem 5. For example, to test $H_0 : \mu_1 = \mu_2$ vs $H_1 : \mu_1 \neq \mu_2$, we have $\mu_1 - \mu_2 = 0$ under H_0. Hence by theorem 5, when H_0 is true the statistic

$$t = \frac{\bar{x}_1 - \bar{x}_2}{s_p \sqrt{\dfrac{1}{n_1} + \dfrac{1}{n_2}}} \qquad (12)$$

is such that

$$P\{|t| > t_{\alpha/2,\nu}\} = \alpha \qquad (\nu = n_1 + n_2 - 2)$$

This provides a two-sided test at level of significance α for H_0. Arguments based on theorem 5 can also be used to construct one-sided tests, using the appropriate upper or lower tail of the t distribution. We summarize the results in

TABLE 7.2
Hypothesis Tests for $\mu_1 - \mu_2$ with Significance Level α
(independent samples of size n_1 and n_2 from two normal
populations with unknown $\sigma_1^2 = \sigma_2^2$)

Let $\nu = n_1 + n_2 - 2$ and t be as in (12).

H_0	H_1	Critical region: reject H_0 if
$\mu_1 = \mu_2$	$\mu_1 \neq \mu_2$	$t > t_{\alpha/2,\nu}$ $\qquad$ or $t < -t_{\alpha/2,\nu}$ (assert $\mu_1 > \mu_2$) $\qquad$ (assert $\mu_1 < \mu_2$)
$\mu_1 \leq \mu_2$	$\mu_1 > \mu_2$	$t > t_{\alpha,\nu}$
$\mu_1 \geq \mu_2$	$\mu_1 < \mu_2$	$t < -t_{\alpha,\nu}$

Example 8
A company has developed a product to be marketed as a nutritious, easily prepared, completely balanced breakfast food. The product can be marketed in either liquid or solid form. Before marketing the product, the company wants to know whether these two forms have equal intake efficiency. A random sample of 20 newly born rats are used for the study. Ten of these rats are randomly assigned to the liquid diet for 30 days and the remaining ten to the solid diet. Each rat is fed the same amount of food in grams per day. The weight gains for the rats over the 30 day period are recorded. Do the two forms of diet yield different mean weight gains (an accepted measure of intake efficiency), and if so, which is better?

Here one might test, say, at level $\alpha = .05$, $H_0: \mu_1 = \mu_2$ vs $H_1:$ $\mu_1 \neq \mu_2$, where μ_1 and μ_2 are the mean weight gains for the populations of rats on the liquid and solid diets, respectively. The results of the experiment were:

Liquid diet: $n_1 = 10$, $\bar{x}_1 = 148.7$ grams, $s_1 = 4.3$ grams

Solid diet: $n_2 = 10$, $\bar{x}_2 = 144.1$ grams, $s_2 = 3.8$ grams

The test is given in table 7.2: Reject H_0 if either $t > 2.101$ or $t < -2.101$, where t is as in (12) and $2.101 = t_{.025, 18}$, since $\nu = n_1 + n_2 - 2 = 10 + 10 - 2 = 18$. The data yield

$$s_p = \sqrt{\frac{(n_1 - 1)s_1^2 + (n_2 - 1)s_2^2}{n_1 + n_2 - 2}} = \sqrt{\frac{9(4.3)^2 + 9(3.8)^2}{18}} = \sqrt{16.465}$$

$$t = \frac{\bar{x}_1 - \bar{x}_2}{s_p \sqrt{\frac{1}{n_1} + \frac{1}{n_2}}} = \frac{148.7 - 144.1}{\sqrt{16.465} \sqrt{\frac{1}{10} + \frac{1}{10}}} = \frac{4.6}{1.81} = 2.54$$

Since $t = 2.54 > 2.101 = t_{.025, 18}$, we reject H_0 and assert that the two diets are *not* equally efficient. The sample results indicate that the liquid diet is the more efficient. (The probability of making this assertion when in fact $\mu_1 \le \mu_2$ is at most $\alpha/2 = .025$.)

PROBLEMS 7.5

1. Construct a 90% confidence interval for the difference $\mu_1 - \mu_2$ between population mean values, based on the following independent samples from normal distributions.

Sample size	Sample mean	Sample standard deviation
$n_1 = 6$	$\bar{x}_1 = 16$	$s_1 = 3.2$
$n_2 = 10$	$\bar{x}_2 = 14$	$s_2 = 3.4$

2. Construct a 95% confidence interval for the difference $\mu_1 - \mu_2$ between population mean values, based on the following independent samples from normal distributions.

Sample size	Sample mean	Sample standard deviation
$n_1 = 15$	$\bar{x}_1 = 241$	$s_1 = 17.8$
$n_2 = 10$	$\bar{x}_2 = 307$	$s_2 = 18.6$

3. Two independent random samples of 15 men and 15 women, newly graduated from a university, gave the following data on annual salaries for their first job.

Sample	Sample mean	Sample standard deviation
Men	$11,228	$1386
Women	$8697	$1161

Find a 95% confidence interval for the difference $\mu_1 - \mu_2$ in mean income for newly graduated men and women.

4. Two independent random samples of 15 mice were raised under identical conditions except for a high level of air pollutants in the atmosphere of the second sample. The resulting data (in months of life) were

Sample	Sample mean	Sample standard deviation
Without pollutants	29.6	6.4
With pollutants	23.4	5.9

Find a 95% confidence interval for the difference $\mu_1 - \mu_2$ in mean lifetimes.

5. Using the data in problem 3, test the hypothesis that new men graduates make more than new women graduates, at the level of significance $\alpha = .05$.

   a. State the null and alternative hypotheses.
   b. State the critical region of the test in terms of $\bar{x}_1$, $\bar{x}_2$, s_1, and s_2.
   c. What conclusion would you reach?

6. Using the data in problem 5, test the hypothesis at the level of significance $\alpha = .01$ that polluted atmosphere decreases the mean lifetime of mice.

   a. State the null and alternative hypotheses.
   b. State the critical region of the test in terms of $\bar{x}_1$, $\bar{x}_2$, s_1, and s_2.
   c. What conclusion would you reach?

7. Two different diets, a standard and an experimental, are fed to pigs to see if there is a difference in weight gain over a month's time. The results given below are for 20 pigs, 10 of which were randomly assigned to each diet.

Diet	Weight gains (pounds)									
Standard	43	49	60	49	44	48	61	41	57	45
Experimental	40	68	57	39	56	53	65	62	64	49

Using these data, test at the level of significance $\alpha = .02$ whether the mean weight gain is the same for the two diets.

a. State the null and alternative hypotheses of the test.
b. State the critical regions of the test.
c. What is your conclusion based on the above data?

8. A manufacturer of cigarettes claims that a new filter reduces the amount of tar in the smoke. Test this claim at the level of significance $\alpha = .05$ based on the following data from a sample of 8 cigarettes with the old filter and 12 cigarettes with the new filter. The amount of smoke drawn through the filters was regulated by an inhaling machine.

Filter	Grams of tar											
Old	15.9	14.2	15.8	17.6	16.8	17.1	15.8	14.5				
New	15.8	19.1	15.5	14.4	14.1	14.6	16.5	15.4	14.7	14.6	15.7	15.9

a. State the null and alternative hypotheses.
b. State the critical region of the test.
c. Do these data support the manufacturer's claim?

9. Independent random samples with $n_1 = 9$ and $n_2 = 15$ of two makes of four-cylinder compact cars were each driven at 40 miles per hour for 200 miles with a single brand of gasoline. The results in gallons consumed were:

Sample size	Sample mean	Sample standard deviation
$n_1 = 9$	$\bar{x}_1 = 8.6$	$s_1 = 1.07$
$n_2 = 15$	$\bar{x}_2 = 7.5$	$s_2 = .86$

Using these data, test the hypothesis of no difference in mileage for the two makes at the level of significance $\alpha = .05$.

a. State the null and alternative hypotheses.
b. State the critical region of the test in terms of $\bar{x}_1, \bar{x}_2, s_1,$ and s_2.
c. Do the data support the claim of a mileage difference in the two compacts?

7.6 Inference Procedures for Paired Dependent Samples from a Normal Population

Example 9

A researcher in physical education wishes to study whether a program of jogging 6 days a week for 2 miles at 8 minutes per mile for 6 weeks will reduce the resting pulse rate of men aged 40 to 50. Using a sample of 8 men, the results before and after completion of the program are

Subject	1	2	3	4	5	6	7	8
Pulse rate (before)	74	86	80	98	85	83	74	92
Pulse rate (after)	70	85	82	90	82	79	71	89

The researcher wishes to test at significance level $\alpha = .05$ the hypothesis $H_0 : \mu_1 \leq \mu_2$ vs $H_1 : \mu_1 > \mu_2$, where μ_1 and μ_2 are the mean resting pulse rates before and after the jogging program of the population of all men in the 40 to 50 age group.

A Faulty Analysis. Suppose the researcher uses the one-sided t test of the previous section, with $n_1 = n_2 = 8$. The sample results yield $\bar{x}_1 = 84$, $\bar{x}_2 = 81$, $s_1^2 = 68.86$, $s_2^2 = 55.43$, and $s_p^2 = 62.14$. From table 7.2 the test would reject H_0 only if $t > t_{.05, 14} = 1.761$, where

$$t = \frac{\bar{x}_1 - \bar{x}_2}{s_p \sqrt{\dfrac{1}{n_1} + \dfrac{1}{n_2}}} = \frac{84 - 81}{\sqrt{62.14} \sqrt{\dfrac{1}{8} + \dfrac{1}{8}}} = \frac{3}{3.94} = .76$$

Since this value does not exceed 1.761, the researcher cannot claim that the jogging program decreases the mean resting pulse rate.

However, this analysis is faulty. In fact, of the 8 subjects tested, all but one (subject 3) show a decrease. Now, the maximum probability under H_0 of getting that many (7 or 8) subjects to show a decrease is $P\{y \geq 7\}$, where y is a binomial random variable with $n = 8$ trials and $p = 1/2$. But, $P\{y \geq 7\} = \binom{8}{7}\left(\dfrac{1}{2}\right)^8 + \binom{8}{8}\left(\dfrac{1}{2}\right)^8 = 9\left(\dfrac{1}{2}\right)^8 = 9/256$

$= .035$. Thus even a one-sided test for a binomial parameter p (section 4.3) would reject H_0 on the evidence of this sample at level $\alpha = .035$ (and therefore at level $\alpha = .05$ also).

The error in this analysis is that these samples are not independent of each other, since both measurements x_{1i} and x_{2i} are on the *same person* (that is, $x_{11} = 74$ and $x_{21} = 70$ are on subject 1, and so forth). A subject having a low (high) rate before tends to have a low (high) rate after. By ignoring this dependence between the two samples and using the test of the previous section one *overestimates the variance* of $\bar{x}_1 - \bar{x}_2$ and hence *decreases the sensitivity* (that is, the power function) of the test to departures from H_0.

Let us reconsider the general problem. Let two sets of random variables $\{x_{11}, \ldots, x_{1n}\}$ and $\{x_{21}, \ldots, x_{2n}\}$ be of the same size. Define new random variables, the n *differences*

$$d_i = x_{1i} - x_{2i}$$

and assume that the d_i are normal with mean value $\mu_d = \mu_1 - \mu_2$ and some common variance σ_d^2. Furthermore, assume that the d_i are independent of each other. (In the example, the persons were randomly chosen and hence the observed differences are independent.) Thus, $\{d_1, \ldots, d_n\}$ represents a random sample of size n from a single normal population with mean value μ_d and variance σ_d^2 Setting

$$\bar{d} = \frac{1}{n} \sum_{i=1}^{n} d_i = \bar{x}_1 - \bar{x}_2$$

and

$$s_d^2 = \frac{1}{n-1} \sum_{i=1}^{n} (d_i - \bar{d})^2 \tag{13}$$

we see by theorem 4 that

$$t = \frac{\bar{d} - \mu_d}{s_d/\sqrt{n}} = \frac{(\bar{x}_1 - \bar{x}_2) - (\mu_1 - \mu_2)}{s_d/\sqrt{n}} \tag{14}$$

has a t distribution with $\nu = n - 1$ d.f. Letting $\mu_d = \mu_1 - \mu_2$ replace μ, and s_d replace s, in table 7.1, we obtain the following tests for the difference $\mu_d = \mu_1 - \mu_2$.

TABLE 7.3

Hypothesis Tests for $\mu_1 - \mu_2$ with Significance Level α Based on a Random Sample of n Paired Differences of Normally Distributed Random Variables

Let $t = \dfrac{\bar{d}}{s_d/\sqrt{n}} = \dfrac{\bar{x}_1 - \bar{x}_2}{s_d/\sqrt{n}}$ with s_d^2 as in (13), $\nu = n - 1$, and $t_{\alpha,\nu}$ such that

$P(t > t_{\alpha,\nu}) = \alpha$.

H_0	H_1	Critical region: reject H_0 if
$\mu_1 \leq \mu_2$ ($\mu_d \leq 0$)	$\mu_1 > \mu_2$ ($\mu_d > 0$)	$t > t_{\alpha, n-1}$
$\mu_1 \geq \mu_2$ ($\mu_d \geq 0$)	$\mu_1 < \mu_2$ ($\mu_d < 0$)	$t < -t_{\alpha, n-1}$
$\mu_1 = \mu_2$ ($\mu_d = 0$)	$\mu_1 \neq \mu_2$ ($\mu_d \neq 0$)	$t > t_{\alpha/2, n-1}$ or $t < -t_{\alpha/2, n-1}$ (assert $\mu_1 > \mu_2$) (assert $\mu_2 > \mu_1$)

Example 9 (correct analysis)

The table of differences for the data of example 9 is

Subject i	Difference $d_i = x_{1i} - x_{2i}$	$d_i - \bar{d}$	$(d_i - \bar{d})^2$
1	$4(74 - 70)$	1	1
2	$1(86 - 85)$	-2	4
3	$-2(80 - 82)$	-5	25
4	$8(98 - 90)$	5	25
5	$3(85 - 82)$	0	0
6	$4(83 - 79)$	1	1
7	$3(74 - 71)$	0	0
8	$3(92 - 89)$	0	0
Sums	24	0	56

with

$$\bar{d} = \frac{1}{n} \sum_{i=1}^{n} d_i = \frac{24}{8} = 84 - 81 = 3 = \bar{x}_1 - \bar{x}_2$$

$$s_d^2 = \frac{1}{n-1} \sum_{i=1}^{n} (d_i - \bar{d})^2 = \frac{56}{7} = 8$$

Therefore

$$t = \frac{\bar{d}}{s_d/\sqrt{n}} = 3$$

The correct test at level of significance $\alpha = .05$ of $H_0 : \mu_1 \leq \mu_2$ vs $H_1 : \mu_1 > \mu_2$ for this example is to reject H_0 if $t > t_{.05,7} = 1.895$. Since $t = 3$, we do reject H_0 in favor of H_1 and claim that the jogging program does lower the mean resting pulse rate for the population in question.

We immediately obtain confidence intervals for $\mu_1 - \mu_2$ in paired dependent samples from the fact that the statistic in (14) has a t distribution with $n - 1$ d.f.

A $100(1 - \alpha)\%$ confidence interval for $\mu_1 - \mu_2$ from a sample of n paired differences of normally distributed random variables:

$$P\left\{ \bar{d} - t_{\alpha/2, n-1} \cdot \frac{s_d}{\sqrt{n}} < \mu_1 - \mu_2 < \bar{d} + t_{\alpha/2, n-1} \cdot \frac{s_d}{\sqrt{n}} \right\} \tag{15}$$

$$= P\{ |t| > t_{\alpha/2, n-1} \} = 1 - \alpha$$

with $\bar{d} = \bar{x}_1 - \bar{x}_2$, s_d^2 as in (13), and t as in (14).

Example 10

A chemist wishes to estimate with 95% confidence the difference between the mean temperatures of discoloration of two paints, measured by a color-sensing device as the temperature is raised. The chemist takes 10 boards and paints at random half of each board with paint A and half with paint B. The boards yield the following temperatures (Fahrenheit) of discoloration.

Board i	1	2	3	4	5	6	7	8	9	10
x_{1i} = paint A	264	301	229	270	316	247	275	264	291	256
x_{2i} = paint B	287	326	222	347	383	327	299	304	289	244
$d_i = x_{1i} - x_{2i}$	−23	−25	7	−77	−67	−80	−24	−40	2	12

For these sample data
$$d = -31.5 \text{ and } s_d = \sqrt{1158.06} = 34.03$$

Since $t_{.025, 9} = 2.262$, the 95% confidence interval (15) is

$$\mu_1 - \mu_2 = \bar{d} \pm t_{.025,9} \cdot \frac{s_d}{\sqrt{n}} = -31.5 \pm (2.262) \frac{(34.03)}{\sqrt{10}}$$
$$= -31.5 \pm 24.34$$

The 95% confidence interval estimate of the difference (mean temperature to discoloration of paint A) − (mean temperature to discoloration of paint B) is therefore

$$-55.84 < \mu_1 - \mu_2 < -7.16$$

This test was carried out as a *paired experiment*, with both paints A and B for each i on the same board. (Hence, x_{1i} and x_{2i} are not independent of each other.) The advantage of doing the experiment in this way is that the *board-to-board variation* (if any) *is removed* by using both paints on each board. If one expects large sources of variation owing to the materials used in an experiment, the technique of pairing the two treatment observations to remove this variation usually yields a shorter confidence interval for the difference of the two population mean values than would two independent samples of the same size.

PROBLEMS 7.6

1. A radiotherapist wishes to see if treatment causes patients to lose sleep. Using a sample of 10 patients she records the amount of sleep (in hours) (1) for a week before treatment and (2) for the first week after treatment. Based on the following data, test the hypothesis at level $\alpha = .05$ that radiotherapy treatment does not cause loss of sleep against the alternative that there is a loss of sleep.

Patient	1	2	3	4	5	6	7	8	9	10
Hours of sleep (before)	51	48	58	44	61	55	59	50	48	52
Hours of sleep (after)	47	46	60	43	54	49	52	47	49	50

   a. State the null and alternative hypotheses.
   b. State the rejection region of your test.
   c. State your conclusion.

2. An English professor wishes to see if a literature course changes racial attitudes. The literature read deals with racial problems. A racial attitude test is given to 12 students at the beginning (score 1) and end (score 2) of the semester. The scale is from 20 to 100, with a high score indicating a high degree of racial bias. The results are:

Student	1	2	3	4	5	6	7	8	9	10	11	12
Score 1	64	78	91	53	48	56	62	47	28	37	46	52
Score 2	58	69	80	54	32	49	64	40	27	34	39	47

   a. State the null and alternative hypotheses for testing the hypothesis of no change in the mean racial attitude score versus a lowering of the score.
   b. State the rejection region of your test.
   c. State your conclusion.

3. A random sample of 25 freshmen at the University of Virginia showed a mean decrease of $\bar{d} = 4.7$ hours per week in the amount of time devoted to study between the first and second semesters. Find a 95% confidence interval for μ_d, the mean decrease of student study time per week, if $s_d = 3.6$.

4. A random sample of 16 wives and their husbands showed the following caloric intake per day for a given week:

$$\text{Wives} \quad \bar{x}_1 = 2540$$
$$\text{Husbands} \quad \bar{x}_2 = 3080$$

Based on $\bar{d} = \bar{x}_1 - \bar{x}_2$, the sample difference in mean caloric intake, find a 98% confidence interval for μ_d if $s_d = 247$.

5. A random sample of 10 sets of twins showed the following birth weights (in pounds).

Twins	1	2	3	4	5	6	7	8	9	10
First born	6.2	4.7	5.1	4.9	6.1	7.2	5.1	5.7	6.2	4.7
Second born	5.9	4.2	5.3	4.0	5.4	5.3	5.5	4.9	5.8	3.8

Based on these data, construct a 90% confidence interval for the mean value of the difference μ_d in the weights of the first born and second born in a set of twins.

6. Redo problem 1 assuming (incorrectly) that the observations before and after radiotherapy are independent observations, using the test in 6(b). Explain the error of this analysis and the conclusion of your test here as opposed to that in problem 1.

7.7 Inference for the Variance σ^2 of a Normal Population

By theorem 2, the statistic

$$\chi^2 = \frac{(n-1)s^2}{\sigma^2} \tag{16}$$

computed from a random sample $\{x_1, \ldots, x_n\}$ from a normal population with variance σ^2, has a chi-squared distribution with $\nu = n - 1$ degrees of freedom. Using this fact, we can give inference procedures for an unknown variance σ^2.

Confidence Intervals for σ^2

Appendix table 8 gives the values of $\chi^2_{\alpha, \nu}$ such that $P\{\chi^2 > \chi^2_{\alpha, \nu}\} = \alpha$ when χ^2 has a chi-squared distribution with ν d.f. Therefore, using (16) we have for any $0 < \alpha < 1$

$$P\left\{\chi^2_{1-\alpha/2, n-1} < \chi^2 = \frac{(n-1)s^2}{\sigma^2} < \chi^2_{\alpha/2, n-1}\right\} = 1 - \alpha \tag{17}$$

Figure 7.5 illustrates this probability statement. We use (17) to form a confidence interval for σ^2.

A 100 $(1 - \alpha)$% confidence interval for σ^2, based on a random sample from a normal population:

$$P\left\{\frac{(n-1)s^2}{\chi^2_{\alpha/2, n-1}} < \sigma^2 < \frac{(n-1)s^2}{\chi^2_{1-\alpha/2, n-1}}\right\} = 1 - \alpha \tag{18}$$

or equivalently,

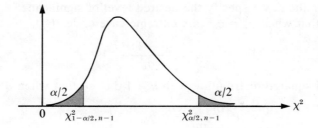

FIGURE 7.5
Tail areas of the chi-squared distribution

$$P\left(\frac{\sqrt{n-1}\ s}{\sqrt{\chi^2_{\alpha/2,\,n-1}}} < \sigma < \frac{\sqrt{n-1}\ s}{\sqrt{\chi^2_{1-\alpha/2,\,n-1}}}\right) = 1 - \alpha \qquad (19)$$

These results follow immediately by noting that the events in (17), (18), and (19) are algebraically equivalent.

Example 11
We wish to estimate with a 90% confidence interval the variance σ^2 of IQ for the population of an elementary school system having about 10,000 students. Using a standard IQ test for a random sample of 20 students, we obtain $s^2 = 214.1$. To find a 90% confidence interval for σ^2, we use (18). Since $\chi^2 = \chi^2_{.95,\,19} = 10.117$, and $\chi^2_{\alpha/2,\,n-1} = \chi^2_{.05,\,19} = 30.144$, we obtain the 90% confidence interval

$$134.9 = \frac{(19)(214.1)}{30.144} < \sigma^2 < \frac{(19)(214.1)}{10.117} = 402.1$$

For the standard deviation σ, the corresponding 90% confidence interval is

$$11.6 = \sqrt{134.} < \sigma < \sqrt{402.1} = 20.1$$

Hypothesis Tests for σ^2

One- and two-sided hypothesis tests for σ^2 are based on theorem 2 for the statistic χ^2 of (16). For example, suppose we wish to test

$$H_0 : \sigma^2 \leq \sigma_0^2 \text{ versus } H_1 : \sigma^2 > \sigma_0^2$$

Since a large value of s^2 (which estimates σ^2) tends to support H_1 over H_0, we take as critical region

$$R = \{s^2 > c\} \qquad (20)$$

To determine c, we specify the desired level of significance α and use the fact that when $\sigma^2 = \sigma_0^2$ (the extreme case under H_0),

$$\chi^2 = \frac{(n-1)s^2}{\sigma_0^2}$$

has a chi-squared distribution with $n - 1$ d.f., so that when $\sigma^2 = \sigma_0^2$

$$P\left\{\frac{(n-1)s^2}{\sigma_0^2} > \chi_{\alpha, n-1}^2\right\} = \alpha \qquad (21)$$

It can be shown that this is the *maximum* probability of a type I error under $H_0 : \sigma^2 \leq \sigma_0^2$. Therefore, taking

$$c = \frac{\chi_{\alpha, n-1}^2 \cdot \sigma_0^2}{n-1}$$

in (20), we get the critical region

$$\text{Reject } H_0 \text{ if } \chi^2 = \frac{(n-1)s^2}{\sigma_0^2} > \chi_{\alpha, n-1}^2$$

Similar tests for other hypotheses can be developed. The results are given in table 7.4 below. $\chi_{\alpha, v}^2$ is given in appendix table 8.

TABLE 7.4
Hypothesis Tests for σ^2 at Level of Significance α
Based on a Random Sample of Size n from a Normal
Population

H_0	H_1	Critical region: reject H_0 if
$\sigma^2 \leq \sigma_0^2$	$\sigma^2 > \sigma_0^2$	$\dfrac{(n-1)s^2}{\sigma_0^2} > \chi_{\alpha, n-1}^2$
$\sigma^2 \geq \sigma_0^2$	$\sigma^2 < \sigma_0^2$	$\dfrac{(n-1)s^2}{\sigma_0^2} < \chi_{1-\alpha, n-1}^2$
$\sigma^2 = \sigma_0^2$	$\sigma^2 \neq \sigma_0^2$	$\dfrac{(n-1)s^2}{\sigma_0^2} > \chi_{\alpha/2, n-1}^2$ or $\dfrac{(n-1)s^2}{\sigma_0^2} < \chi_{1-\alpha/2, n-1}^2$ In the first case assert that $\sigma^2 > \sigma_0^2$ and in the second that $\sigma^2 < \sigma_0^2$.

Example 12

A proposed method of ultrasound scanning allows a doctor to estimate tumor size without surgery. From past data, we know that the surgical method of measurement has standard deviation $\sigma = 80.2$ c.c. The ultrasound method will be considered adequate if it can be shown at level $\alpha = .05$ that the standard deviation with ultrasound is no more than 25 percent greater than that of the surgical method; that is, that $\sigma < 100$ c.c.

If a random sample of 41 ultrasound measurements yield $s = 76.3$, what conclusion can be drawn? Here we wish to test with $\alpha = .05$, say,

$$H_0 : \sigma \geq 100 \text{ vs } H_1 : \sigma < 100$$

By table 7.4, the test is:

$$\text{Reject } H_0 \text{ if } \chi^2 = \frac{(n-1)s^2}{\sigma_0^2} = \frac{40\, s^2}{(100)^2} < \chi^2_{.95,\, 40} = 26.509$$

From the data we have

$$\chi^2 = 40\left(\frac{76.3}{100}\right)^2 = 23.287$$

Since $\chi^2 = 23.287 < 26.509 = \chi^2_{.95,\, 40}$, we reject H_0 and decide that the ultrasound method has a standard deviation no more than 25 percent greater ($\sigma < 100$) than the surgical method.

PROBLEMS 7.7

1. Find a 90% confidence interval for the variance, based on a random sample of 10 observations from a normal population for which $s^2 = 21.5$.

2. Find a 95% confidence interval for the standard deviation of weights of college men, based on a sample of 25 men with $s = 16.8$ lbs. Assume that the weights follow an approximately normal distribution.

3. A supplier of laboratory mice advertises in *Science* that his strain has a weight variance of at most .25. Based on a sample of 30 such mice, test the supplier's claim against the alternative $\sigma^2 > .25$ at level $\alpha = .05$, if $s^2 = .39$. State the null and alternative hypotheses of your test, the rejection region, and your conclusion.

4. The Garrett Company manufactures drill bits. Its quality control standards call for a variance of $\sigma^2 \leq 1.5$ mm. Based on a sample of 25 drill bits produced, test the hypothesis that the variance

meets the above standard, versus the alternative it does not, at level $\alpha = .05$, if $s = .85$. State the null and alternative hypotheses, the rejection region, and your conclusion.

7.8 Inference about the Variances of Two Normal Populations

The F Distribution

One of the *assumptions* used in section 7.3 to make inferences about the difference $\mu_1 - \mu_2$ between two population mean values was that the two unknown population variances are equal; that is, that $\sigma_1^2 = \sigma_2^2$. In this section, we discuss a *test* of the hypothesis $H_0 : \sigma_1^2 = \sigma_2^2$ vs the alternative $H_1 : \sigma_1^2 \neq \sigma_2^2$, based on the statistic s_1^2/s_2^2, the *ratio of the sample variances* from two independent random normal samples $\{x_{11}, \ldots, x_{1n_1}\}$ and $\{x_{21}, \ldots, x_{2n_2}\}$.

Definition 4

Let χ_1^2 and χ_2^2 be independent chi-squared random variables with ν_1 and ν_2 degrees of freedom, respectively. The distribution of

$$F = F_{\nu_1, \nu_2} = \frac{\chi_1^2/\nu_1}{\chi_2^2/\nu_2} = \frac{\nu_2}{\nu_1} \cdot \frac{\chi_1^2}{\chi_2^2}$$

is called an *F distribution with ν_1 degrees of freedom in the numerator and ν_2 degrees of freedom in the denomiator.*

Before discussing how to compute probabilities from the tabled values for the F distribution in appendix table 9, let us see how definition 4 yields the distribution of s_1^2/s_2^2.

By theorem 2, since the samples are from normal populations with variances σ_1^2 and σ_2^2, respectively, we see that

$$\chi_i^2 = \frac{(n_i - 1)s_i^2}{\sigma_i^2} \qquad i = 1, 2,$$

has a chi-squared distribution with $\nu_i = n_i - 1$ degrees of freedom. Furthermore, χ_1^2 and χ_2^2 are independent of each other, since s_1^2 and s_2^2 are computed from independent samples. The next result now follows from definition 4.

Theorem 6

Let $\{x_{i1}, \ldots, x_{in_i}\}$, $i = 1, 2$, be independent random samples from two normal populations with mean values μ_i and variances σ_i^2. Then the statistic

$$F = \frac{(s_1^2/\sigma_1^2)}{(s_2^2/\sigma_2^2)}$$

has a F distribution, with $\nu_1 = n_1 - 1$ and $\nu_2 = n_2 - 1$ degrees of freedom in the numerator and denominator, respectively.

Appendix table 9 gives the upper-tail .01 and .05 points of the F distribution. Let F_{ν_1,ν_2} have an F distribution with (ν_1, ν_2) degrees of freedom. In writing (ν_1, ν_2) in this order, it is understood that the first position stands for the degrees of freedom in the numerator of F above, and that the second position stands for the degrees of freedom in the denominator. Then $F_{\nu_1,\nu_2,\alpha}$ is the value such that

$$P\{F_{\nu_1,\nu_2} > F_{\nu_1,\nu_2,\alpha}\} = \alpha$$

This probability is represented by the shaded area in figure 7.6.

For example, if $\alpha = .01$, $\nu_1 = 6$, and $\nu_2 = 9$, column 4 and row 9 of appendix table 9 give $F_{6,9,.01} = 5.80$; that is, $P(F_{6,9} > 5.80) = .01$, where $F_{6,9}$ has an F distribution with (6,9) d.f. Again, if $\alpha = .05$, $\nu_1 = 4$, and $\nu_2 = 28$, column 4 and row 28 of appendix table 9 give $F_{4,28,.05} = 2.71$; that is, $P(F_{4,28} > 2.71) = .05$, where $F_{4,28}$ has an F distribution with (4, 28) d.f.

We can also compute lower-tail probabilities from appendix table 9. To see this, note that in definition 4 we can interchange numerator and denominator and write

$$\frac{1}{F_{\nu_1,\nu_2}} = \frac{(\chi_2^2/\nu_2)}{(\chi_1^2/\nu_1)} = F_{\nu_2,\nu_1}$$

That is, for $c > 0$

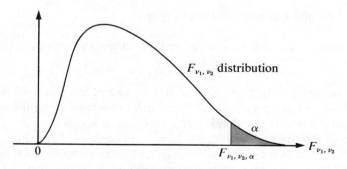

FIGURE 7.6
Tail areas of the F distribution

$$P\left\{F_{\nu_1, \nu_2} < \frac{1}{c}\right\} = P\left\{\frac{1}{F_{\nu_1, \nu_2}} > c\right\} = P\{F_{\nu_2, \nu_1} > c\}$$

and a lower-tail probability is converted to an upper-tail probability. Therefore, with $c = F_{\nu_2, \nu_1, \alpha}$, we have

$$P\left\{F_{\nu_1, \nu_2} < \frac{1}{F_{\nu_2, \nu_1, \alpha}}\right\} = P\{F_{\nu_2, \nu_1} > F_{\nu_2, \nu_1, \alpha}\} = \alpha$$

For example, if $\alpha = .05$, $\nu_1 = 30$, and $\nu_2 = 20$, from appendix table 9, $F_{20, 30, .05} = 1.93$. Therefore

$$P\left\{F_{30, 20} < \frac{1}{1.93}\right\} = P\{F_{20, 30} > 1.93\} = .05$$

Example 13
Samples of size $n_1 = 10$ and $n_2 = 8$ are drawn independently from two normal populations, with resulting sample variances s_1^2 and s_2^2. Under the assumption that $\sigma_1^2 = \sigma_2^2$, find the value c such that $P\{s_1^2 > c\, s_2^2\} = .01$. What might one conclude if $s_1 = 11.9$ and $s_2 = 3.2$?

Here, $F = s_1^2/s_2^2$ has an F distribution with $(n_1 - 1, n_2 - 1) = (9,7)$ degrees of freedom. Thus, the value of c such that

$$P(s_1^2 > c\, s_2^2) = P(F_{9,7} > c) = .01$$

from appendix table 9 is $c = F_{9,7,.01} = 6.71$. Since for the samples given

$$F = \frac{s_1^2}{s_2^2} = \left(\frac{11.9}{3.2}\right)^2 = 13.83 > 6.71 = F_{9,7,.01}$$

it is highly unlikely that the samples did come from distributions with $\sigma_1^2 = \sigma_2^2$, and it is reasonable to infer that $\sigma_1^2 > \sigma_2^2$.

A Test for the Equality of Two Variances

Suppose that we wish to test the equality of two variances

$$H_0 : \sigma_1^2 = \sigma_2^2 \text{ vs } H_1 : \sigma_1^2 \neq \sigma_2^2$$

based on independent samples of size n_1 and n_2 from normal populations with unknown variances σ_1^2 and σ_2^2. Let s_1^2 and s_2^2 be the respective sample variances. Under H_0, theorem 6 states that $F = s_1^2/s_2^2$ has an F distribution with $(n_1 - 1, n_2 - 1)$ degrees of freedom. Since large values of F suggest that $\sigma_1^2 > \sigma_2^2$, while small values of F suggest that $\sigma_1^2 < \sigma_2^2$, we take as the critical region R of our test the event

$$R = [\{F > c_1\} \text{ or } \{F < c_2\}]$$

that is, we agree to reject H_0 if F is either *too large* or *too small*. Since $P[\{F > c_1\} \text{ or } \{F < c_2\}] = P\{F > c_1\} + P\{F < c_2\}$, we can choose c_1 and c_2 for a test of level α by making each of these probabilities under H_0 equal to $\alpha/2$,

$$P\{F_{\nu_1, \nu_2} > c_1\} = P\{F_{\nu_1, \nu_2} < c_2\} = \frac{\alpha}{2}$$

where $\nu_1 = n_1 - 1$ and $\nu_2 = n_2 - 1$. Therefore, $c_1 = F_{\nu_1, \nu_2, \alpha/2}$, and since

$$P\{F_{\nu_1, \nu_2} < c_2\} = P\left\{\frac{1}{F_{\nu_1, \nu_2}} > \frac{1}{c_2}\right\} = P\left\{F_{\nu_2, \nu_1} > \frac{1}{c_2}\right\}$$

it follows that

$$\frac{1}{c_2} = F_{\nu_2, \nu_1, \alpha/2} \qquad c_2 = \frac{1}{F_{\nu_2, \nu_1, \alpha/2}},$$

Our test thus becomes: reject H_0 if $F = s_1^2/s_2^2$ is either

$$> F_{\nu_1, \nu_2, \alpha/2} \quad \text{or} \quad < \frac{1}{F_{\nu_2, \nu_1, \alpha/2}} \qquad (\nu_i = n_i - 1; \ i = 1,2)$$

In the former case we assert that $\sigma_1^2 > \sigma_2^2$, and in the latter case that $\sigma_1^2 < \sigma_2^2$. The error probability when $\sigma_1^2 \neq \sigma_2^2$ is then at most $\alpha/2$. Tests of $H_0 : \sigma_1^2 \leq \sigma_2^2$ vs $H_1 : \sigma_1^2 > \sigma_2^2$, or of $H_0 : \sigma_1^2 \geq \sigma_2^2$ vs $H_1 : \sigma_1^2 < \sigma_2^2$, involve determining the cut-off points by using only one tail of the F distribution. A summary of these tests is given in table 7.5.

TABLE 7.5
Tests for Equality of Variances Based on Two Independent Samples from Normal Populations

Let $F_{\nu_1, \nu_2, \alpha}$ be defined by $P\{F_{\nu_1, \nu_2} > F_{\nu_1, \nu_2, \alpha}\} = \alpha$.

H_0	H_1	Critical region: reject H_0 if
$\sigma_1^2 = \sigma_2^2$	$\sigma_1^2 \neq \sigma_2^2$	$F = \dfrac{s_1^2}{s_2^2} > F_{n_1-1, n_2-1, \alpha/2}$ (assert $\sigma_1^2 > \sigma_2^2$) or $\quad < \dfrac{1}{F_{n_2-1, n_1-1, \alpha/2}}$ (assert $\sigma_1^2 < \sigma_2^2$)
$\sigma_1^2 \leq \sigma_2^2$	$\sigma_1^2 > \sigma_2^2$	$F = \dfrac{s_1^2}{s_2^2} > F_{n_1-1, n_2-1, \alpha}$
$\sigma_1^2 \geq \sigma_2^2$	$\sigma_1^2 < \sigma_2^2$	$F = \dfrac{s_1^2}{s_2^2} < \dfrac{1}{F_{n_2-1, n_1-1, \alpha}}$

Example 14

A zoologist wants to use mice whose weights at birth have low variability. Two different strains of mice are available. She takes at random 10 mice from strain 1 and 16 mice from strain 2, and decides to test at level $\alpha = .02$ the null hypothesis that the two strains have equal variance of birth weights. If she concludes that they do not, she will obtain her experimental mice from the strain with the lower estimated variability, if not, she will use whichever strain is more convenient to obtain.

The appropriate test here is that for $H_o : \sigma_1^2 = \sigma_2^2$ vs $H_1 : \sigma_1^2 \neq \sigma_2^2$ in table 7.5. Suppose that the samples yield $s_1 = .36$ grams and $s_2 = .87$ grams. Do they show evidence of a difference in variability significant at level $\alpha = .02$?

For $\alpha = .02$, $n_1 - 1 = 9$, $n_2 - 1 = 15$, the F values are $F_{9, 15, .01} = 3.89$ and $1/F_{15, 9, .01} = 1/496 = .20$. Thus, H_0 (equality of variances) would be rejected if

$$F = \frac{s_1^2}{s_2^2} > 3.89 \text{ or } < .20$$

Using the sample results, $F = (.36/.87)^2 = .17$. Since $.17 < .20$, she rejects H_0 and concludes that $\sigma_1^2 \neq \sigma_2^2$. Since $s_1^2 < s_2^2$, she uses mice of strain 1. (The probability that $s_1^2/s_2^2 < .20$ if in fact $\sigma_1^2 \geq \sigma_2^2$ is at most .01, its value when $\sigma_1^2 = \sigma_2^2$.)

A preliminary test of $H_0 : \sigma_1^2 = \sigma_2^2$ vs $H_1 : \sigma_1^2 \neq \sigma_2^2$ can in principle be carried out to validate the hypothesis of equality of variances in the procedures of section 7.5. If that hypothesis is not valid, one is confronted with what is known as the *Behrens-Fisher problem*. Approximate inference procedures for $\mu_1 - \mu_2$ are available in this case.

Confidence intervals for the ratio σ_1/σ_2 of two standard deviations can be obtained by using the F distribution of $(s_1^2/\sigma_1^2)/(s_2^2/\sigma_2^2)$. For details see problems 7 to 9 below.

PROBLEMS 7.8

1. For the F distribution with $v_1 = 8$ and $v_2 = 5$, find c to make (a) $P(F > c) = .01$; (b) $P(F > c) = .05$; and (c) $P(F < c) = .05$.

2. For the F distribution with $v_1 = 15$ and $v_2 = 10$, find c to make (a) $P(F > c) = .05$; (b) $P(F < c) = .01$; and (c) $P(F < c) = .05$.

3. Independent samples of $n_1 = 10$ and $n_2 = 4$ are drawn from two normal populations with the same variance. Let s_1^2 and s_2^2 be the variances of the two samples. Find c to make (a) $P(s_1^2 > c \, s_2^2) = .01$; (b) $P(s_1 < c \, s_2) = .05$; and (c) $P(s_1^2 < c \, s_2^2) = .99$

4. Two independent samples of sizes $n_1 = 18$ and $n_2 = 23$ are drawn from two normal populations with the same variance. Let s_1 and s_2 be the standard deviations of the two samples. Find c to make (a) $P(s_1 < c\, s_2) = .05$; (b) $P(s_1^2 > c\, s_2^2) = .01$; and (c) $P(s_1 > c\, s_2) = .95$.

5. An experimental psychologist wishes to use students from two different colleges for an experiment on IQ's. Before conducting the experiment she wants to determine if IQ's of students at the two colleges have the same amount of variability. The sample results are

$$n_1 = 10 \qquad s_1^2 = 14.7$$
$$n_2 = 15 \qquad s_2^2 = 18.9$$

State the null and alternative hypotheses, rejection region, and conclusion of the test the psychologist should use. Use level $\alpha = .10$.

6. An economist wishes to compare the variability in incomes between men and women employed full time in Indiana. The sample results are:

$$\text{Men: } n_1 = 25; \ s_1 = \$1984$$
$$\text{Women: } n_2 = 18; \ s_2 = \$1108$$

Based on these data, test, at level $\alpha = .01$, the hypothesis that there is no difference in variability against the alternative that men's incomes are more variable than women's. State the null and alternative hypotheses, the rejection region, and the conclusion of the appropriate test.

7. Let s_1^2 and s_2^2 be the variances of random samples from two independent normal populations of sizes n_1 and n_2 respectively, with respective variances σ_1^2 and σ_2^2.

a. State the distribution of $F = (s_1^2/\sigma_1^2)/(s_2^2/\sigma_2^2)$

b. Using (a), find values a and b such that:

(i) $P\left(\dfrac{\sigma_1^2}{\sigma_2^2} \leq a\, \dfrac{s_1^2}{s_2^2}\right) = .01$

(ii) $P\left(\dfrac{\sigma_1^2}{\sigma_2^2} \geq b\, \dfrac{s_1^2}{s_2^2}\right) = .01$

c. By combining statements (i) and (ii) in (b), show that

$$P\left(a\, \frac{s_1^2}{s_2^2} < \frac{\sigma_1^2}{\sigma_2^2} < b\, \frac{s_1^2}{s_2^2}\right) = .98$$

that is, the interval $\left(a\, \dfrac{s_1^2}{s_2^2}, \ b\, \dfrac{s_1^2}{s_2^2}\right)$ constitutes a 98% confidence interval for σ_1^2/σ_2^2.

8. Using the results of problem 7, find a 98% confidence interval for σ_1^2/σ_2^2 in problems 5 and 6.

9. Develop results similar to that of problem 7 where (i) and (ii) in (b) are computed with .05 replacing .01. Based on these results, give a 90% confidence interval for σ_1^2/σ_2^2 in problems 5 and 6.

The Analysis of Variance

8 The Analysis of Variance

8.1 One-Way Analysis of Variance

In chapter 7 we showed how to test whether the means μ_1, μ_2 of two normal populations are the same, assuming that the population variances are equal. We now generalize this to the problem of testing whether the means $\mu_1, \ldots, \mu_I$ of $I > 2$ normal populations are all the same, again assuming that the population variances are equal. The null hypothesis to be tested is thus

$$H_0 : \mu_1 = \mu_2 = \ldots = \mu_I \tag{1}$$

The data available for the test are the values of the $n = n_1 + \ldots + n_I$ random variables x_{ij} = the jth observation from the ith population ($i = 1, \ldots, I$ and $j = 1, \ldots, n_i$, where n_i is the size of the sample from the ith population.) It is assumed that the x_{ij} are normally distributed and mutually independent, with μ_i = mean value of ith population, σ^2 = common variance of all I populations. The true values of the μ_i and of σ^2 are unknown.

Example 1
Three brands G_1, G_2, G_3 of gasoline are to be tested for mileage, using 20 more or less identical motors adjusted to run at a fixed speed. Of these, seven motors are randomly chosen to be used with gasoline G_1, seven are randomly assigned to gasoline G_2, and six to gasoline

G_3. Each motor runs with five gallons of gasoline until it is out of fuel, and the number of minutes of running time is recorded. The observed sample values x_{ij} are given in table 8.1.

Question: Are the sample means $\bar{x}_1$, $\bar{x}_2$, $\bar{x}_3$ *sufficiently* different (in view of the considerable variation *within* each sample) to justify asserting that the three brands of gasoline do not all give equal mean mileages under the test conditions?

TABLE 8.1
Running Times for Three Brands of Gasoline

Population G_i	G_1	G_2	G_3
Observed sample values $x_{i1}, \ldots, x_{in_i}$	$x_{11} = 74.4$ $x_{12} = 87.0$ $x_{13} = 88.8$ $x_{14} = 79.4$ $x_{15} = 73.3$ $x_{16} = 85.2$ $x_{17} = 72.6$	$x_{21} = 80.2$ $x_{22} = 69.8$ $x_{23} = 79.3$ $x_{24} = 71.2$ $x_{25} = 87.1$ $x_{26} = 85.4$ $x_{27} = 70.9$	$x_{31} = 76.3$ $x_{32} = 60.7$ $x_{33} = 76.2$ $x_{34} = 72.3$ $x_{35} = 57.5$ $x_{36} = 70.4$
$\bar{x}_i = \dfrac{1}{n_i} \displaystyle\sum_{j=1}^{n_i} x_{ij}$	$\dfrac{560.7}{7}$ $= 80.1(\bar{x}_1)$	$\dfrac{543.9}{7}$ $= 77.7(\bar{x}_2)$	$\dfrac{413.4}{6}$ $= 68.9(\bar{x}_3)$
$s_i^2 = \dfrac{1}{n_i - 1} \displaystyle\sum_{j=1}^{n_i} (x_{ij} - \bar{x}_i)^2$	$\dfrac{284.78}{6}$ $= 47.463(s_1^2)$	$\dfrac{307.36}{6}$ $= 51.227(s_2^2)$	$\dfrac{319.06}{5}$ $= 63.812(s_3^2)$

Example 2

Four methods M_1, M_2, M_3, M_4 of teaching reading to first graders are tested for effectiveness. A group of 24 students is selected, all with about the same reading ability as measured by a standard test at the beginning of the school year. The 24 students are then randomly assigned to the four different methods, six to each method. They are all taught by the same teacher, each group using its method exclusively for a year. At the end of the year another version of the reading ability test is administered, and the *improvement** in each student's score is recorded. Does the evidence in table 8.2 below justify asserting that

---

*To eliminate the effect of the difference in scores at the beginning of the year for the 24 randomly assigned students.

the four methods do not all produce the same mean improvement effects under the conditions of the experiment?

TABLE 8.2
Improvements in Reading Ability for Four Methods of Teaching

Population M_i	M_1	M_2	M_3	M_4
Observed sample values $x_{i1}, \ldots, x_{in_i}$	24 13 18 24 16 23	13 21 11 23 28 18	21 13 26 23 16 12	27 30 24 29 26 34
$\bar{x}_i = \dfrac{1}{n_i} \displaystyle\sum_{j=1}^{n_i} x_{ij}$	$19.67 = \dfrac{118}{6}$	$19 = \dfrac{114}{6}$	$18.5 = \dfrac{111}{6}$	$28.33 = \dfrac{170}{6}$
$s_i^2 = \dfrac{1}{n_i - 1} \displaystyle\sum_{j=1}^{n_i} (x_{ij} - \bar{x}_i)^2$	21.87	40.40	32.30	12.27

In the *general case* of a *one-way analysis of variance*, so-called because the different populations involve variation in only one factor (brand of gasoline in example 1, method of teaching in example 2), we compute the following quantities from the observed values x_{ij}:

$$\bar{x}_i = \frac{1}{n_i} \sum_{j=1}^{n_i} x_{ij} = \text{sample mean of } i\text{th population}$$

$$s_i^2 = \frac{1}{n_i - 1} \sum_{j=1}^{n_i} (x_{ij} - \bar{x}_i)^2 = \text{sample variance of } i\text{th population}$$

$$\bar{x} = \frac{1}{n} \sum_{i=1}^{I} \sum_{j=1}^{n_i} x_{ij} = \frac{1}{n} \sum_{i=1}^{I} n_i \bar{x}_i = \begin{array}{l}\text{grand sample mean of all } n \\ \text{observations}\end{array}$$

$$SS_E = \sum_{i=1}^{I} (n_i - 1) s_i^2 = \begin{array}{l}\text{``error'' or ``within populations'' sum} \\ \text{of squares}\end{array}$$

$$SS_T = \sum_{i=1}^{I} n_i (\bar{x}_i - \bar{x})^2 = \begin{array}{l}\text{``treatment'' or ``among populations''} \\ \text{sum of squares}\end{array}$$

$$F = \frac{SS_T/(I - 1)}{SS_E/(n - I)} = \text{``F ratio''}$$

We shall see in the following section that the denominator and numerator of F are such that

a. Whether the population mean values μ_i are equal or not, the mean value of the denominator $SS_E/(n - I)$ is σ^2.

b. The mean value of the numerator $SS_T/(I - 1)$ is $\geq \sigma^2$, with equality if and only if H_0 is true.

We therefore take as our critical region for rejecting H_0 the event $\{F > c\}$, where c is some constant greater than 1, since large values of F are more likely to occur when H_0 is false than when H_0 is true. To specify the value of c we use the fact that the numerator and denominator of F can be shown to be independent random variables such that

c. SS_E/σ^2 has a chi-squared distribution, with $n - I$ d.f., and

d. when H_0 is true, SS_T/σ^2 also has a chi-squared distribution, with $I - 1$ d.f.

Hence, from definition 7.4 and theorem 7.6, *under* H_0 *the* ratio

$$F = \frac{SS_T/(I - 1)}{SS_E/(n - I)} = \frac{SS_T/[\sigma^2(I - 1)]}{SS_E/[\sigma^2(n - I)]}$$

has an F *distribution with* $(I - 1, n - I)$ *d.f., irrespective of the value of σ^2 and of the assumed common value of the μ_i. Accordingly, if $F_{I-1, n-I, \alpha}$ denotes that number which leaves probability α to the right of it for the F distribution with $(I - 1, n - I)$ d.f., then for $c = F_{I-1, n-I, \alpha}$ the event $\{F > c\}$ will have a desired small probability α when H_0 is true. We thus obtain

The F *test of level* α *for equality of population means in one-way analysis of variance:*

$$\text{Reject } H_0 : \mu_1 = \mu_2 = \ldots = \mu_I \text{ if } F > F_{I-1, n-I, \alpha} \tag{2}$$

The statistics in the denominator and numerator of F are called *mean squares:*

$$MS_E = \frac{SS_E}{n - I} = \text{mean square due to error} \tag{3}$$

$$MS_T = \frac{SS_T}{I - 1} = \text{mean square due to treatments} \tag{4}$$

We shall obtain the mean values of MS_E and MS_T in the next section.

To carry out the analysis of variance test (2) we construct table 8.3, the analysis of variance table.

TABLE 8.3
The One-Way Analysis of Variance

Source of variation	Degrees of freedom	Sum of squares	Mean square	F ratio
Treatments	$I - 1$	SS_T	$MS_T = \dfrac{SS_T}{I - 1}$	$F = \dfrac{MS_T}{MS_E}$
Error	$n - I$	SS_E	$MS_E = \dfrac{SS_E}{n - I}$	

For the data of table 8.1, we find by computation

TABLE 8.4
Analysis of Variance Table for Example 1

Source of variation	Degrees of freedom	Sum of squares	Mean square	F ratio
Treatments (gasolines)	2	440.16	220.08	4.10
Error	17	911.20	53.60	$F_{2, 17, .05} = 3.59$

For table 8.2, we have

TABLE 8.5
Analysis of Variance Table for Example 2

Source of variation	Degrees of freedom	Sum of squares	Mean square	F ratio
Treatments (teaching methods)	3	391.11	130.37	4.27
Error	20	534.20	26.71	$F_{.3, 20, .05} = 4.88$

The values $F_{2, 17, .05} = 3.59$ and $F_{3, 20, .05} = 3.10$ are obtained from appendix table 9. In both cases, the null hypothesis H_0 will be rejected at the .05 level of significance by the test (2), since the probability of obtaining such a large value of F is $< .05$ when H_0 is true.

PROBLEMS 8.1

1. Three brands of sausages are tested for fat content. The data for samples of five sausages of each brand are

Brand	1	2	3
Fat content (%)	32	39	28
	34	44	31
	39	40	25
	33	33	36
	41	45	33

a. Compute the sample means and variances for each brand.
b. Give the analysis of variance table for these data.
c. Test the hypothesis of the equality of the mean values of the fat content percentages for the three brands of sausages at the level of significance $\alpha = .05$. State your conclusion.

2. A random sample of six students from each undergraduate year at the University of Wisconsin, Whitewater, gave the following one-year grade point averages:

Freshman	Sophomore	Junior	Senior
2.21	3.31	2.73	3.26
1.86	2.25	2.95	2.87
2.89	2.69	2.86	2.96
2.06	2.28	2.17	3.54
1.96	2.72	3.44	2.80
2.34	2.59	2.65	2.45

a. Compute the sample means and variances for each class.
b. Give the analysis of variance table for these data.
c. Test the hypothesis of the equality of means of the grade point averages for the four classes at the level of significance $\alpha = .05$. State your conclusion.

3. The following data represent the acreage of farms in samples from three Midwestern states.

Wisconsin	Michigan	Minnesota
195	168	340
120	110	254
160	245	190
254	97	296
142	148	230
220	224	
211	160	
146	113	
	165	
	90	

a. Compute the sample means and variances for the above data.
b. Give the analysis of variance table for these data.
c. Test the hypothesis of equality of farm acreage mean sizes in these three states at the level of significance $\alpha = .01$. State your conclusion.

4. A consumer group studying the sales of Corvairs in Columbus, Ohio, obtained the following sample data on the costs of standard Corvairs at five dealers in the city.

I	II	III	IV	V
2848	2820	2655	3040	2742
2490	2944	2410	2750	2960
2630	2765	2350	2886	
	2490	2871		
	2631	2554		
		2614		
		2550		

a. Compute the sample means and variances for the above data.
b. Give the analysis of variance table for these data.
c. Test the hypothesis of equality of the mean costs of Corvairs for the dealers in Columbus at the level of significance $\alpha = .05$. State your conclusion.

8.2 Motivation of the F Test: The Total Sum of Squares and Its Decomposition

In the general one-way analysis of variance, if SS denotes the *total squared variation of all the* $n = n_1 + \ldots + n_I$ *observations* x_{ij} *about their global average* $\bar{x}$, then by algebra

$$SS = \sum_{i=1}^{I} \sum_{j=1}^{n_i} (x_{ij} - \bar{x})^2 \tag{5}$$

$$= \sum_i \sum_j [(x_{ij} - \bar{x}_i) + (\bar{x}_i - \bar{x})]^2$$

$$= \sum_i \sum_j (x_{ij} - \bar{x}_i)^2 + \sum_i \sum_j (\bar{x}_i - \bar{x})^2 + 2 \sum_i \sum_j (x_{ij} - \bar{x}_i)(\bar{x}_i - \bar{x})$$

Now, the last term of (5) is 0, since it is equal to

$$\sum_i \left\{ (\bar{x}_i - \bar{x}) \sum_j (x_{ij} - \bar{x}_i) \right\} = \sum_i \left\{ (\bar{x}_i - \bar{x})(n_i \bar{x}_i - n_i \bar{x}_i) \right\}$$

$$= \sum_i \left\{ (\bar{x}_i - \bar{x}) \cdot 0 \right\} = 0$$

Moreover, the first two terms reduce to

$$\sum_i \sum_j (x_{ij} - \bar{x}_i)^2 = \sum_i (n_i - 1)s_i^2 = SS_E$$

$$\sum_i \sum_j (\bar{x}_i - \bar{x})^2 = \sum_i n_i(\bar{x}_i - \bar{x})^2 = SS_T$$

We therefore have the relation

$$SS = SS_E + SS_T \tag{6}$$

which decomposes the "total" sum of squares SS into two parts:

SS_E, the sum of squares of the x_{ij} about their individual sample means $\bar{x}_i$.

SS_T, the weighted sum of squares of the individual sample means $\bar{x}_i$ about the grand sample mean $\bar{x}$.

The probability distribution of SS_E does not depend on the values μ_i, since the difference $x_{ij} - \bar{x}_i$ is unaffected by the addition of any constant to the values $x_{i1}, \ldots, x_{in_i}$. In fact, whatever the values of $\mu_1, \ldots, \mu_I$, we have by the assumption (3) for the mean values of SS_E and MS_E

$$m.v.(SS_E) = m.v.\left(\sum_i (n_i - 1)s_i^2\right) = \sum_i (n_i - 1)\sigma^2 = (n - I)\sigma^2 \tag{7}$$

so that

$$m.v.(MS_E) = m.v.\left(\frac{SS_E}{n - I}\right) = \sigma^2$$

whether H_0 *is true or not.* The mean value of SS_T, however, does depend on the values of the μ_i. In fact, since

$$SS_T = \sum_i n_i[(\bar{x}_i - \bar{x})^2] = \sum_i n_i\{\bar{x}_i^2 - 2\bar{x}\,\bar{x}_i + \bar{x}^2\}$$

$$= \sum_i n_i\bar{x}_i^2 - 2\bar{x}\sum_i n_i\bar{x}_i + n\bar{x}^2$$

$$= \sum_i n_i\bar{x}_i^2 - 2\bar{x}\cdot n\bar{x} + n\bar{x}^2 = \sum_i n_i\bar{x}_i^2 - n\bar{x}^2$$

it follows that

$$m.v.(SS_T) = \sum_i n_i\,\mu_{\bar{x}_i^2} - n(\mu_{\bar{x}^2})$$

$$= \sum_i n_i\{\sigma_{\bar{x}_i}^2 + (\mu_{\bar{x}_i})^2\} - n\{\sigma_{\bar{x}}^2 + (\mu_{\bar{x}})^2\}$$

$$= \sum_i n_i\left\{\frac{\sigma^2}{n_i} + \mu_i^2\right\} - n\left\{\frac{\sigma^2}{n} + \left(\frac{1}{n}\sum_i n_i\mu_i\right)^2\right\}$$

$$= \sum_i \sigma^2 + \sum_i n_i\mu_i^2 - \sigma^2 - \frac{1}{n}\left(\sum_i n_i\mu_i\right)^2$$

$$= (I-1)\sigma^2 + \sum_i n_i\mu_i^2 - \frac{1}{n}\left(\sum_i n_i\mu_i\right)^2$$

$$= (I-1)\sigma^2 + \sum_i n_i(\mu_i - \bar{\mu})^2$$

where by definition we have put

$$\bar{\mu} = \frac{1}{n}\sum_i n_i\mu_i = \text{weighted average of the population mean values.}$$

The term $\sum_i n_i (\mu_i - \bar{\mu})^2$ is always ≥ 0, and is 0 only when $\mu_i = \bar{\mu}$

for every $i = 1, \ldots, I$; that is, only when all the μ_i are equal. Hence

$$m.v.(MS_T) = m.v.\left(\frac{SS_T}{I-1}\right) = \sigma^2 + \frac{1}{I-1}\sum_i n_i(\mu_i - \bar{\mu})^2$$

$$\begin{cases} = \sigma^2 \text{ if } H_0 \text{ is true} \\ > \sigma^2 \text{ if } H_0 \text{ is false} \end{cases} \qquad (8)$$

Thus

$$F = \frac{(MS_T/\sigma^2)}{(MS_E/\sigma^2)} \qquad (9)$$

is the ratio of two quantities such that the ratio of their *mean values* is

$$\frac{m.v.(MS_T/\sigma^2)}{m.v.(MS_E/\sigma^2)} = 1 + \frac{1}{(I-1)\sigma^2}\sum_i n_i(\mu_i - \bar{\mu})^2 \qquad (10)$$

If all sample sizes n_i are large then both the numerator and denominator of (9) will with high probability be close to their respective mean values and hence F itself will be close to (10), which is 1 when H_0 is true and > 1 when H_0 is false. *The F statistic is in fact an estimate of the value* (10). For given values n_i of the sample sizes, (10) depends on the ratio

$$\frac{\sum_i n_i(\mu_i - \bar{\mu})^2}{\sigma^2} \qquad (11)$$

which measures the departure of the μ's from equality, compared to the common variance σ^2 of the individual observations. When this ratio is large the F test will reject H_0 with high probability.

It must be emphasized that when the F test (2) rejects H_0 it *merely asserts that the μ's are not all equal* (since if they were equal, a value of F greater than $F_{I-1, n-I, \alpha}$ would occur only about 100α percent of the time). Now, it really makes very little sense to test the null hypothesis $H_0 : \mu_1 = \mu_2 = \ldots = \mu_I$ of *strict equality* of $I \geq 2$ population mean values in any practical situation. For, unless the I treatments (brands of gasoline, teaching methods, and so on) differ in name only, there will always be *some* difference between the μ's, and *with sufficiently large sample sizes* n_i *the F test will be almost certain to reject* H_0 *even if the differences among the μ's are negligible for all practical purposes*. In other words, an F test may be highly "significant" ($F > F_{I-1, n-I, \alpha}$ with $\alpha = .01$, say) of a *practically* insignificant difference among the μ's. Hence, why bother to test the hypothesis H_0, which we know from the beginning to be false?

One answer to this question is that the F test, which rejects H_0 with small probability α when it is true, will reject H_0 with probability only a little greater than α when H_0 is only "slightly" false; that is, when the μ's are *nearly* equal. (The actual "power function" of the F test—its probability of rejecting H_0—depends on the parameter (11), and can be found by consulting available tables.) We should, however, avoid using the F test on samples so large that H_0 will have a high probability of being rejected even though it may be sufficiently true for all practical purposes.

A much more satisfactory procedure is to replace the problem of *testing* by one of *confidence interval estimation* of the differences $\mu_i - \mu_j$ of the population means. This we shall do in the next section for the case of a one-way analysis of variance. The F test itself must be regarded as a very crude and incomplete way of presenting the total information available in an analysis of variance problem.

PROBLEMS 8.2

1. Suppose that in problem 1 of section 8.1 the data for brand i come from a normal distribution with mean value μ_i and variance 18, $i = 1, 2, 3$ where $\mu_1 = 36$, $\mu_2 = 40$, and $\mu_3 = 30$. Find m.v. (MS_T), m.v.(MS_E), and the ratio (10) in this situation. Would one expect the F test to be significant at level $\alpha = .05$?

2. Suppose that in problem 3 of section 8.1 the samples are from a normal distribution with $\sigma = 52$ and mean values given by

State	Sample size	Population mean value
Wisconsin	$n_1 = 8$	$\mu_1 = 180$
Michigan	$n_2 = 10$	$\mu_2 = 153$
Minnesota	$n_3 = 5$	$\mu_3 = 265$

Find m.v.(MS_T), m.v.(MS_E), and the ratio (10) for this situation. Would one expect the F test to be significant at level $\alpha = .01$?

8.3 Multiple Comparison of Means

When the F test in a one-way analysis of variance rejects the null hypothesis $H_0: \mu_1 = \ldots = \mu_I$, it asserts only that the μ's are not all equal. The question of *how much* the μ's differ from each other is not answered by the F test. Now, instead of merely testing H_0, let us ask, for the data in table 8.1 (with $\bar{x}_1 = 80.1$, $\bar{x}_2 = 77.7$, and $\bar{x}_3 = 68.9$), whether there is enough evidence to say with assurance that $\mu_1 > \mu_3$, $\mu_2 > \mu_3$, or $\mu_1 > \mu_2$? Again, the data in table 8.2 (with $\bar{x}_1 = 19.67$, $\bar{x}_2 = 19$, $\bar{x}_3 = 18.5$, and $\bar{x}_4 = 28.33$) suggest that the method M_1 of teaching reading is definitely better than any of the other three methods. With what assurance can this be asserted?

When (as in example 2) *the number of observations is the same for each treatment*, we can use a method proposed by J. W. Tukey for obtaining *simultaneous confidence intervals for the differences* $\mu_i - \mu_j$ *of each pair of population mean values*. Let $m = n_1 = \ldots = n_I$ be the common sample size for each treatment, so that the total sample size is $n = mI$ and the mean square due to error is

$$s^2 = MS_E = \frac{1}{I(m-1)} \sum_{i=1}^{I} (m-1)s_i^2 \tag{12}$$

The (unobservable) quantity

$$Q = \text{maximum for all pairs } i \neq i' \text{ of the } \binom{I}{2} = I(I-1)/2 \text{ quantities}$$

$$\frac{|(\bar{x}_i - \mu_i) - (\bar{x}_{i'} - \mu_{i'})|}{s/\sqrt{m}}$$

can be shown to have a distribution (the "Studentized range distribution") which depends only on I and m. In fact, Q will have a "Q distribution with I degrees of freedom for the numerator and $I(m-1)$ d.f. for the denominator," and appendix table 10 gives the value $Q_{I, I(m-1), \alpha}$, which is such that $P\{Q < Q_{I, I(m-1), \alpha}\} = 1 - \alpha$. It can be shown by simple algebra that the event $\{Q < Q_{I, I(m-1), \alpha}\}$ is equivalent to the event that *for every* $i \neq i'$

$$(\bar{x}_i - \bar{x}_{i'}) - Q_{I, I(m-1), \alpha} \cdot \frac{s}{\sqrt{m}} < \mu_i - \mu_{i'} < (\bar{x}_i - \bar{x}_{i'}) \tag{13}$$

$$+ Q_{I, I(m-1), \alpha} \cdot \frac{s}{\sqrt{m}}$$

Hence with probability $1 - \alpha$ *all of the statements* (13) *will be true.*

The virtue of this procedure is that we compare all pairs of means μ_i, $\mu_{i'}$ simultaneously, and that $100(1 - \alpha)$ percent of the time *all* the confidence interval statements (13) will be true. (No preliminary F test of H_0 need be made; in fact, it would be improper to make the assertions (13) only when H_0 is rejected at level α by the F test, since in so doing the (conditional) probability that all the statements 13 will hold would no longer be $1 - \alpha$.)

For the data of example 2 we have

$$s = \sqrt{MS_E} = \sqrt{26.71} = 5.168$$

with $m = 6$ and $I = 4$, so that from appendix table 10 with $\alpha = .05$

$$Q_{I,I(m-1),\alpha} = Q_{4,20,.05} = 3.96$$

Hence, in the simultaneous confidence intervals (13)

$$Q_{I,I(m-1),\alpha} \cdot \frac{s}{\sqrt{m}} = \frac{(3.96)(5.168)}{\sqrt{6}} = 8.35$$

and using the values $\bar{x}_i - \bar{x}_{i'}$ from table 8.2 we construct the following six simultaneous confidence intervals:

Unknown population mean difference $\mu_i - \mu_{i'}$	Observed sample mean difference $\bar{x}_i - \bar{x}_{i'}$	Lower confidence limit $(\bar{x}_i - \bar{x}_{i'}) - 8.35$	Upper confidence limit $(\bar{x}_i - \bar{x}_{i'}) + 8.35$
$\mu_1 - \mu_2$	$19.67 - 19 = .67$	-7.68	9.02
$\mu_1 - \mu_3$	$19.67 - 18.5 = 1.17$	-7.18	9.52
$\mu_1 - \mu_4$	$19.67 - 28.33 = -8.66$	$-17.01*$	$-.31*$
$\mu_2 - \mu_3$	$19.00 - 18.5 = .5$	-7.85	8.85
$\mu_2 - \mu_4$	$19.00 - 28.33 = -9.33$	$-17.68*$	$-.98*$
$\mu_3 - \mu_4$	$18.50 - 28.33 = -9.83$	$-18.18*$	$-1.48*$

The only confidence intervals not containing zero are the three starred ones. Since these three intervals lie to the left of zero, we can assert that

$$\mu_4 > \mu_1, \ \mu_4 > \mu_2, \text{ and } \mu_4 > \mu_3$$

and hence that method M_4 has a mean reading performance increase μ_4 greater than that of either M_1, M_2, or M_3. Since the three confidence intervals for $\mu_1 - \mu_2$, $\mu_1 - \mu_3$, and $\mu_2 - \mu_3$ all contain zero, we cannot assert that *these* comparisons of pairs are sufficient to establish the sign of the difference in population means. Since the upper confidence limit for $\mu_1 - \mu_4$ is close to zero we can claim with 95% confidence that $\mu_4 > \mu_1$. If the experiment had been conducted with a somewhat smaller sample of students, such a conclusion may not have been reached.

When the sample sizes are not equal, a method introduced by H. Scheffé can be used to derive simultaneous multiple comparisons.

Note: If our object before the samples were taken had been only to compare μ_4 and μ_1, say, it would have been legitimate to use the statistic

$$t = \frac{(\bar{x}_4 - \mu_4) - (\bar{x}_1 - \mu_1)}{s\sqrt{\dfrac{1}{n_1} + \dfrac{1}{n_4}}}$$

which has a t distribution with 20 d.f., and yields the 95% confidence interval for $\mu_4 - \mu_1$ with $t_{.025, 20} = 2.086$ given by $2.44 = 8.66 - 6.22 < \mu_4 - \mu_1 < 8.66 + 6.22 = 14.88$, since $t_{.025, 20}\, s\sqrt{1/n_1 + 1/n_4} = (2.086)$ $(5.168)\sqrt{1/6 + 1/6} = 6.22$. We would therefore have been able to say with 95% confidence that $\mu_4 > \mu_1$. However, although any *preassigned* difference $\mu_i - \mu_{i'}$ could in this manner be enclosed in a 95% confidence interval smaller than that obtained by Tukey's method, the probability that *all* six of the differences $\mu_i - \mu_{i'}$ would be within such 95% confidence intervals would be considerably less than the 95% associated with the simultaneous intervals (13).

PROBLEMS 8.3

1. For the data of problem 1, section 8.1, find the simultaneous confidence intervals (13) with $\alpha = .05$. Which means are different at level $\alpha = .05$?

2. For the data of problem 2, section 8.1, find the simultaneous confidence intervals (13) with $\alpha = .05$. Which means are different at level $\alpha = .05$?

3. In problem 1, section 8.1, construct the confidence interval for $\mu_3 - \mu_2$ by using a t statistic with confidence coefficient $1 - \alpha = .95$, and compare it with the simultaneous interval for $\mu_3 - \mu_2$ given by problem 1.

4. In problem 2, section 8.1, construct the confidence interval for $\mu_4 - \mu_1$ (μ_4 = mean for seniors, μ_1 = mean for freshmen), by using a t statistic with the confidence coefficient $1 - \alpha = .95$, and compare it with the simultaneous interval for $\mu_4 - \mu_1$ given by problem 2.

8.4 Two-Way Analysis of Variance

The analysis of variance can be extended to the case in which there are two different factors in the experiment. For example, in table 8.1

besides having three brands of gasoline G_1, G_2, G_3, we might also have four different additives A_1, A_2, A_3, A_4 that we could use in combination with each gasoline. An experiment could then be conducted in which a certain number of motors are run with five gallons of each gasoline and with each additive present. The mileages obtained would then depend on *two* factors: the kind of gasoline G_1, G_2, G_3 and the additive A_1, A_2, A_3, A_4. We might wish then to test hypotheses about differences in population means due (1) to the gasoline, or (2) to the additive, or (3) to the interaction of the gasoline with the additive. Consider the following example.

Example 3
A platelet is a cell component of blood that plays an important role in blood coagulation. The normal platelet count in humans is between 200,000 to 400,000 per cc of blood. Certain drugs used in treating cancer are known to lower the platelet count. Suppose that three different drugs D_1, D_2, D_3 are used at three different dosage levels L_1, L_2, L_3 on four patients each. Suppose each patient has a platelet count of approximately 300,000 before treatment. We record this count as 300 (300 $\times$ 1000). After treatment, the counts for the 36 patients are taken (see table 8.6). Without a systematic method of analysis little can be inferred from these data because of the inevitable random variation within each group.

TABLE 8.6
Platelet Counts

Dosage level i (factor A)	Drug j (factor B)		
	D_1	D_2	D_3
light L_1	245	248	355
	302	213	298
	289	283	218
	252	255	315
medium L_2	246	278	253
	250	194	263
	323	278	326
	235	298	234
heavy L_3	206	228	198
	254	241	190
	137	164	165
	237	191	231

In table 8.6 each cell has $K = 4$ observations. For example, drug

D_1 was administered at a light level L_1 to four patients chosen at random among those who had initial platelet counts of approximately 300. Given the above data, what conclusions can we draw about the effect of the various levels, the various drugs, and the interactions between these two factors? We shall take the following model as the basis for our analysis.

The Model: Let $\{x_{ij1}, \ldots, x_{ijK}\}$ $(i = 1, \ldots, I; j = 1, \ldots, J)$ be independent samples, each of size K, from populations with means μ_{ij} and a common variance σ^2. For example, x_{124} is the fourth observation at factor A, level 1, and factor B, level 2. We assume $I \geq 2$, $J \geq 2$ and $K \geq 2$. We define

$$\bar{\mu}_{i.} = \frac{1}{J} \sum_{j=1}^{J} \mu_{ij}, \ \bar{\mu}_{.j} = \frac{1}{I} \sum_{i=1}^{I} \mu_{ij}$$

$$\bar{\mu} = \frac{1}{IJ} \sum_{i=1}^{I} \sum_{j=1}^{J} \mu_{ij} = \frac{1}{I} \sum_{i=1}^{I} \bar{\mu}_{i.} = \frac{1}{J} \sum_{j=1}^{J} \bar{\mu}_{.j}$$

and call

$$\alpha_i = \bar{\mu}_{i.} - \bar{\mu} \text{ the "effect" of factor } A \text{ at level } i$$

$$\beta_j = \bar{\mu}_{.j} - \bar{\mu} \text{ the "effect" of factor } B \text{ at level } j$$

The quantity

$$\gamma_{ij} = \mu_{ij} - (\bar{\mu} + \alpha_i + \beta_j) = \mu_{ij} - \bar{\mu}_{i.} - \bar{\mu}_{.j} + \mu$$

is called the "interaction" between factor A at level i and factor B at level j; it is the amount by which μ_{ij} differs from {the average population mean $\bar{\mu}$ plus the effect α_i plus the effect β_j}, and hence measures the departure, if any, from "additivity" of the effects of the two factors in the model.

We therefore have the representation

$$\mu_{x_{ijk}} = \mu_{ij} = \bar{\mu} + \alpha_i + \beta_j + \gamma_{ij}$$

as the *general mean* $\bar{\mu}$, plus the *A effect*, plus the *B effect*, plus an *interaction effect*. Note that by the definitions above

$$\sum_{i=1}^{I} \alpha_i = \sum_{i=1}^{I} \bar{\mu}_{i.} - I\bar{\mu} = 0, \ \sum_{j=1}^{J} \beta_j = \sum_{j=1}^{J} \bar{\mu}_{.j} - J\bar{\mu} = 0$$

$$\sum_{j=1}^{J} \gamma_{ij} = \sum_{j=1}^{J} \mu_{ij} - J\bar{\mu}_{i.} - \sum_{j=1}^{J} \bar{\mu}_{.j} + J\bar{\mu}$$

$$= J\bar{\mu}_{i.} - J\bar{\mu}_{i.} - J\bar{\mu} + J\bar{\mu} = 0 \qquad (i = 1, \ldots, I)$$

and similarly

$$\sum_{i=1}^{I} \gamma_{ij} = 0 \qquad (j = 1, \ldots, J)$$

Since $\mu_{x_{ijk}} = \mu_{ij}$, we can write

$$x_{ijk} = \bar{\mu} + \alpha_i + \beta_j + \gamma_{ij} + \epsilon_{ijk}$$

where ϵ_{ijk}, called the "error" of the observation χ_{ijk}, has mean value 0 and variance σ^2, assumed to be the same for all i, j, k values. We shall assume in addition that the ϵ_{ijk} (and hence the x_{ijk}) are normally distributed. In table 8.6, factor B is the drug and factor A is the dosage level at which the drug is administered.

We now consider tests of the following different hypotheses:

$$H_A : \alpha_1 = \alpha_2 = \ldots = \alpha_I = 0$$

$$H_B : \beta_1 = \beta_2 = \ldots = \beta_J = 0$$

$$H_{AB} = \gamma_{ij} = 0 \text{ for all } i = 1, \ldots, I; j = 1, \ldots, J$$

The hypothesis H_A (H_B) is that there is no *effect* due to factor A (B), while H_{AB} is the hypothesis that there is no *interaction* between A and B; that is, that the effects of A and B are *additive*. As in a one-way analysis of variance, our tests will be based on various terms in a partitioned total sum of squares about the grand sample mean. We partition this total sum of squares into four parts, attributable respectively to factor A, factor B, interaction of A and B, and random error. Comparisons of the ratios of SS_A, SS_B, and SS_{AB} to SS_E (each divided by the appropriate number of degrees of freedom) will allow us to test separately each of the three null hypotheses H_A, H_B, and H_{AB}.

The grand sample mean is

$$\bar{x} = \frac{1}{IJK} \sum_{i=1}^{I} \sum_{j=1}^{J} \sum_{k=1}^{K} x_{ijk} \qquad (= \text{estimate of } \bar{\mu})$$

and the *cell means* are

$$\bar{x}_{ij} = \frac{1}{K} \sum_{k=1}^{K} x_{ijk} \qquad (= \text{estimate of } \mu_{ij})$$

We define

$$\bar{x}_{i.} = \frac{1}{JK} \sum_{j=1}^{J} \sum_{k=1}^{K} x_{ijk} = \text{mean of the observations at level } i \text{ of factor } A \; (= \text{estimate of } \bar{\mu}_{i.})$$

$$\bar{x}_{.j} = \frac{1}{IK} \sum_{i=1}^{I} \sum_{k=1}^{K} x_{ijk} = \text{mean of the observations at level } j \text{ of factor } B \; (= \text{estimate of } \bar{\mu}_{.j})$$

so that

$$\bar{x}_{i.} - \bar{x} = \text{estimate of } \alpha_i$$
$$\bar{x}_{.j} - \bar{x} = \text{estimate of } \beta_j$$
$$\bar{x}_{ij} - \bar{x}_{i.} - \bar{x}_{.j} + \bar{x} = \text{estimate of } \gamma_{ij}$$

and the sums of squares

$$SS = \sum_{i=1}^{I} \sum_{j=1}^{J} \sum_{k=1}^{K} (x_{ijk} - \bar{x})^2 = \text{total sum of squares}$$

$$SS_A = \sum_{i=1}^{I} \sum_{j=1}^{J} \sum_{k=1}^{K} (\bar{x}_{i.} - \bar{x})^2$$

$$= JK \sum_{i=1}^{I} (\bar{x}_{i.} - \bar{x})^2 = \text{sum of squares for factor } A$$

$$SS_B = \sum_{i=1}^{I} \sum_{j=1}^{J} \sum_{k=1}^{K} (\bar{x}_{.j} - \bar{x})^2$$

$$= IK \sum_{j=1}^{J} (\bar{x}_{.j} - \bar{x})^2 = \text{sum of squares for factor } B$$

$$SS_{AB} = \sum_{i=1}^{I} \sum_{j=1}^{J} \sum_{k=1}^{K} (\bar{x}_{ij} - \bar{x}_{i.} - \bar{x}_{.j} + \bar{x})^2$$

$$= K \sum_{i=1}^{I} \sum_{j=1}^{J} (\bar{x}_{ij} - \bar{x}_{i.} - \bar{x}_{.j} + \bar{x})^2 = \begin{array}{l} \text{sum of squares} \\ \text{for interaction} \end{array}$$

$$SS_E = \sum_{i=1}^{I} \sum_{j=1}^{J} \sum_{k=1}^{K} (x_{ijk} - \bar{x}_{ij})^2 = \text{sum of squares for error}$$

By algebra similar to that used to verify (6), it can be shown that

$$SS = SS_A + SS_B + SS_{AB} + SS_E \qquad (14)$$

Now, SS_A measures the variation of the sample means of factor A (the $\bar{x}_{i.}$) from the grand mean $\bar{x}$. This will usually be small if there is little or no effect due to A. Similarly, SS_B measures the variation about $\bar{x}$ of the factor B sample means (the $\bar{x}_{.j}$), and this will usually be small if factor B has little or no effect, while SS_{AB} will usually be small if there is no interaction effect.

SS_E measures variation of the observations x_{ijk} from their respective sample cell means $\bar{x}_{ij}$. This variation is that which is due to the unexplained variability in the data after the effects and interaction have been accounted for.

PROBLEMS 8.4

To illustrate the meaning of the sums of squares in (14), consider the following sets of hypothetical data. For each case compute the cell means $\bar{x}_{ij}$, the factor A means $\bar{x}_{i.}$, the factor B means $\bar{x}_j$, SS, SS_A, SS_B, SS_{AB}, and SS_E.

1.

Factor A \ Factor B	B_1	B_2
A_1	$-3, -2, -1$	$-3, -2, -1$
A_2	$-1, \ 0, \ 1$	$-1, \ 0, \ 1$
A_3	$1, \ 2, \ 3$	$1, \ 2, \ 3$

2.

Factor A \ Factor B	B_1	B_2	B_3
A_1	$-1, -3$	$-1, 1$	$1, 3$
A_2	$-1, -3$	$-1, 1$	$1, 3$
A_3	$-1, -3$	$-1, 1$	$1, 3$
A_4	$-1, -3$	$-1, 1$	$1, 3$

3.

Factor A \ Factor B	B_1	B_2	B_3
A_1	$-3, -2, -1$	$-1, 0, 1$	$3, \ 2, \ 1$
A_2	$-1, \ 0, \ 1$	$-1, 0, 1$	$-1, \ 0, \ 1$
A_3	$3, \ 2, \ 1$	$-1, 0, 1$	$-3, -2, -1$

4.

Factor A \ Factor B	B_1	B_2	B_3	B_4	B_5
A_1	$0, \ 0$	$1, \ 1$	$2, \ 2$	$3, \ 3$	$4, 4$
A_2	$-4, -4$	$-3, -3$	$-2, -2$	$-1, -1$	$0, 0$

8.5 The Mean Squares and Their Expected Values: The F Test

Just as in the one-way case, we define the mean square connected with each sum of squares:

$$MS_A = \frac{SS_A}{I - 1} = \text{mean square for factor } A \tag{15}$$

$$MS_B = \frac{SS_B}{J - 1} = \text{mean square for factor B} \tag{16}$$

$$MS_{AB} = \frac{SS_{AB}}{(I - 1)(J - 1)} = \text{mean square for interaction} \tag{17}$$

$$MS_E = \frac{SS_E}{IJ(K - 1)} = \text{mean square for error} \tag{18}$$

It can be shown that

$$m.v.(MS_A) = \sigma^2 + \frac{JK}{I-1} \sum_{i=1}^{I} \alpha_i^2$$

$$m.v.(MS_B) = \sigma^2 + \frac{IK}{J-1} \sum_{j=1}^{J} \beta_j^2$$

$$m.v.(MS_{AB}) = \sigma^2 + \frac{K}{(I-1)(J-1)} \sum_{i=1}^{I} \sum_{j=1}^{J} \gamma_{ij}^2$$

$$m.v.(MS_E) = \sigma^2$$

Whether or not any of the hypotheses H_A, H_B, H_{AB} are true we see from this that MS_E is an unbiased estimator of σ^2. Under $H_A : \alpha_1 = \alpha_2 = \ldots = \alpha_I = 0$ we see also that MS_A is an unbiased estimator of σ^2, but overestimates σ^2 if H_A is not true (for then $m.v.\,(MS_A) = \sigma^2 + JK(I-1)^{-1} \sum_{i=1}^{I} \alpha_i^2 > \sigma^2$). Thus if we form the ratio

$$F_A = \frac{MS_A}{MS_E}$$

then when MS_A and MS_E are near their mean values we shall have (compare (10))

$$F_A \cong \frac{m.v.\,(MS_A)}{m.v.\,(MS_E)} = 1 + \frac{JK \sum_{i=1}^{I} \alpha_i^2}{(I-1)\sigma^2} \tag{19}$$

so that F_A will tend to be large if H_A is not true. It can be proved that under H_A, F_A has an F distribution, with $I - 1$ degrees of freedom in the numerator and $IJ\,(K-1)$ degrees of freedom in the denominator. Thus, we agree to reject H_A at level α if F_A exceeds the value $F_{I-1, IJ(K-1), \alpha}$ of appendix table 9.

Similarly, level α tests of $H_B : \beta_1 = \beta_2 = \ldots = \beta_J = 0$, and $H_{AB} : \gamma_{ij} = 0$ for all $i = 1, \ldots, I; j = 1, \ldots, J$, are given by

$$\text{Reject } H_B \text{ if } F_B = \frac{MS_B}{MS_E} > F_{J-1, IJ(K-1), \alpha}$$

$$\text{Reject } H_{AB} \text{ if } F_{AB} = \frac{MS_{AB}}{MS_E} > F_{(I-1)(J-1), IJ(k-1), \alpha}$$

We summarize these results in the two-way analysis of variance table shown on the facing page.

TABLE 8.7
Two-Way Analysis of Variance Table with K Observations per Cell

Source of variation	Degrees of freedom	Sum of squares	Mean square	F ratio	Level α test
Factor A	$I-1$	SS_A	$MS_A = \dfrac{SS_A}{IJ(K-1)}$	$F_A = \dfrac{MS_A}{MS_E}$	Reject H_A if $F_A >$ $F_{I-1,IJ(K-1),\alpha}$
Factor B	$J-1$	SS_B	$MS_B = \dfrac{SS_B}{J-1}$	$F_B = \dfrac{MS_B}{MS_E}$	Reject H_B if $F_B >$ $F_{J-1,IJ(K-1),\alpha}$
Interaction	$(I-1)(J-1)$	SS_{AB}	$MS_{AB} = \dfrac{SS_{AB}}{(I-1)(J-1)}$	$F_{AB} = \dfrac{MS_{AB}}{MS_E}$	Reject H_{AB} if $F_{AB} >$ $F_{(I-1)(J-1),IJ(K-1),\alpha}$
Error	$IJ(K-1)$	SS_E	$MS_E = \dfrac{SS_E}{IJ(K-1)}$		

The computation of SS, SS_A, SS_B, SS_{AB}, and SS_E is simplified by the formulas we now introduce. The verification of these formulas is a straightforward exercise in algebra and the use of the summation notation. Define

$$T_{ij} = \sum_{k=1}^{K} x_{ijk} \qquad \text{(the sum of the observations in cell } (i, j)) \tag{20}$$

$$T_{i.} = \sum_{j=1}^{J} \sum_{k=1}^{K} x_{ijk} \qquad \text{(the sum of all observations at level } i \text{ of factor } A) \tag{21}$$

$$T_{.j} = \sum_{i=1}^{I} \sum_{k=1}^{K} x_{ijk} \qquad \text{(the sum of all observations at level } j \text{ of factor } B)$$

$$T = \sum_{i=1}^{I} \sum_{j=1}^{J} \sum_{k=1}^{K} x_{ijk} \qquad \text{(the sum of all observations)} \tag{23}$$

$$C = \frac{T^2}{IJK} \tag{24}$$

Then

$$SS_A = \frac{1}{JK} \sum_{i=1}^{I} T_{i.}^2 - C \tag{25}$$

$$SS_B = \frac{1}{IK} \sum_{j=1}^{J} T_{.j}^2 - C \tag{26}$$

$$SS_E = \sum_{i=1}^{I} \sum_{j=1}^{J} \sum_{k=1}^{K} x_{ijk}^2 - \frac{1}{K} \sum_{i=1}^{I} \sum_{j=1}^{J} T_{ij}^2 \tag{27}$$

$$SS = \sum_{i=1}^{I} \sum_{j=1}^{J} \sum_{k=1}^{K} x_{ijk}^2 - C \tag{28}$$

$$SS_{AB} = SS - SS_A - SS_B - SS_E \tag{29}$$

We now apply formulas 20 to 29 to the data of table 8.6 and construct the analysis of variance table for this example, in which $I = 3(L_1, L_2, L_3)$, $J = 3(D_1, D_2, D_3)$, and $K = 4$. From table 8.6 we obtain

TABLE 8.8
Sums of Observations for Table 8.6

i \ j	1	2	3	Sums
1	$T_{11} = 1088$	$T_{12} = 999$	$T_{13} = 1186$	$T_{1.} = 3273$
2	$T_{21} = 1054$	$T_{22} = 1048$	$T_{23} = 1076$	$T_{2.} = 3178$
3	$T_{31} = 834$	$T_{32} = 824$	$T_{33} = 784$	$T_{3.} = 2442$
Sums	$T_{.1} = 2976$	$T_{.2} = 2871$	$T_{.3} = 3046$	$T = 8893$

For example, $T_{32} = x_{321} + x_{322} + x_{323} + x_{324} = 228 + 241 + 164 + 191 = 824$. From table 8.8 we compute the quantities

$$\sum_{i=1}^{3} \sum_{j=1}^{3} T_{ij}^{\,2} = 8{,}944{,}525$$

$$\sum_{i=1}^{3} T_{i.}^{\,2} = 26{,}775{,}577$$

$$\sum_{j=1}^{3} T_{.j}^{\,2} = 26{,}377{,}333$$

$$C = \frac{T^2}{3.3.4} = \frac{79{,}085{,}449}{36} = 2{,}196{,}818.03$$

$$\sum_{i=1}^{3} \sum_{j=1}^{3} \sum_{k=1}^{4} x_{ijk}^{\,2} = 2{,}280{,}829$$

Using formulas 25 to 29 we then have

$$SS_A = \frac{26{,}775{,}577}{12} - C = 2{,}231{,}298.08 - 2{,}196{,}818.03 = 34{,}480.05$$

$$SS_B = \frac{26{,}377{,}333}{12} - C = 2{,}198{,}111.08 - 2{,}196{,}818.03 = 1293.05$$

$$SS_E = 2{,}280{,}829 - \frac{8{,}944{,}525}{4} = 2{,}280{,}829 - 2{,}236{,}131.25 = 44{,}697.75$$

$$SS = 2{,}280{,}829 - C = 84{,}010.97$$

$$SS_{AB} = SS - SS_A - SS_B - SS_E$$
$$= 84{,}010.97 - 1293.05 - 34{,}480.05 - 44{,}697.75 = 3540.12.$$

We now form the analysis of variance table as in table 8.7.

TABLE 8.9
Analysis of Variance Table for Table 8.6

Source of variation	Degrees of freedom	Sum of squares	Mean square	F ratio
Level (L)	2	34,480.05	17,240.30	10.41
Drug (D)	2	1293.05	646.53	.39
Interaction	4	3540.12	885.03	.53
Error	27	44,697.75	1655.47	

To carry out the appropriate F tests at level $\alpha = .05$, we note that from appendix table 9 $F_{2.27, .05} = 3.35$, $F_{4.27, .05} = 2.73$. Since $F_A = 10.41 > 3.35$, $F_B = .39 < 3.35$, $F_{AB} = .53 < 2.73$, we conclude that $H_A : \alpha_1 = \alpha_2 = \alpha_3 = 0$ is false and that there is an effect on platelet count of different dosage level. There is no significant effect of different drug (for these three drugs only) or of interaction between the drug and its dosage level.

From table 8.6 we can construct a table of sample means for the various treatments to see more clearly what the data are trying to tell us.

TABLE 8.10
Table of Sample Means for Table 8.6

Dosage \ Drug	D_1	D_2	D_3	Dosage means
L_1	$\bar{x}_{11} = 272$	$\bar{x}_{12} = 249.8$	$\bar{x}_{13} = 296.5$	$\bar{x}_{1.} = 272.8$
L_2	$\bar{x}_{21} = 263.5$	$\bar{x}_{22} = 262$	$\bar{x}_{23} = 269$	$\bar{x}_{2.} = 264.8$
L_3	$\bar{x}_{31} = 208.5$	$\bar{x}_{32} = 206$	$\bar{x}_{33} = 196$	$\bar{x}_{3.} = 203.5$
Drug means	$\bar{x}_{.1} = 248$	$\bar{x}_{.2} = 239.3$	$\bar{x}_{.3} = 253.8$	$\bar{x} = 247$ Grand mean

From this table we see that $\bar{x}_{3.} = 203.5$ is considerably less than $\bar{x}_{2.} = 264.8$, which is in turn less than $\bar{x}_{1.} = 272.8$. Thus, the data strongly suggests that increasing the dosage level lowers platelet count, although there is an apparent exception to this in the case of drug 2 in going from level 1 to level 2.

PROBLEMS 8.5

1. Twelve women and twelve men, each approximately 30 lbs overweight, were randomly assigned to two diet regimens. After six weeks the weight losses (in lbs) were

	Diet I		Diet II	
Men	9.5	8.6	17.4	13.5
	8.8	13.3	13.8	11.4
	12.6	11.4	20.4	15.5
Women	12.4	9.2	16.2	7.4
	6.3	7.8	9.7	12.7
	16.0	14.6	11.8	14.1

a. Compute a table of means for these data.
b. Give the analysis of variance table for these data.
c. Test the hypotheses of no diet effect, no sex effect, and no diet-sex interaction effect, at the level of significance $\alpha = .05$. State your conclusions.

2. A forest products researcher wishes to compare the breaking strength of laminated beams made up of three different types of glue and three varieties of wood. Four beams of each combination were manufactured and put under a stress test. The data given in the following table indicate the pressure readings at which the beams broke.

Wood \ Glue	G_1	G_2	G_3
W_1	196	310	387
	247	268	298
	327	360	353
	274	204	426
W_2	178	307	365
	361	224	248
	268	329	319
	285	390	292
W_3	318	185	437
	248	402	291
	159	313	385
	223	240	516

a. Compute a table of means.
b. Give the analysis of variance table.
c. Test the hypotheses of no glue effect, no wood effect, and no glue-wood interaction, at the level of significance $\alpha = .05$. State your conclusions.

3. To study the aftereffect of noise on the performance of tasks, subjects were assigned to a proofreading task after being subjected to 30 minutes of one of three levels of noise, either predictably (at regularly spaced intervals) or unpredictably (at randomly spaced intervals). Eight subjects were assigned randomly to each group; the scores (0 to 100) represent the number of proofreading corrections made out of a possible 100. The data are given in the table at the top of the following page.

Type of noise \ Noise level	Very Loud	Loud	Soft
Predictable	52 79 61 66 47 59 71 73 55 54	74 82 62 66 53 70 68 55 62 59	80 63 58 85 82 81 73 64 68 57
Unpredictable	40 61 62 47 63 51 45 46 39 68	75 50 57 64 46 63 57 53 66 52	82 78 49 83 62 66 70 65 52 74

a. Compute a table of means.
b. Give the analysis of variance table.
c. Test at the level of significance $\alpha = .05$ whether or not there is an aftereffect due to loudness of noise, to predictability of noise, and to interaction of predictability and loudness. State your conclusions.

4. Four types of commercial grass seeds are planted on one-half acre plots with three different fertilizers. Four plots are assigned at random to each fertilizer-grass seed combination. The table below gives the density of coverage (%) for each plot as measured by a technique that regards a small grid square as uncovered if less than half is covered by grass.

Fertilizer \ Brand of seed	B_1	B_2	B_3	B_4
F_1	78 69 73 66	68 82 74 80	89 77 65 69	80 75 63 62
F_2	84 72 75 91	75 69 84 82	87 82 70 93	94 83 69 80
F_3	96 85 88 73	74 90 80 86	90 98 87 79	64 73 86 89

a. Compute a table of means.
b. Give the analysis of variance table.
c. Test at the level of significance $\alpha = .05$ whether there is an effect due to fertilizer type, brand of seed, or interaction between fertilizer and brand. State your conclusions.

8.6 An Example with Interactions

In example 3 no significant interaction effect was present. We now give an example in which interactions are present.

Example 4

At a four-year liberal arts college three men and three women were randomly chosen from each college class. The average number of study hours per week was recorded for each of these 24 students for a semester. All students chosen had about the same credit load. The resulting data are given in table 8.11.

TABLE 8.11
Amount of Study Time per Week (in hours)

Sex i \ Class j	Freshman	Sophomore	Junior	Senior	Row totals
Male	16.2 25.5 18.9 60.6 (T_{11})	31.1 24.1 19.8 75.0 (T_{12})	24.8 36.3 34.9 96.0 (T_{13})	38.7 28.8 30.9 98.4 (T_{14})	$T_{1.} =$ 330.0
Female	26.4 28.0 33.8 88.2 (T_{21})	23.6 21.0 28.0 72.6 (T_{22})	24.3 19.7 25.6 69.6 (T_{23})	22.8 31.2 33.6 87.6 (T_{24})	$T_{2.} =$ 318.0
Column totals	$T_{.1} =$ 148.8	$T_{.2} =$ 147.6	$T_{.3} =$ 165.6	$T_{.4} =$ 186.0	$T =$ 648.0

From table 8.11 we compute the following quantities with the aid of formulas 20 to 29.

$$\sum_{i=1}^{2} \sum_{j=1}^{4} \sum_{k=1}^{3} x_{ijk}^{2} = (16.2)^2 + \ldots + (33.6)^2 = 18,304.18$$

$$\sum_{i=1}^{2} \sum_{j=1}^{4} T_{ij}^{2} = 53,763.84$$

$$\sum_{j=1}^{4} T_{.j}^{2} = 105,946.56$$

$$\sum_{i=1}^{2} T_{i.}^{2} = 210,024.00$$

$$C = \frac{T^2}{IJK} = \frac{(648)^2}{4 \cdot 2 \cdot 3} = \frac{419{,}904}{24} = 17{,}496$$

$$SS_B = \frac{105{,}946.56}{6} - C = 161.76$$

$$SS_A = \frac{210{,}024.00}{12} - C = 6.00$$

$$SS_E = 18{,}304.18 - \frac{53{,}763.84}{3} = 382.90$$

$$SS = 18{,}304.18 - 17{,}496 = 808.18$$

$$SS_{AB} = SS - SS_A - SS_B - SS_E = 257.52$$

From this we construct the following analysis of variance table, as in table 8.7.

TABLE 8.12
Analysis of Variance Table for Table 8.11

Source of variation	Degrees of freedom	Sum of squares	Mean square	F ratio
Class	3	161.76	53.92	2.25
Sex	1	6.00	6.00	.25
Interaction	3	257.52	85.84	3.59
Error	16	382.90	23.93	

To carry out the appropriate F tests at level $\alpha = .05$ we note that

$$F_{3,16,.05} = 3.24 \qquad F_{1,16,.05} = 4.49$$

Since $F_{AB} = 3.59 > 3.24$, we conclude that the null hypothesis H_{AB}: $\gamma_{ij} = 0$ for all $i = 1, 2, 3, 4$, and $j = 1, 2$ is false, and that there *is* an interaction effect between class and sex. Since $F_B = 2.25 < 3.24$ and $F_A = .25 < 4.49$, there is not enough evidence from the data to claim an effect due to class or sex individually.

To see more clearly what the interactions are, we compute the following table of means and corresponding graph that shows the interaction between class and sex.

TABLE 8.13
Table of Sample Means for Table 8.11

Sex \ Class	Freshman	Sophomore	Junior	Senior	Mean
Male	$\bar{x}_{11} = 20.2$	$\bar{x}_{12} = 25.0$	$\bar{x}_{13} = 32.0$	$\bar{x}_{14} = 32.8$	$\bar{x}_{1.} = 27.5$
Female	$\bar{x}_{21} = 29.4$	$\bar{x}_{22} = 24.2$	$\bar{x}_{23} = 23.2$	$\bar{x}_{24} = 29.2$	$\bar{x}_{2.} = 26.5$
Mean	$\bar{x}_{.1} = 24.8$	$\bar{x}_{.2} = 24.6$	$\bar{x}_{.3} = 27.6$	$\bar{x}_{.4} = 31.0$	$\bar{x} = 27.0$

Figure 8.1 illustrates the interaction effect by showing the sample means for the two sexes for each class level. From this it appears that freshmen behave quite differently from the other classes. The difference between the study habits of males and females must be viewed with regard to the class in question, since from the test for interactions and the graph we can see that the effects of class and sex interact in a complex way. It follows that the analysis of sex differences in study habits should be done for each class separately.

A plot of the means is always useful whenever the hypothesis H_{AB} is rejected, since it can suggest the directions of the interactions and possible future questions to study.

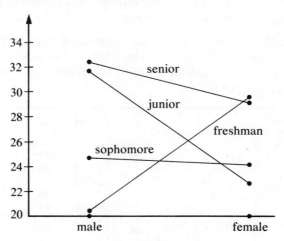

FIGURE 8.1
Plot of the sample means showing interaction

PROBLEMS 8.6

1. The following "whiteness" readings on a scale of 0 to 100 are the results of tests on soiled sheets washed at four different temperatures with two detergents. The sheets were all washed in the same machine.

Detergent \ Temp.	120°	140°	160°	180°
D_1	61	63	54	63
	73	42	72	54
	45	55	61	61
	59	46	59	72
D_2	32	61	69	86
	40	44	84	93
	58	68	60	74
	46	57	79	69

 a. Compute a table of means.
 b. Give the analysis of variance table.
 c. Test the hypotheses of no detergent effect, no temperature effect, and no detergent-temperature interaction, at the level of significance $\alpha = .05$. State your conclusions.
 d. Plot the mean values at the different temperatures for the two detergents. Discuss these plots.

2. In a study of how the concentration of a certain drug in the blood is influenced by age and sex, analysis of blood samples from 50 persons given the drug gave the following concentrations (in milligrams per cc).

Sex \ Age	13–20	21–35	36–50	51–65	over 65
Male	68	132	73	122	62
	48	74	64	69	37
	112	107	142	55	107
	85	144	103	94	59
	56	83	68	81	83
Female	108	68	116	75	133
	73	53	53	136	99
	124	77	80	107	159
	86	105	69	108	106
	143	76	74	88	86

 a. Compute a table of means.
 b. Give the analysis of variance table.

   c. Test the hypotheses of no age effect, no sex effect, and no age-sex interaction, at the level of significance $\alpha = .05$. State your conclusions.

   d. Plot the mean values at the different age levels for the two sexes. Discuss these plots.

3. In problem 1, section 8.5, plot the means of diet I and diet II for each sex. Discuss this plot, where no interaction is present. Compare with problem 1 above.

4. In problem 3, section 8.5, plot the means of the noise levels for the two types of noise. Discuss this plot, where no interaction is present. Compare with problem 2 above.

8.7   The Case $K = 1$ and the Effect of Blocking

In a two-way analysis of variance with only $K = 1$ observation per cell we cannot test for interaction between factors A and B, since for $K = 1$ the SS_E term vanishes. However, if we are willing to *assume that all the interactions γ_{ij} are 0*, then $m.v.(MS_{AB}) = \sigma^2$, so that MS_{AB} can be used to replace MS_E in the F test of H_A or H_B. The analysis of variance table is shown below.

TABLE 8.14
Two-Way Analysis of Variance Table with One Observation per Cell

Source of variation	Degrees of freedom	Sum of squares	Mean square	F ratio	Level α test
Factor A	$I - 1$	SS_A	$MS_A = \dfrac{SS_A}{I - 1}$	$F_A = \dfrac{MS_A}{MS_{AB}}$	Reject H_A if $F_A >$ $F_{I-1,(I-1)(t-1),\alpha}$
Factor B	$J - 1$	SS_B	$MS_B = \dfrac{SS_B}{J - 1}$	$F_B = \dfrac{MS_B}{MS_{AB}}$	Reject H_B if $F_B >$ $F_{J-1,(I-1)(J-1),\alpha}$
Error	$(I - 1)(J - 1)$	SS_{AB}	$MS_{AB} = \dfrac{SS_{AB}}{(I - 1)(J - 1)}$		

    Whether $K = 1$ or $K > 1$, the factor B is sometimes introduced not because of its intrinsic interest but to reduce the value of σ^2 by "blocking." Suppose, for example, that factor A represents the type of fertilizer used in a field trial of corn yield. If each of the I types of fertilizer is used K times within each of J relatively homogeneous blocks of land, then the effect of variable fertility among blocks is eliminated from the analysis, with a consequent reduction of the error variance σ^2 and an increased sensitivity of the analysis of variance test to departures from the null hypothesis H_A. By this we mean that for a given value of $\sum_{i=1}^{I} \alpha_i^2 \neq 0$, the F test at a given level is more likely to reject H_A when σ^2 is small than when it is large, as is apparent from the relation (19). Consider the following example.

Example 5

A dairy scientist wishing to study the effectiveness of four milk preservatives splits each of five different pints of milk (from different cows) into four 4-ounce portions and adds each preservative to one of the four portions. The following spoilage times (in hours) were recorded. All 20 samples (4×5) were kept under identical storage conditions.

TABLE 8.15
Spoilage Times

Preservative (i)	Block (j)(pint)					Sums ($T_{i.}$)	Means
	B_1	B_2	B_3	B_4	B_5		
P_1	71	86	69	93	74	393	78.6
P_2	84	90	77	89	82	422	84.4
P_3	73	78	63	78	80	372	74.4
P_4	64	86	61	90	74	375	75.0
Sums ($T_{.j}$)	292	340	270	350	310	1562 = T	

If we now use formulas 20–29 with $K = 1$ ($SS_E = 0$ in formula 27) we have

$$\sum_{i=1}^{4} T_{i.}^2 = 611{,}542 \qquad \sum_{j=1}^{5} T_{.j}^2 = 492{,}364$$

$$\sum_{i=1}^{4} \sum_{j=1}^{5} T_{ij}^2 = (71)^2 + (86)^2 + \ldots + (90)^2 + (74)^2 = 123{,}708$$

$$C = \frac{T^2}{4 \cdot 5} = \frac{(1562)^2}{20} = 121{,}992.2 , \quad SS_A = \frac{611{,}542}{5} - C = 316.2$$

$$SS_B = \frac{492{,}364}{4} - C = 1098.8 , \qquad SS = 123{,}708 - C = 1715.8$$

$$SS_{AB} = SS - SS_A - SS_B = 300.8$$

We now form the analysis of variance table as in table 8.14.

TABLE 8.16
Analysis of Variance Table for Table 8.15

Source of variation	Degrees of freedom	Sum of squares	Mean square	F ratio
Preservative	3	316.2	105.4	4.20
Block (pint)	4	1098.8	274.7	10.96
Error	12	300.8	25.07	

To carry out the appropriate F tests at level $\alpha = .05$ we note that

$$F_{3,12,.05} = 3.49 \quad , \quad F_{4,12,.05} = 3.26$$

Since $F_A = 4.20 > 3.49$, we conclude there is an effect due to the preservative; that is, the null hypothesis $H_A : \alpha_1 = \alpha_2 = \alpha_3 = \alpha_4$ is false. Since $F_B = 10.96 > 3.26$, there is also a significant block effect.

If the experimenter had ignored this variability in different pints of milk in designing the experiment (and had not split each pint into four 4-ounce portions), the perservative effect may not have been detected by a one-way analysis. The column of means in table 8.15 suggests that P_2 is the best preservative.

PROBLEMS 8.7

1. Three different varieties of oats are planted on six different blocks of land (one-third of each block is randomly assigned to each variety). The yields in bushels per acre are given in the following table.

Variety \ Block	1	2	3	4	5	6
V_1	54.4	64.8	69.7	63.3	49.9	59.7
V_2	46.7	43.5	60.2	52.8	55.8	46.4
V_3	64.8	72.3	56.7	62.7	70.4	58.9

   a. Compute the means for varieties and blocks.
   b. Give the analysis of variance table (see table 8.14).
   c. Test the hypotheses of no variety effect and no block effect on oat yield at the level of significance $\alpha = .05$, assuming no interaction between block and variety. State your conclusions.

2. Each of five students in engineering is given a battery of standarized tests (0 to 100, with a median of 50) in four aptitude areas. The results are as follows.

Area \ Student	1	2	3	4	5
Verbal	76	73	35	84	57
Mathematical	83	68	52	97	78
Scientific	91	85	63	93	83
Artistic	72	58	46	76	62

a. Compute the means for students and aptitude areas.
b. Give the analysis of variance table.
c. Test the hypotheses of no student effect and no aptitude area effect for the scores of these students, assuming no interaction. Use $\alpha = .01$. State your conclusions.

LINEAR REGRESSION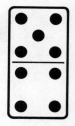

9 Linear Regression

The central problems in many branches of science concern the way in which a change in one quantity affects the value of another quantity. For example, a physiologist might want to know to what extent $y =$ weight loss over a month's time in the overweight adult male depends on $x =$ amount of exercise, or a college admissions officer might want to find how much $y =$ the GPA at the end of the freshman year depends on $x =$ the entering student's IQ score. To study such problems, statisticians use a method called *regression analysis*. The present chapter gives a brief introduction to the simplest of such problems: finding the extent to which a single "dependent" quantity y is linearly related to a single "independent" quantity x.

9.1 Linear Regression of Data on One Independent Variable

When the value of one variable y is determined by the value of another variable x by a functional relationship of the form

$$y = \alpha + \beta x$$

where α and β are constants, we say that y depends on x *linearly*, since the graph of y as a function of x is a straight line. If the coefficient β

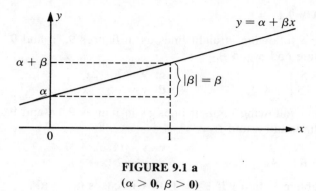

FIGURE 9.1 a
($\alpha > 0$, $\beta > 0$)

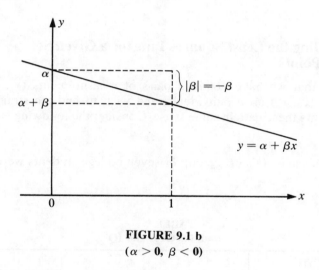

FIGURE 9.1 b
($\alpha > 0$, $\beta < 0$)

is positive, as in figure 9.1a, then y *increases* as x increases. If β is negative, as in figure 9.1b, then y *decreases* as x increases. In either case, β is the amount by which y changes (positively or negatively) per unit change in the value of x.

The equation $y = \alpha + \beta x$ is a deterministic equation, since the value of y is completely determined by the value of x. We shall be concerned, however, with the nondeterministic case in which y and x are only *approximately* linearly related through a set of data points. This is expressed by saying that y exhibits a certain amount of "linear regression" on x.

PROBLEMS 9.1

1. Plot the following straight lines as in figures 9.1a and 9.1b. For each line find α and β.

   a. $y = 5 + 3x$ **c.** $y = 7 - 2x$
   b. $y = .5x - 4$ **d.** $y = -5 - x$

2. Plot the following straight lines as in figures 9.1a and 9.1b. For each line, find α and β.

   a. $y = 3x + 2$ **c.** $y = (1/2)x - 1/4$
   b. $y = 6 - .8x$ **d.** $y = 2\,(x - 3)$

3. In problem 1, find y if $x = -1, 0, 1$ in cases (a) to (d).

4. In problem 2, find y if $x = -2, .5, 6$ in cases (a) and (d).

9.2 Finding the Least Squares Line for a Given Set of Data Points

Suppose that we have obtained pairs of measurements (x_1, y_1) $(x_2, y_2), \ldots, (x_n, y_n)$ on n individuals, and wish to find the straight line that best fits these data in some sense. Consider the following example.

Example 1
The GPA's and IQ's of a group of seven college students were found to be

TABLE 9.1
Data for GPA and IQ

Student (i)	1	2	3	4	5	6	7
IQ (x_i)	106	110	121	129	134	140	156
GPA (y_i)	2.10	1.70	2.78	3.07	2.94	3.44	3.92

To see whether it is reasonable to try to fit a straight line to these data, in figure 9.2 we plot a "scattergram" to get a visual impression of the nature of the relationship between x and y. (Thus, in the scattergram of figure 9.3 the data points clearly do not show a linear trend, and any attempt to fit a straight line to them would be a meaningless exercise.)

The data points in figure 9.2 do seem to show an approximately linear relation between x and y, with the y values generally increasing

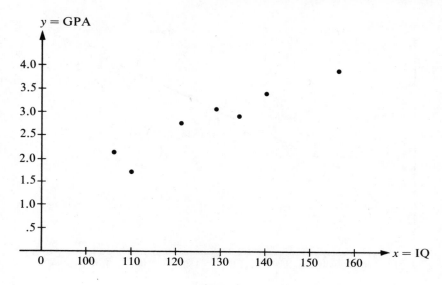

FIGURE 9.2
The scattergram for table 9.1

FIGURE 9.3
A scattergram of data not linearly related

as x increases. We shall therefore try to "smooth out" the scattergram of figure 9.3 the data points clearly do not show a linear trend, and any attempt to fit a straight line to them would be a meaningless exercise.) points showing the smallest and largest x values. This method would be very sensitive to variation in these two points, and would make no use of the other five points. How then shall we draw a line that best fits the data as a whole? Although the answer to this question is somewhat arbitrary, it is convenient in practice to define the "best fitting"

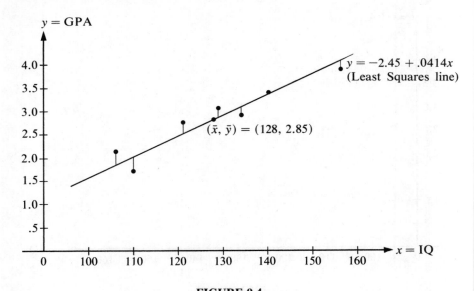

FIGURE 9.4
Least squares line for figure 9.2

straight line as the one that *minimizes the sum of the squares of the vertical distances between the line and the given data points.* This is called the *Least Squares* line, and is shown in figure 9.4. Of all possible straight lines in the x, y plane, it is the one for which the sum of the squared vertical distances to the seven given data points is a minimum.

In general, let $(x_1, y_1), \ldots, (x_n, y_n)$ be any n data points in the x, y plane. Suppose that we wish to approximate the data points (x_i, y_i) by a new set of points (x_i, Y_i) with the same x_i values but new Y_i values of the form

$$Y_i = \alpha + \beta x_i$$

so that the "adjusted" or "fitted" points $(x_1, Y_1), \ldots, (x_n, Y_n)$ will all lie on some straight line $y = \alpha + \beta x$. In so doing we agree to choose the two constants α, β at our disposal in such a way that if $d_i = |y_i - Y_i|$ denotes the vertical distance between the data point (x_i, y_i) and the fitted point (x_i, Y_i), then the *sum of the squares* of these distances

$$S(\alpha, \beta) = d_1^2 + d_2^2 + \ldots + d_n^2 = \sum_{i=1}^{n} (y_i - Y_i)^2 \qquad (1)$$

$$= \sum_{i=1}^{n} [(y_i - (\alpha + \beta x_i)]^2$$

shall be a minimum.

Definition 1

The particular values $\hat{\alpha}$ and $\hat{\beta}$ which minimize the sum of squares (1) are called the *Least Squares values* of α and β. The corresponding straight line

$$y = \hat{\alpha} + \hat{\beta} x \tag{2}$$

is called the *Least Squares line* for the given set of data points $(x_1, y_1), \ldots, (x_n, y_n)$.

The solution of the minimization problem and hence the equation (2) of the Least Squares line is given by

Theorem 1

Let $(x_1, y_1), \ldots, (x_n, y_n)$ be any set of n data points in the x, y plane such that not all the x_i values are equal. Then the values of α and β that minimize the quantity (1) are given by

$$\hat{\beta} = \frac{S_{xy}}{S_x^{\,2}} \qquad \hat{\alpha} = \bar{y} - \hat{\beta}\,\bar{x} \tag{3}$$

where throughout this chapter we use the notation

$$\bar{x} = \frac{1}{n} \sum_{i=1}^{n} x_i \quad , \quad \bar{y} = \frac{1}{n} \sum_{i=1}^{n} y_i \tag{4}$$

$$S_{xy} = \sum_{i=1}^{n} (x_i - \bar{x})(y_i - \bar{y}) = \sum_{i=1}^{n} x_i y_i - n\bar{x}\bar{y}$$

$$S_x^{\,2} = \sum_{i=1}^{n} (x_i - \bar{x})^2 = \sum_{i=1}^{n} x_i^2 - n\bar{x}^2$$

$$S_y^{\,2} = \sum_{i=1}^{n} (y_i - \bar{y})^2 = \sum_{i=1}^{n} y_i^2 - n\bar{y}^2$$

A proof of theorem 1 is given in the appendix at the end of this chapter. The details of the proof are not essential in understanding the following sections.

To illustrate the use of theorem 1, we shall find the Least Squares line for the data of table 9.1. The calculations are given in table 9.2.

TABLE 9.2
Calculation of $\hat{\alpha}$ and $\hat{\beta}$ for Table 9.1

i	x_i	y_i	$x_i - \bar{x}$	$y_i - \bar{y}$	$(x_i - \bar{x})^2$	$(y_i - \bar{y})^2$	$(x_i - \bar{x})(y_i - \bar{y})$
1	106	2.10	−22	− .75	484	.5625	16.50
2	110	1.70	−18	−1.15	324	1.3225	20.70
3	121	2.78	− 7	− .07	49	.0049	.49
4	129	3.07	1	.22	1	.0484	.22
5	134	2.94	6	.09	36	.0081	.54
6	140	3.44	12	.59	144	.3481	7.08
7	156	3.92	28	1.07	784	1.1449	29.96
Sums	896	19.95	0	0	1822	3.4394	75.49

$$\bar{x} = \frac{896}{7} = 128, \ \bar{y} = \frac{19.95}{7} = 2.85, \ S_x^2 = 1822, \ S_{xy} = 75.49,$$

$$\hat{\beta} = \frac{75.49}{1822} = .0414, \ \hat{\alpha} = 2.85 - (.0414)(128) = -2.45.$$

The Least Squares line $y = \hat{\alpha} + \hat{\beta}x = -2.45 + .0414x$ is plotted in figure 9.4. By theorem 1, it is the line that minimizes the sum of the squared distances $S(\alpha, \beta) = \sum_{i=1}^{7} [(y_i - (\alpha + \beta x_i)]^2$ for all possible choices of the constants α and β.

PROBLEMS 9.2

1. The following data (*American Scientist*, 1974, p. 197) give the average U.S. price of crude oil (dollars/bbl) for 1950–1970:

Year (x)	1950	1955	1960	1965	1970
Price (y)	2.51	2.77	2.88	2.86	3.13

   a. Plot the scattergram for these data. Does it look linear?
   b. Find $\bar{x}$, $\bar{y}$, S_x^2, S_y^2, and S_{xy}.
   c. Find the Least Squares line and plot it on the same paper with the scattergram. Does the fit look good?

2. The following data represent the sales of a department store (in millions) for the last 10 years (year 1 = 10 years ago):

Year (x)	1	2	3	4	5	6	7	8	9	10
Sales (y)	1.32	1.40	1.68	1.80	2.14	2.39	2.71	2.77	2.95	3.14

   a. Plot the scattergram for these data. Does it look linear?
   b. Find $\bar{x}$, $\bar{y}$, S_x^2, S_y^2, and S_{xy}.
   c. Find the Least Squares line and plot it on the same paper with the scattergram. Does the fit look good?

3. The following data give the U.S. divorce rate per 1000 population for 1890–1970 (National Center for Health Statistics):

Year (x)	1890	1900	1910	1920	1930	1940	1950	1960	1970
Divorce rate (y)	.5	.7	.9	1.6	1.6	2.0	2.6	2.2	3.5

a. Plot the scattergram for these data. Does it look linear?
b. Find $\bar{x}$, $\bar{y}$, S_x^2, S_y^2, and S_{xy}.
c. Find the Least Squares line data and plot it on the same paper with the scattergram. Does the fit look good?

4. The following data give the verbal and math. scores of 10 students on a college entrance examination:

Verbal (x)	68	52	78	29	87	61	91	37	62	53
Math. (y)	59	65	93	42	88	73	82	63	56	47

a. Arrange the verbal score in ascending order and plot the scattergram of the data. Does it look linear?
b. Find $\bar{x}$, $\bar{y}$, S_x^2, S_y^2, and S_{xy}.
c. Find the Least Squares line and plot it on the same paper with the scattergram. Does the fit look good?

5. The following data represent the mean body temperatures of 10 Puerto Rican lizards as a function of time of day (habitat in forest):

Time (x)	0200	0400	0600	0800	1000	1200
Temp. (C.)(y)	24.3	24.0	23.9	25.3	27.6	28.9

Time (x)	1400	1600	1800	2000	2200	2400
Temp. (C.)(y)	29.2	30.1	28.3	26.2	25.6	24.5

a. Plot the scattergram of the data. Does it look linear?
b. Find $\bar{x}$, $\bar{y}$, S_x^2, S_y^2, and S_{xy}.
c. Find the Least Squares line and plot it on the same paper with the scattergram. Does the fit look good?

9.3 The Correlation Coefficient r. Alternative Forms of the Least Squares Line

The correlation coefficient r of any n data points $(x_1, y_1), \ldots, (x_n, y_n)$ is defined by

Definition 2

$$r = \frac{S_{xy}}{S_x \cdot S_y} \tag{5}$$

where S_{xy}, S_x, and S_y are defined by (4). It is easily seen that r is a "dimensionless" number; that is, it does not depend on the origin or unit of measurement of x or y.

We can now rewrite (2) in the two alternative forms

$$y = \bar{y} + \hat{\beta}(x - \bar{x}) \tag{6}$$

or, more symmetrically,

$$\frac{y - \bar{y}}{S_y} = r \cdot \frac{x - \bar{x}}{S_x} \tag{7}$$

Equation 6 is obtained by substituting the Least Squares coefficient $\hat{\alpha} = \bar{y} - \hat{\beta}\,\bar{x}$ in (2). Equation 7 follows immediately from (6) on dividing both sides by S_y and noting that from (3) and (5)

$$\hat{\beta} = \frac{S_{xy}}{S_x^2} = r \cdot \frac{S_y}{S_x} \tag{8}$$

From (6) or (7) it is clear that *the Least Squares line always passes through the point* $(\bar{x}, \bar{y})$ *of average values in the* x, y *plane (as in figure 9.4)*, even though $(\bar{x}, \bar{y})$ may not be a data point itself.

We now examine the value $S(\hat{\alpha}, \hat{\beta})$ of the minimized sum of squares and show its relation to the correlation coefficient r defined by (5).

Definition 3

The minimized sum of squares $S(\hat{\alpha}, \hat{\beta})$, called the *sum of squares due to error* and denoted by SS_E, is defined by

$$SS_E = S(\hat{\alpha}, \hat{\beta}) = \sum_{i=1}^{n} [y_i - (\hat{\alpha} + \hat{\beta} x_i)]^2 \tag{9}$$

The values

$$\hat{y}_i = \hat{\alpha} + \hat{\beta} x_i = \bar{y} + \hat{\beta}(x_i - \bar{x}) \tag{10}$$

corresponding to the points on the Least Squares line for each x_i, are called the *fitted values* of the y_i. The sum of squares due to error, SS_E, is the sum of the squared "residuals"

$$y_i - \hat{y}_i = y_i - (\hat{\alpha} + \hat{\beta} x_i) = (y_i - \bar{y}) - \hat{\beta}(x_i - \bar{x}) \tag{11}$$

between the actual y_i's and the corresponding fitted $\hat{y}_i$'s on the Least Squares line.

An important relationship among the quantities SS_E, S_y^2, and r is given by

Theorem 2

$$SS_E = S_y^2 - \frac{S_{xy}^2}{S_x^2} = S_y^2(1 - r^2) \tag{12}$$

To verify this we note that by (9) and (10)

$$
\begin{aligned}
SS_E &= \sum_{i=1}^{n} [(y_i - \bar{y}) - \hat{\beta}(x_i - \bar{x})]^2 \\
&= \sum_{i=1}^{n} (y_i - \bar{y})^2 - 2\hat{\beta} \sum_{i=1}^{n} (x_i - \bar{x})(y_i - \bar{y}) + \hat{\beta}^2 \sum_{i=1}^{n} (x_i - \bar{x})^2 \\
&= S_y^2 - 2 \frac{S_{xy}^2}{S_x^2} + \frac{S_{xy}^2}{S_x^4} \cdot S_x^2 \quad \text{by (3)} \\
&= S_y^2 - \frac{S_{xy}^2}{S_x^2} = S_y^2 \cdot (1 - r^2) \quad \text{by (5)}
\end{aligned}
$$

Since SS_E and S_y^2 are both ≥ 0, it follows from (12) that $1 - r^2 \geq 0$, and hence that

$$-1 \leq r \leq +1$$

Thus, *the correlation coefficient* r *cannot exceed* 1 *in magnitude.*

From (7) we see that if $r = 0$ the Least Squares line becomes $y = \bar{y}$ and is a *horizontal* line, so that the values x_i do not affect the corresponding fitted values $\hat{y}_i = \bar{y}$. At the other extreme, if $r = \pm 1$ then by (12) $SS_E = 0$, and hence all the residuals $y_i - \hat{y}_i$ are 0, so that the y_i lie *exactly* on the Least Squares line (2).

PROBLEMS 9.3

1. For problem 1, section 9.2, find the correlation coefficient r. Rewrite the Least Squares line as in (6) and (7). Plot the point $(\bar{x}, \bar{y})$ on it. Find SS_E by the formula

$$SS_E = S_y^2 - \frac{S_{xy}^2}{S_x^2}$$

2. Repeat problem 1 using the results of problem 2, section 9.2.

3. Repeat problem 1 using the results of problem 3, section 9.2.

4. Repeat problem 1 using the results of problem 4, section 9.2.

9.4 The Coefficient of Determination r^2

It is an algebraic identity, the straightforward but somewhat lengthy proof of which we omit, that

$$\sum_{i=1}^{n} (y_i - \bar{y})^2 = \sum_{i=1}^{n} (\hat{y}_i - \bar{y})^2 + \sum_{i=1}^{n} (y_i - \hat{y}_i)^2 \tag{13}$$

Each term in this identity has a specific name and meaning.

a. The quantity $S_y^2 = \sum_{i=1}^{n} (y_i - \bar{y})^2$ is called the *total sum of squares*, and is denoted by SS_T. It measures the sum of the squared differences of the data values y_i about their average $\bar{y}$.

b. The quantity $\sum_{i=1}^{n} (\hat{y}_i - \bar{y})^2$ is called the *sum of squares explained by linear regression*, and is denoted by SS_R. It measures the sum of the squared differences of the fitted $\hat{y}_i$ values about their average, which is by (10) also equal to $\bar{y}$, since

$$\frac{1}{n} \sum_{i=1}^{n} \hat{y}_i = \frac{1}{n} \sum_{i=1}^{n} [\bar{y} + \hat{\beta}(x_i - \bar{x})] = \bar{y} + \frac{\hat{\beta}}{n} \sum_{i=1}^{n} (x_i - \bar{x}) = \bar{y}$$

c. The quantity $\sum_{i=1}^{n} (y_i - \hat{y}_i)^2$ is by (9) the *sum of squares due to error*, and is denoted by SS_E.

Thus the identity (13) can be written as

$$SS_T = SS_R + SS_E \tag{14}$$

In words, the total sum of squares equals the sum of squares explained by linear regression plus the sum of squares due to error.

Now, (12) can be written as

$$1 - r^2 = \frac{SS_E}{SS_T} \tag{15}$$

and hence from (14)

$$r^2 = 1 - \frac{SS_E}{SS_T} = \frac{SS_T - SS_E}{SS_T} = \frac{SS_R}{SS_T} \tag{16}$$

Thus r^2, called the *coefficient of determination*, is the ratio of the sum of squares SS_R explained by linear regression to the total sum of squares SS_T, while $1 - r^2$ is the ratio of the "error" or "unexplained" sum of squares SS_E to the total sum of squares SS_T.

From table 9.2 we have for example 1

$$S_x^2 = 1822 \qquad S_y^2 = 3.4394 \qquad S_{xy} = 75.49$$

and hence the coefficient of determination is

$$r^2 = \frac{S_{xy}^2}{S_x^2 \cdot S_y^2} = \frac{(75.49)^2}{(1822)(3.4394)} = \frac{5698.7401}{6266.5868} = .909$$

The correlation coefficient itself (since $S_{xy} > 0$) is given by

$$r = +\sqrt{.909} = .954$$

Observe that in computing r it is easier to compute r^2 first and then to put $r = +\sqrt{r^2}$ or $-\sqrt{r^2}$ depending on whether $S_{xy} > 0$ or < 0, rather than to compute r directly from (5).

In example 1 approximately 91 percent ($r^2 = .91$) of the total variation SS_T in the GPA scores is "explained" by linear regression on the IQ score. Furthermore, since $r = .954$, there is a high degree of positive correlation between GPA and IQ, suggesting a strong association between y and x, with $\hat{\beta} = .0414 > 0$.* This is clearly noticeable in figure 9.4.

Everything we have done thus far has been purely "descriptive" for a given set of data points $(x_1, y_1), \ldots, (x_n, y_n)$. We have given no answer, for example, to the question of how closely we could expect a future observation y_0, taken at some preassigned value x_0 of x, to lie on the Least Squares line $y = \hat{\alpha} + \hat{\beta}x$ obtained from the given data. We shall only be able to answer such questions by formulating a specific probabilistic model in which the y_i's are random variables.

PROBLEMS 9.4

1. Compute SS_R and r^2 for the data of problem 1, sections 9.2 and 9.3. Explain what r^2 means.

2. Repeat problem 1 for problem 2, sections 9.2 and 9.3.

3. Repeat problem 1 for problem 3, sections 9.2 and 9.3.

4. Repeat problem 1 for problem 4, sections 9.2 and 9.3.

---

*Although r is near 1, $\hat{\beta}$ is small because S_y is much greater than S_x in this example.

9.5 A Probabilistic Model for Linear Regression on One Independent Variable

Assume for simplicity that the values $x_1, \ldots, x_n$ of the variable x, the "independent" or "control" variable, are fixed, perhaps chosen by the experimenter. The values $y_1, \ldots, y_n$ of y, the "dependent" or "response" variable, are now thought of as random observations or responses that are linearly related *only with respect to their mean values* to the respective x values $x_1, \ldots, x_n$, but are masked by experimental error so that they do not lie exactly on a line but scatter about a line. Consider the following example.

Example 2

A physiologist wishes to study how a running exercise program affects weight loss in middle-aged males. Using 10 men in the 35 to 45 age group, each about 25 pounds overweight, he establishes a normal fixed caloric intake per unit of body weight for each man and then places him on a running program for 4 weeks. Each subject runs x miles per day, 6 days a week, at the rate of 8 minutes per mile. At the end of 4 weeks the weight loss y is recorded for each subject. The subjects are randomly assigned to the various running regimens. The results are given in table 9.3

TABLE 9.3
Weight Loss Data

Subject (i)	1	2	3	4	5	6	7	8	9	10
Miles run (x_i)	1.0	1.0	1.5	1.5	2.0	2.0	2.5	2.5	3.0	3.0
Wt. loss (y_i)	5.6	3.4	5.8	5.4	9.4	7.8	9.8	6.6	10.3	8.3

In contrast to example 1, the experimenter here had the x values under his control, and chose to have two subjects run one mile per day, two one and one-half miles per day, and so on. However, the dependent or response variable y = weight loss was not under his control, and the values $y_1, y_2, \ldots, y_{10}$, although influenced by their corresponding x values, are random variables. If, as we assume, the relationship of the y values to the x values is in fact *linear in the mean plus an unknown amount of experimentally uncontrolled error*, then each of the y_i can be thought of as being of the form

$$y_i = \alpha + \beta x_i + \epsilon_i \tag{17}$$

where x_i is the chosen x value for the ith subject (miles per day in the example) and y_i is the observed response, a random variable, for the ith subject (weight loss in the example). The ϵ_i in (17) is thought of as the unexplained experimental error that causes y_i to differ from the ideal "regression" value $\alpha + \beta x_i$, the mean value of y in repeated observations *with the same fixed* x_i. The ϵ_i are unobservable random variables, since α and β are unknown. In example 2 the random errors ϵ_i arise from individual subject variability, measurement error, and various other factors not under experimental control, even though all subjects were roughly the same age (35-45), the same sex, fed the same diet (fixed caloric intake per unit of body weight), overweight to the same amount (about 25 lbs), and ran at the same rate (8 minutes per mile). These factors were controlled (that is, held at the same levels) so that the changes in the dependent variable y would be due primarily to changes in the independent variable x. Whatever is not explained by the assumed linear function $\alpha + \beta x_i$ for the ith subject forms the "error" term, ϵ_i. We can now state the general model:

The Probabilistic Model of Linear Regression
Assume that the values of some "dependent" variable y are related to values of an "independent" variable x as follows. For the ith observation $(i = 1, \ldots, n)$

$$y_i = \alpha + \beta x_i + \epsilon_i \tag{18}$$

where α and β are two unknown constants and

a. $x_1, \ldots, x_n$ are the values of the independent variable x, considered as *fixed*.
b. $y_1, \ldots, y_n$ are the observations on the dependent variable y. They are *random variables*, since
c. the "errors" $\epsilon_1, \ldots, \epsilon_n$ are independent random variables, each of which is *normally distributed* with a *mean value zero*, $\mu_{\epsilon_i} = 0$, and a *constant variance*, $\sigma_{\epsilon_i}^2 = \sigma^2$, $i = 1, \ldots, n$. Here σ^2 is also an unknown constant.

Equation 18, together with the fact that ϵ_i is assumed to have a mean value 0, implies that

$$m.v.(y_i) = \alpha + \beta x_i$$

In other words, the linear "regression" function $\alpha + \beta x$ gives the mean value of a random y taken at any fixed value of x.

The model may be visualized as in figure 9.5. Each y_i is a normally distributed random variable centered at its mean value $\mu_{y_i} = \alpha + \beta x_i$ on the (unknown) regression line $y = \alpha + \beta x$, and with the (unknown) variance σ^2 at all x values.

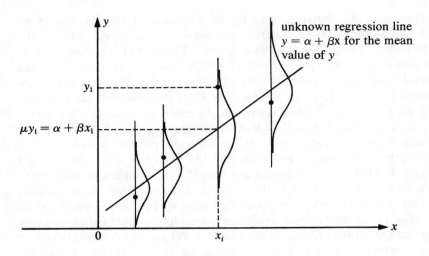

FIGURE 9.5
The linear regression model

PROBLEMS 9.5

1. Discuss problem 1, section 9.2, in connection with the model in (18). Are the years random variables? Are the prices random variables? What assumptions are made?

2. Discuss problem 2, section 9.2, in connection with the model in (18). Are the years random variables? Are the sales random variables? What assumptions are made?

3. Discuss problems 3 and 4, section 9.2, in connection with the model in (18). Can the x values be considered fixed in both these problems? Can the y values be considered random variables in both these problems? Do you see any differences between reasonable models in these two problems? What assumptions would have to be made to conform to the model in (18)?

9.6 Estimation of α, β, and σ^2 in the Model

Postponing other inference problems to the next section, we shall first obtain good *point estimators* for the unknown constants α, β, and σ^2 of the model. The Least Squares approach discussed in section 9.2 suggests that we do this for α and β by choosing as estimates the values $\hat{\alpha}$ and $\hat{\beta}$ that minimize the sum of squares (1). By theorem 1 the values of $\hat{\alpha}$ and $\hat{\beta}$ are given by

$$\hat{\beta} = \frac{S_{xy}}{S_x^2} \qquad \hat{\alpha} = \bar{y} - \hat{\beta}\bar{x} \tag{19}$$

where $\bar{x}$, $\bar{y}$, S_x, S_y, S_{xy} are defined in (4). The corresponding Least Squares estimate of the unknown regression line on which the mean values $\mu_{y_i} = \alpha + \beta x_i$ are assumed to lie is then, as in (2) and (6),

$$y = \hat{\alpha} + \hat{\beta}x = \bar{y} + \hat{\beta}(x - \bar{x}) \tag{20}$$

The values $\hat{\alpha}$ and $\hat{\beta}$, being functions of the random variables $y_1, \ldots,$ y_n, are themselves random variables, and will fluctuate from sample to sample when $x_1, \ldots, x_n$ are fixed. We refer to the statistics $\hat{\alpha}$ and $\hat{\beta}$ as the *Least Squares estimators* of the unknown parameters α and β. The following theorem states some important properties of $\hat{\alpha}$ and $\hat{\beta}$,

Theorem 3

For the model in section 9.5, the Least Squares estimators (19) have the following properties.

a. $\hat{\alpha}$ and $\hat{\beta}$ are *unbiased* estimators of the true but unknown α and β. That is, whatever be the true values of α and β.

$$\mu_{\hat{\alpha}} = \alpha, \text{ and } \mu_{\hat{\beta}} = \beta \tag{21}$$

b. The variances of $\hat{\alpha}$ and $\hat{\beta}$ are

$$\sigma_{\hat{\alpha}}^2 = \sigma^2\left(\frac{1}{n} + \frac{\bar{x}^2}{S_x^2}\right) \tag{22}$$

and

$$\sigma_{\hat{\beta}}^2 = \frac{\sigma^2}{S_x^2} \tag{23}$$

c. $\hat{\alpha}$ and $\hat{\beta}$ are normally distributed random variables.

A proof of theorem 3 is given in the appendix at the end of this chapter.

If σ^2 were known, we could at once from theorem 3 obtain confidence intervals for the unknown true values of α and β, since the standardized random variables $z_1 = (\hat{\alpha} - \alpha)/\sigma_{\hat{\alpha}}$ and $z_2 = (\hat{\beta} - \beta)/\sigma_{\hat{\beta}}$ have a standard normal distribution. However, in our model σ^2 is unknown. The next theorem provides an estimator for σ^2 and states some of its properties. We omit the proof.

Theorem 4
The random variable s^2 defined by

$$s^2 = \frac{SS_E}{n-2} = \frac{\sum_{i=1}^{n}(y_i - \hat{y}_i)^2}{n-2} \tag{24}$$

where $\hat{y}_i = \hat{\alpha} + \hat{\beta}\,x_i$, is called the *residual or error mean square*, and has the following properties:

a. s^2 is an unbiased estimator of σ^2; that is, $\mu_{s^2} = \sigma^2$. **(25)**
b. $(n-2)s^2/\sigma^2 = SS_E/\sigma^2$ has a chi-squared distribution with $n-2$ degrees of freedom. From this it follows (page 203) that the variance of $(n-2)s^2/\sigma^2$ is $2(n-2)$, so that $\sigma^2_{s^2} = 2\sigma^4/(n-2)$.
c. s^2 is independent of $\hat{\alpha}$ and $\hat{\beta}$.

The following basic theorem is used in making statistical inferences about α and β.

Theorem 5

$$t_1 = \frac{\hat{\alpha} - \alpha}{s\sqrt{\frac{1}{n} + \frac{\bar{x}^2}{S_x^2}}} \quad \text{has a } t \text{ distribution with } n-2 \text{ d.f.} \tag{26}$$

and

$$t_2 = \frac{\hat{\beta} - \beta}{s/S_x} \quad \text{has a } t \text{ distribution with } n-2 \text{ d.f.} \tag{27}$$

Proof. To show this for t_2, we write t_2 in the form

$$t_2 = \frac{S_x(\hat{\beta} - \beta)}{\sigma} \bigg/ \sqrt{\frac{s^2}{\sigma^2}}$$

where by theorem 3, $S_x(\hat{\beta} - \beta)/\sigma$ has a standard normal distribution, and by theorem 4,

$$\frac{s^2}{\sigma^2} = \frac{(n-2)s^2}{\sigma^2} \bigg/ (n-2)$$

is a chi-squared random variable divided by its degrees of freedom and is independent of the standard normal numerator $S_x(\hat{\beta} - \beta)/\sigma$. Theorem 7.4 now applies to give the result (27) for t_2. A similar argument establishes (26) for t_1.

In the next sections we shall treat inference problems concerning α and β by using the t distributions (26) and (27).

PROBLEMS 9.6

1. Using the results from problem 1 in sections 9.2 and 9.5,

   a. Find an unbiased estimator for α and β in the unknown line $y = \alpha + \beta x$.
   b. Find an unbiased estimator for σ^2 by formula 24.
   c. Find an unbiased estimator for $\sigma_{\hat{\alpha}}^2$ and $\sigma_{\hat{\beta}}^2$ by (22) and (23). (Hint: replace σ^2 by s^2.)
   d. State the distributions of

$$\frac{(n-2)s^2}{\sigma^2} = \frac{SS_E}{\sigma^2}, \ t_1 = \frac{\hat{\alpha} - \alpha}{s\sqrt{\dfrac{1}{n} + \dfrac{\bar{x}^2}{S_x^2}}}, \text{ and } t_2 = \frac{\hat{\beta} - \beta}{s/S_x}$$

2. Repeat problem 1 using the results from problem 2 in sections 9.2 to 9.5.

3. Repeat problem 1 using the results from problem 3, sections 9.2 to 9.5.

4. Repeat problem 1 using the results from problem 4 in sections 9.2 to 9.5. (Note: verbal scores are thought of as fixed.)

9.7 Confidence Intervals for α and β

Theorem 5 yields at once confidence intervals for the unknown values of α and β.

Let $u = s\sqrt{1/n + \bar{x}^2/S_x^2}$, $v = s/S_x$, and $t_{\delta, \nu} =$ the value from appendix table 7 (the t distribution) with ν d.f. that satisfies

$$P(t \geq t_{\delta, \nu}) = \delta$$

(We are using δ instead of the usual α because α has another meaning here.)

Then

$$P\{\hat{\alpha} - t_{\delta/2, n-2} \cdot u < \alpha < \hat{\alpha} + t_{\delta/2, n-2} \cdot u\} = 1 - \delta \qquad (28)$$

and similarly

$$P\{\hat{\beta} - t_{\delta/2, n-2} \, v < \beta < \hat{\beta} + t_{\delta/2, n-2} \cdot v\} = 1 - \delta \qquad (29)$$

As an example, let us find 95% confidence intervals for α and β based on the data in table 9.3. To do this we must first compute $\hat{\alpha}$ and $\hat{\beta}$ from the observed values of $\bar{x}$, $\bar{y}$, S_{xy}, S_x^2, and S_y^2. Instead of proceeding directly, as in table 9.2, to compute $(x_i - \bar{x})^2$, and so forth, it is a little simpler to form the following table.

TABLE 9.4
Computation of $\hat{\alpha}$, $\hat{\beta}$, and s^2

i	x_i	y_i	x_i^2	y_i^2	$.x_i y_i$
1	1	5.6	1.00	31.36	5.6
2	1	3.4	1.00	11.56	3.4
3	1.5	5.8	2.25	33.64	8.7
4	1.5	5.4	2.25	29.16	8.1
5	2	9.4	4.00	88.36	18.8
6	2	7.8	4.00	60.84	15.6
7	2.5	9.8	6.25	96.04	24.5
8	2.5	6.6	6.25	43.56	16.5
9	3	10.3	9.00	106.09	30.9
10	3	8.3	9.00	68.89	24.9
Sum	20	72.4	45.00	569.50	157

and to calculate

$$\bar{x} = \frac{1}{n} \sum_{i=1}^{n} x_i = \frac{20}{10} = 2 \qquad \bar{y} = \frac{1}{n} \sum_{i=1}^{n} y_i = \frac{72.4}{10} = 7.24$$

$$S_x^2 = \sum_{i=1}^{n} x_i^2 - n\bar{x}^2 = 45 - 10(4) = 5$$

$$S_y^2 = \sum_{i=1}^{n} y_i^2 - n\bar{y}^2 = 569.50 - 10(7.24)^2 = 45.324$$

$$S_{xy} = \sum_{i=1}^{n} x_i y_i - n\bar{x}\bar{y} = 157 - (10)(2)(7.24) = 12.2$$

From these quantities we compute the Least Squares estimates

$$\hat{\beta} = \frac{S_{xy}}{S_x^2} = \frac{12.2}{5} = 2.44$$

$$\hat{\alpha} = \bar{y} - \hat{\beta}\bar{x} = 7.24 - 2.44(2) = 2.36$$

and the equation of the Least Squares line

$$y = \hat{\alpha} + \hat{\beta}x = 2.36 + 2.44x$$

Also, by (12) we have

$$SS_E = S_y^2 - \frac{S_{xy}^2}{S_x^2} = 45.324 - \frac{(12.2)^2}{5} = 15.556$$

from which we get our estimate s^2 of σ^2 by (24)

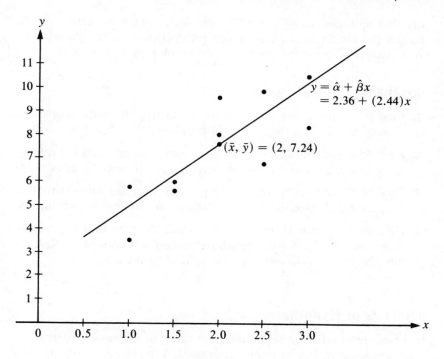

FIGURE 9.6
Scattergram and Least Squares line for the data of table 9.3

$$s^2 = \frac{SS_E}{n-2} = \frac{15.556}{8} = 1.945 \quad , \quad s = \sqrt{1.945} = 1.395$$

Figure 9.6 shows the scattergram of the data as well as the Least Squares line $y = \hat{\alpha} + \hat{\beta}x$.

To construct 95% confidence intervals for α and β we note that with $n - 2 = 8$, $t_{.025,\,8} = 2.306$, and that

$$u = s\sqrt{\frac{1}{n} + \frac{\bar{x}^2}{S_x^2}} = 1.395\sqrt{.1 + .8} = 1.323, \quad v = \frac{s}{S_x} = \frac{1.395}{\sqrt{5}} = 6.24$$

Hence, by (28), a 95% confidence interval for α is

$$-0.69 = 2.36 - (2.306)(1.323) < \alpha < 2.36 + (2.306)(1.323) = 5.41$$

and by (29) a 95% confidence interval for β is

$$1.00 = 2.44 - (2.306)(.624) < \beta < 2.44 + (2.306)(.624) = 3.88$$

The width of the confidence interval (29) for β depends on v in such a way that large values of $v = s/S_x$ yield wide confidence intervals. To shorten the length of the confidence interval (that is, to minimize v), the x_i values of the experiment should be chosen so that S_x is large.

PROBLEMS 9.7

1. Find 95% confidence intervals for α and β for the data in problem 1, section 9.2. Use the results of problem 1 in section 9.6.

2. Find 95% confidence intervals for α and β for the data in problem 2, section 9.2. Use the results obtained in problem 2, section 9.6.

3. Find 98% confidence intervals for α and β for the data in problem 3, section 9.2. Use the results obtained in problem 3, section 9.6.

4. Find 98% confidence intervals for α and β for the data in problem 4, section 9.2. Use the results obtained in problem 4, Section 9.6. (Note: verbal scores are thought of as fixed.)

9.8 Tests of Hypotheses for β

In linear regression on one variable it is often of interest to test hypotheses about β. For example, in example 2 the physiologist naturally suspects that as exercise increases, weight loss also increases. He may attempt to confirm this surmise by testing

$$H_0 : \beta \le 0 \text{ vs } H_1 : \beta > 0.$$

If the test rejects H_0, he will then claim that $\beta > 0$; that is, that y (expected weight loss) increases as x (miles run per day) increases.

Let us consider the slightly more general case of testing $H_0 : \beta \le \beta_0$ vs $H_1 : \beta > \beta_0$, where β_0 is any preassigned value, not necessarily 0. The test is based on the statistic

$$t_2 = \frac{\hat{\beta} - \beta_0}{s/S_x}$$

which by (27) has, at the point $\beta = \beta_0$ separating H_0 and H_1, a t distribution with $n - 2$ d.f. It is reasonable to reject H_0 for large values of t_2, because these values tend to support $\beta > \beta_0$ (since $\hat{\beta}$ tends to be close to the true value of β, t_2 tends to be larger under H_1 than under H_0). Therefore, the critical region should be of the form $\{t_2 > c\}$, where c is determined for $\beta = \beta_0$ to be that value leaving probability δ in the upper tail of the t distribution with $n - 2$ d.f.; that is, $c = t_{\delta, n-2}$. The test is therefore

$$\text{Reject } H_0 \text{ if } t_2 = \frac{\hat{\beta} - \beta_0}{s/S_x} > t_{\delta, n-2}$$

In example 2

$$t_2 = \frac{\sqrt{5}\,(2.24 - 0)}{1.395} = 3.59$$

while $t_{.05, 8} = 3.59$. Therefore, since $2.75 > 1.86$, the physiologist rejects H_0 with a good deal to spare at the .05 level of significance, and asserts with assurance that $\beta > 0$; that is, that weight loss increases with the amount of running (for this age and amount of overweight, over the range of x in question, for a four-week period).

A two-sided test for β based on a two-sided rejection region is also available, as well as a one-sided test in the opposite direction. The results are summarized in table 9.5 below. (In the two-sided test, if we agree to assert that $\beta > \beta_0$ if $t_2 > t_{\delta/2, n-2}$, and that $\beta < \beta_0$ if $t_2 < -t_{\delta/2, n-2}$, then the probability of asserting that $\beta > \beta_0$ when in fact $\beta \le \beta_0$, or of asserting that $\beta < \beta_0$ when in fact $\beta \ge \beta_0$, is at most $\delta/2$.)

TABLE 9.5
Hypothesis Tests for β at Level δ Based on $t_2 = (\hat{\beta} - \beta_0)/(s/S_x)$

H_0	H_1	R: reject H_0 (accept H_1) if
$\beta \le \beta_0$	$\beta > \beta$	$t_2 > t_{\delta, n-2}$
$\beta \ge \beta_0$	$\beta < \beta$	$t_2 < -t_{\delta, n-2}$
$\beta = \beta_0$	$\beta \ne \beta_0$	$t_2 > t_{\delta/2, n-2}$ or $t_2 < -t_{\delta/2, n-2}$

PROBLEMS 9.8

1. Test the hypothesis $H_0 : \beta \le 0$ vs $H_1 : \beta > 0$ in problem 1, section 9.2, at the level of significance .01. State the rejection region and conclusion of your test.

2. Test the hypothesis $H_0 : \beta \le .2$ vs $H_1 : \beta > .2$ in problem 2, section 9.2, at the level of significance $\alpha = .05$. State the rejection region and conclusion of your test.

3. Test the hypothesis $H_0 : \beta = 0$ vs the alternative $H_1 : \beta \ne 0$ in

problem 3, section 9.2, at the level of significance .01. State the rejection region and conclusion of your test.

4. Test the hypothesis $H_0 : \beta = 0$ vs the alternative $H_1 : \beta \neq 0$ in problem 4, section 9.2, at the level of significance .05. State the rejection region and conclusion of your test. Again consider the verbal scores as fixed.

9.9 Confidence Intervals for the Mean Value of y for a Fixed Value x_0 of the Independent Variable

The experiment in example 2 was conducted only at the x values 1, 1.5, 2, 2.5, and 3. Suppose that we want to estimate the mean value, μ_{y_0}, of the dependent variable y at some specified value x_0 of the dependent variable. For instance, we may want to estimate μ_{y_0} for $x_0 = 2.2$ (a value not used in the experiment) or for $x_0 = 2$ (a value that was used). Under our model, the random variable y_0 can be written as

$$y_0 = \alpha + \beta x_0 + \epsilon_0$$

where ϵ_0 has a normal distribution with mean value 0 and variance σ^2. Hence y_0 is normally distributed, with mean and variance

$$\mu_0 = \mu_{y_0} = \alpha + \beta x_0 \quad , \quad \sigma_0^2 = \sigma_{y_0}^2 = \sigma^2$$

Since $\hat{\alpha}$ and $\hat{\beta}$ are our estimators of α and β, we naturally take as our estimator of μ_0 the statistic

$$\hat{\mu}_0 = \hat{\alpha} + \hat{\beta} x_0 \tag{30}$$

which is an unbiased estimator of μ_0, since from the unbiasedness of $\hat{\alpha}$ and $\hat{\beta}$

$$m.v.(\hat{\mu}_0) = \mu_{\hat{\alpha}} + \mu_{\hat{\beta}} \cdot x_0 = \alpha + \beta x_0 = \mu_0$$

We state without proof the following useful facts about the estimator μ_0 given by (30):

$$var(\hat{\mu}_o) = \sigma^2 \left(\frac{1}{n} + \frac{(x_0 - \bar{x})^2}{S_x^2} \right)$$

and

$$t_3 = \frac{\hat{\mu}_0 - \mu_0}{s\sqrt{\dfrac{1}{n} + \dfrac{(x_0 - \bar{x})^2}{S_x^2}}} \tag{31}$$

has a t distribution with $n - 2$ d.f.

From (31) we have

A 100 (1 − δ)% confidence interval for $\mu_0 = \mu_{y0} = \alpha + \beta x_0$:

$$\hat{\mu}_0 - t_{\delta/2,\,n-2} \cdot a < \mu_0 < \hat{\mu}_0 + t_{\delta/2,\,n-2} \cdot a \qquad (32)$$

where

$$a = s\sqrt{\frac{1}{n} + \frac{(x_0 - \bar{x})^2}{S_x^{\,2}}} \qquad (33)$$

In example 2, suppose that we want to estimate the mean value $\mu_0 = \alpha + \beta x_0$ at, say, $x_0 = 2.2$. Then by the calculations on pages 290–91

$$a = 1.395\sqrt{\frac{1}{10} + \frac{(2.2 - 2.0)^2}{5}}$$
$$= 1.395\sqrt{.108} = .458$$

and $\hat{\mu}_0 = \hat{\alpha} + \hat{\beta} x_0 = (2.36) + (2.44)(2.2) = 7.73$. Thus, since $t_{.025,\,8} = 2.306$, a 95% confidence interval for $\mu_0 = \mu_{y0}$ is $6.67 = 7.73 - (2.306)(.458) < \mu_0 < 7.73 + (2.306)(.458) = 8.79$.

Note: In (33), as the term $(x_0 - \bar{x})^2$ increases, so does a (and hence the width of the confidence interval for μ_0). In designing the experiment, the experimenter should therefore choose values $x_1, \ldots, x_n$ of the controlled variable so that $\bar{x}$ is close to the values x_0 that are of greatest interest. Note that the special case $x_0 = 0$ of (33) gives the confidence interval (28) for α.

PROBLEMS 9.9

1. In problem 1, section 9.2, find 95% confidence intervals for the 1958 and 1968 prices of crude oil. Use (32).

2. In problem 3, section 9.2, find 98% confidence intervals for the divorce rates in 1933 and 1965. Use (32).

9.10 Prediction of a Future Value of y

Suppose that we wish to predict a single unknown future value of the dependent variable y_0, corresponding to a given value of x_0 and an independent observation not yet taken there. For instance, in example 2 we may wish to predict, for a new subject fitting the criteria of subjects studied, his weight loss after four weeks of running at, say, $x_0 = 2.5$ miles per day.

In general, we wish to predict the value

$$y_0 = \alpha + \beta x_0 + \epsilon_0$$

at some specified value, x_0, of a single new observation y_0, independent of previous values $y_1, \ldots, y_n$. We naturally take as our predictor

$$\hat{y}_0 = \hat{\alpha} + \hat{\beta} x_0$$

This is also the estimator $\hat{\mu}_0$ of the mean value $\mu_0 = \mu_{y_0} = \alpha + \beta x_0$. But predicting y_0 is not the same as estimating μ_0, since the error of $\hat{y}_0$ as a predictor of $y_0 = \alpha + \beta x_0 + \epsilon_0$ will include not only the variability of the estimator $\hat{\mu}_0 = \hat{\alpha} + \hat{\beta} x_0$ of μ_{y_0} but also some additional variability due to the experimental error ϵ_0 for the new subject. To see this, we write

$$\hat{y}_0 - y_0 = (\hat{y}_0 - \mu_0) - (y_0 - \mu_0) = (\hat{\mu}_0 - \mu_0) - \epsilon_0$$

Then, since ϵ_0 is independent of $y_1, \ldots, y_n$ and hence independent of $\hat{\mu}_0$, we have

$$\sigma_{\hat{y}_0}^2 = \sigma_{\hat{\mu}_0}^2 + \sigma_{\epsilon_0}^2 = \sigma^2 \left(\frac{1}{n} + \frac{(x_0 - \bar{x})^2}{S_x^2} \right) + \sigma^2 = \sigma^2 \left(1 + \frac{1}{n} + \frac{(x_0 - \bar{x})^2}{S_x^2} \right)$$

It can be shown that

$$t_4 = \frac{\hat{y}_0 - y_0}{s \sqrt{1 + \frac{1}{n} + \frac{(x_0 - \bar{x})^2}{S_x^2}}} \tag{34}$$

has a t distribution with a $n - 2$ d.f. Based on this fact we obtain

A 100 $(1 - \delta)\%$ confidence interval for a new value y_0 of the dependent random variable at a fixed x_0:

$$P\{\hat{y}_0 - t_{\delta/2, n-2} \cdot b < y_0 < \hat{y}_0 + t_{\delta/2, n-2} \cdot b\} = 1 - \delta \tag{35}$$

where

$$\hat{y}_0 = \hat{\alpha} + \hat{\beta} x_0, \, b = s \sqrt{1 + \frac{1}{n} + \frac{(x_0 - \bar{x})^2}{S_x^2}}$$

In example 2, if y_0 denotes the weight loss of someone belonging to the population in question who intends to run $x_0 = 2.5$ miles per day for four weeks, the 95% confidence interval for y_0 is given by (35) with

$$\hat{y}_0 = 2.36 + (2.24)(2.5) = 7.96$$

and

$$b = 1.395 \sqrt{1 + \frac{1}{10} + \frac{(2.5 - 2.0)^2}{5}} = 1.496$$

This yields the 95% confidence interval $4.51 = 7.96 - (2.306)(1.496) < y_0 < 7.96 + (2.306)(1.496) = 11.41$.

Again we note that owing to the term $(x_0 - \bar{x})^2$ in (34), the farther x_0 is from $\bar{x}$, the wider the 95% confidence interval for y_0.

PROBLEMS 9.10

1. In problem 1, section 9.2, find 90% confidence intervals for predicted 1973 and 1975 prices of crude oil. Use (35).

2. In problem 2, section 9.2, find a 95% confidence interval for predicted sales in year 11 (one year in the future).

3. In problem 4, section 9.2, find 90% confidence intervals for the math. scores of students whose verbal scores are (a) 60; (b) 70; (c) 90.

9.11 Inference When the Observations on the Independent Variable Are Random or Not Controlled

In example 2 the physiologist was free to control the various values $x_1, \ldots, x_{10}$ of the dependent variable. However, in example 1, if the sample of college students was chosen at random from the population of college students under study, then $x_1, \ldots, x_7$ are themselves random variables, just as are $y_1, \ldots, y_7$. The analysis in such cases regarding α, β, μ_0, or y_0 is as before, but the interpretation is slightly different: the probability statements are now *conditional* probability statements *given the observations* $x_1, \ldots, x_n$.

Thus, suppose we wish to estimate by a 90% confidence interval the mean GPA μ_0 of students with an IQ of $x_0 = 125$, based on the data in table 9.2 for which

$$S_x^2 = 1822 \qquad S_y^2 = 3.4394 \qquad S_{xy} = 75.49$$

$$SS_E = S_y^2 - \frac{S_{xy}^2}{S_x^2} = .3117$$

and

$$s = \sqrt{\frac{SS_E}{n-2}} = \sqrt{\frac{.3117}{5}} = .25$$

From (33)

$$a = s\sqrt{\frac{1}{n} + \frac{(x_0 - \bar{x})^2}{S_x^2}} = .25\sqrt{\frac{1}{7} + \frac{(125 - 128)^2}{1822}} = .096$$

and

$$\hat{\mu}_0 = \hat{\alpha} + \hat{\beta}x_0 = -2.45 + (.0414)(125) = 2.73$$

With $t_{.05,5} = 2.015$ the 90% confidence interval for μ_0 is therefore $2.54 = 2.73 - (2.015)(.096) < \mu_0 < 2.73 + (2.015)(.096) = 2.92$, *provided that the values* $x_1, \ldots, x_7$ *are considered as given.*

Similarly, a one-sided test of $H_0 : \beta \leq 0$ vs $H_1 : \beta > 0$ at level $= .01$, using table 9.5, is based on the statistic

$$t_1 = \frac{\hat{\beta} - \beta_0}{s/S_x} = \frac{(42.68)(.0414 - 0)}{.25} = \frac{1.767}{.25} = 7.07$$

and since $t_{.01,5} = 3.365$ we know that *for the given values* $x_1, \ldots, x_7$ there will be less than a .01 chance of deciding that $\beta > 0$ and hence asserting a positive effect of IQ on GPA, if in fact $\beta \leq 0$.

Remarks

a. The confidence intervals and tests of this chapter are, of course, based on the model in section 9.5. If any of the assumptions (a)–(c) fail to hold, at least approximately, we may be in trouble. A case of this sort arises when the assumed linear relation $\alpha + \beta x$ for the mean value of y holds only in some restricted interval $a \leq x \leq b$ of x values in which the observations are taken, but we attempt to predict a future value y_0 corresponding to an x_0 value outside this interval, where the linear model may be badly in error.

b. The concept of "linear regression" first arose in studies of the inheritance of body characteristics. To simplify somewhat, let x denote (father's height plus mother's height)/2 and y the height of the child, adjusted for sex. Francis Galton's observational data suggested a linear relation $\mu_y = \bar{y} + \beta(x - \bar{x})$, with β about equal to .5 and $\bar{y}$ about the same as $\bar{x}$. Thus the mean height of children whose parents' mean height is x deviates from the mean height $\bar{x}$ of the general population by only about one-half the amount $x - \bar{x}$ by which the parents' height x differs from $\bar{x}$. In other words, *children tend to deviate less from the general population mean than do their parents.*

Galton realized, even before the modern theory of genetics was developed, that one of the reasons for this phenomenon is that some of the genetic material transmitted from parents to children, coming from remote ancestors, remains latent in the parents but manifests itself in the children. Current statistical methods for studying the effect of environmental pollution, schooling, and so forth, on various aspects of human welfare rely greatly on the techniques developed by Galton and his followers, notably Karl Pearson.

PROBLEMS 9.11

1. Discuss problem 4, section 9.2 in view of the discussion in this section. Are the inferences in problem 3 of section 9.10, and problem 4 of sections 9.7 and 9.8, to be thought of as conditional?

2. Carry out an analysis of the data in problem 5, section 9.2 *ignoring the nonlinearity*. Specifically,
   a. Find 95% confidence intervals for α and β.
   b. Find 95% confidence for predicted values at the times of day 500, 1300, and 2100, using formula (34).
   c. Comment on the appropriateness of the intervals in (b).

9.12 Appendix

Proof of Theorem 1
An algebraic proof of theorem 1 is based on the following *Lemma*.

Let $c_1, \ldots, c_n$ and $d_1, \ldots, d_n$ be any constants, with the d_i's not all zero, and consider the expression

$$g(t) = \sum_{i=1}^{n} (c_i - d_i t)^2$$

as a function of t. This expression attains its minimum value for

$$t = t_0 = \frac{\sum_{i=1}^{n} c_i d_i}{\sum_{i=1}^{n} d_i^2}$$

and this minimum value is

$$g_{min} = g(t_0) = \frac{\left(\sum_{i=1}^{n} c_i^2\right)\left(\sum_{i=1}^{n} d_i^2\right) - \left(\sum_{i=1}^{n} c_i d_i\right)^2}{\sum_{i=1}^{n} d_i^2} \geq 0$$

Proof We have

$$g(t) = \sum_{i=1}^{n} (c_i - d_i t)^2 = \sum_{i=1}^{n} (c_i^2 - 2c_i d_i t + d_i^2 t^2) = a^2 t^2 - 2bt + c^2$$

where $a^2 = \sum_{i=1}^{n} d_i^2$, $b = \sum_{i=1}^{n} c_i d_i$,   and $c^2 = \sum_{i=1}^{n} c_i^2$.

"Completing the square" in $g(t)$ gives

$$g(t) = \left(a^2 t^2 - 2bt + \frac{b^2}{a^2}\right) + \left(c^2 - \frac{b^2}{a^2}\right)$$

$$= \left(at - \frac{b}{a}\right)^2 + \left(\frac{c^2 a^2 - b^2}{a^2}\right)$$

Since $(at - b/a)^2 \geq 0$, and since the term $(c^2 a^2 - b^2)/a^2$ does not depend on t, $g(t)$ is minimized by making $(at - b/a)^2 = 0$; that is, by choosing t equal to

$$t_0 = \frac{b}{a^2} = \frac{\sum\limits_{i=1}^{n} c_i d_i}{\sum\limits_{i=1}^{n} d_i^2}$$

The minimum value of $g(t)$ is then given by

$$g_{min} = g(t_0) = \frac{c^2 a^2 - b^2}{a^2} = \frac{\left(\sum\limits_{i=1}^{n} c_i^2\right)\left(\sum\limits_{i=1}^{n} d_i^2\right) - \left(\sum\limits_{i=1}^{n} c_i d_i\right)^2}{\sum\limits_{i=1}^{n} d_i^2}$$

This completes the proof of the lemma.

To prove theorem 1 we first consider $S(\alpha, \beta) = \sum\limits_{i=1}^{n} (y_i - \alpha - \beta x_i)^2$ as a function of α, regarding β as fixed. Let $t = \alpha$, $d_i = 1$, and $c_i = y_i - \beta x_i$ in the lemma. Then $S(\alpha, \beta)$ is minimized with respect to α for

$$\hat{\alpha} = \frac{\sum\limits_{i=1}^{n} c_i d_i}{\sum\limits_{i=1}^{n} d_i^2} = \frac{\sum\limits_{i=1}^{n} (y_i - \beta x_i)}{n} = \bar{y} - \beta \bar{x}$$

regardless of how β was chosen. Substituting this value $\hat{\alpha}$ in $S(\alpha, \beta)$ gives

$$S(\hat{\alpha}, \beta) = \sum\limits_{i=1}^{n} [(y_i - \bar{y}) - \beta(x_i - \bar{x})]^2 \, ,$$

a function of β alone. We now minimize this as a function of β by applying the lemma again with $t = \beta$, $c_i = y_i - \bar{y}$ and $d_i = x_i - \bar{x}$. The value of β that minimizes $S(\hat{\alpha}, \beta)$ is thus

$$\hat{\beta} = \frac{\sum\limits_{i=1}^{n} c_i d_i}{\sum\limits_{i=1}^{n} d_i^2} = \frac{\sum\limits_{i=1}^{n} (x_i - \bar{x})(y_i - \bar{y})}{\sum\limits_{i=1}^{n} (x_i - \bar{x})^2} = \frac{S_{xy}}{S_x^2}$$

verifying the first part of (3). Now, with $\hat{\beta}$ so defined, the $\hat{\alpha}$ above becomes $\hat{\alpha} = \bar{y} - \hat{\beta}\bar{x}$, verifying the second part of (3).

Proof of Theorem 3

Since $\sum\limits_{i=1}^{n} (x_i - \bar{x})\bar{y} = \left(\sum\limits_{i=1}^{n} x_i\right)\bar{y} - n\bar{x}\bar{y} = 0$, $S_{xy} = \sum\limits_{i=1}^{n} (x_i - \bar{x})(y_i - \bar{y}) = \sum\limits_{i=1}^{n} (x_i - \bar{x})y_i$, and we may write $\hat{\beta}$ as a linear combination of the y_i values

$$\hat{\beta} = \frac{S_{xy}}{S_x^2} = \frac{\sum\limits_{i=1}^{n} (x_i - \bar{x})\,y_i}{S_x^2} = \sum\limits_{i=1}^{n} c_i y_i \tag{36}$$

where $c_i = (x_i - \bar{x})/S_x^2$. In the model of section 9.5 the y_i are independent normal random variables with mean values $\mu_i = \alpha + \beta x_i$ and variances $\sigma_i^2 = \sigma^2$. A linear combination of independent normal random variables is itself normally distributed, so by (36) $\hat{\beta}$ is normal with mean value

$$\mu_{\hat{\beta}} = m.v. \left(\sum\limits_{i=1}^{n} c_i y_i\right) = \sum\limits_{i=1}^{n} c_i \mu_i = \alpha \left(\sum\limits_{i=1}^{n} c_i\right) + \beta \sum\limits_{i=1}^{n} c_i x_i = \beta$$

where the last equality follows from the relations

$$\sum\limits_{i=1}^{n} c_i = \frac{1}{S_x^2} \sum\limits_{i=1}^{n} (x_i - \bar{x}) = 0$$

$$\sum\limits_{i=1}^{n} c_i x_i = \frac{1}{S_x^2} \left(\sum\limits_{i=1}^{n} x_i^2 - \sum\limits_{i=1}^{n} x_i \bar{x}\right) = \frac{S_x^2}{S_x^2} = 1$$

Since the y_i's are independent with a common variance σ^2, it follows from (36) that

$$\sigma_{\hat{\beta}}^2 = \sigma^2 \sum\limits_{i=1}^{n} c_i^2 = \frac{\sigma^2}{S_x^2}$$

since

$$\sum\limits_{i=1}^{n} c_i^2 = \frac{1}{S_x^4} \sum\limits_{i=1}^{n} (x_i - \bar{x})^2 = \frac{1}{S_x^2}$$

A similar argument may be used to obtain the mean value and variance of $\hat{\alpha} = \sum\limits_{i=1}^{n} d_i y_i$, where

$$d_i = \frac{1}{n} - \frac{\bar{x}}{S_x^2} (x_i - \bar{x}) \ ,$$

by showing that $\sum\limits_{i=1}^{n} d_i = 1$, $\sum\limits_{i=1}^{n} d_i x_i = 0$, and $\sum\limits_{i=1}^{n} d_i^2 = \frac{1}{n} + \frac{\bar{x}^2}{S_x^2}$.

Analysis of
Categorical Data

10 Analysis of Categorical Data

In this chapter we consider hypothesis tests for random variables that are categorical rather than quantative, so that the data are in the form of counts. Often more than one categorization is involved. For example, in studies of college students the categories may be {freshman, sophomore, junior, senior} on the one hand, and {male, female} on the other. Such data, when cross-classified, give eight cell counts: freshman-male, freshman-female, sophomore-male, and so on. Again, in a medical study one categorization may be presence or absence of a certain disease, and the question at issue will be whether this is independent of or associated with another categorization, say blood type O, A, B, or AB. Here again there will be $8 = 2 \times 4$ cells for the cross-categorized data.

When data are categorized in two ways, the resulting cross-categorized table of counts in the cells is called a *contingency table*. In section 10.1, we discuss the 2×2 contingency table, where each of the two categorizations is a dichotomy: male-female, Republican-Democrat, Yes-No, and so forth. Section 10.2 treats a general multi-nomial model for categorical data, and section 10.3 the $r \times c$ contingency table of r rows (first category) and c columns (second category).

10.1 The 2×2 Contingency Table

Suppose that n observations are categorized according to each of two dichotomous attributes. The categorization for the first attribute consists of the events A or A' (not A); for the second, the events B or B'

(not B). This double dichotomization produces a $2 \times 2 = 4$-way cross-classification: (A and B), (A and B'), (A' and B), (A' and B'), and the data are summarized in a 2×2 *contingency table* of cell counts.

TABLE 10.1
The General 2 × 2 Contingency Table

Categorical variable 1 \ Categorical variable 2	B	B'	Totals
A	a	b	$n_1 = a + b$
A'	c	d	$n_2 = c + d$
Totals	$m_1 = a + c$	$m_2 = b + d$	$n = m_1 + m_2 = n_1 + n_2$

In this table, $a =$ the number of observations classified as (A and B), and so forth, n_1 and n_2 are the row totals ($n_1 =$ the number of observations classified as A; $n_2 = n - n_1$ the number classified as A'), and similarly for the column totals m_1 and m_2.

There is essentially only one hypothesis testing problem concerning a 2×2 contingency table, but it occurs in two forms, depending upon how the data are generated: (a) a test for *homogeneity*, based on two separate samples, and (b) a test for *independence*, based on a single sample.

10.1.1 Test for Homogeneity (Two Samples)

Example 1
Random samples of 100 men and 100 women were asked whether they agreed or disagreed with the statement "Women receive the same pay as men for equal work." The resulting 2×2 contingency table of cell counts is shown in table 10.2.

TABLE 10.2
Attitude Poll

Sex \ Attitude	Agree	Disagree	Sample sizes
Female	30	70	100
Male	45	55	100
Totals	75	125	200

Does table 10.2 justify asserting that the two populations, men and women, are *differently divided* with regard to the question?

In general, suppose that two independent binomial samples of sizes n_1 and n_2, lead to a and c "successes," respectively. We arrange the data in the 2×2 contingency table shown below. Tables 10.3 and 10.1 are formally the same. However, the row totals (sample sizes) n_1 and n_2 in table 10.3 are fixed by the experimenter.

TABLE 10.3
A 2×2 Contingency Table for Testing
Homogeneity of Two Independent Samples

Outcome / Population	Success	Failure	Sample sizes
Population 1	a	b	$n_1 = a + b$
Population 2	c	d	$n_2 = c + d$
Totals	$m_1 = a + c$	$m_2 = b + d$	$n = n_1 + n_2$

Suppose now that for population i, the probability of success in a single trial is p_i; $i = 1, 2$. A test for "homogeneity" of the two binomial populations amounts to testing $H_0 : p_1 = p_2$ vs $H_1 : p_1 \neq p_2$, a problem already treated in section 6.9. Here we shall reformulate the test of that section in terms of the following test statistic:

$$Y = \frac{n(ad - bc)^2}{m_1 \, m_2 \, n_1 \, n_2} \tag{1}$$

Under H_0, *and when* n_1 *and* n_2 *are large,* Y *has approximately a chi-squared distribution with 1 d.f.* To see this, we observe that by algebra it can be shown that $Y = z^2$, where

$$z = \frac{\hat{p}_1 - \hat{p}_2}{\sqrt{\left(\dfrac{1}{n_1} + \dfrac{1}{n_2}\right) \hat{p}(1 - \hat{p})}} \tag{2}$$

$$\hat{p}_1 = \frac{a}{n_1} \qquad \hat{p}_2 = \frac{c}{n_2} \qquad \hat{p} = \frac{a + c}{n}$$

It was shown in section 6.4 that under H_0, z has approximately a standard normal distribution when n_1 and n_2 are large, so that $Y = Z^2$ has a chi-squared distribution with 1 d.f. (definition 7.1).

From (2) we see that if $|z|$ is large then $|\hat{p}_1 - \hat{p}_2|$ is large, so that large values of $z^2 = Y$ suggest that $p_1 \neq p_2$. We therefore adopt as our critical region for testing H_0 the region $\{Y > c\}$, and choose c according to the chi-squared distribution with 1 d.f. The resulting test is

   An α-level test of homogeneity for the 2 × 2 contingency table 10.3 (two independent samples):

Null hypothesis: $H_0 : p_1 = p_2$ (homogeneity of populations 1 and 2)

Alternative hypothesis: $H_1 : p_1 \neq p_2$

Critical region: Reject H_0 if $Y = \dfrac{n(ad - bc)^2}{m_1 \, m_2 \, n_1 \, n_2} > \chi^2_{\alpha, 1}$ **(3)**

where $\chi^2_{\alpha, 1}$ is the value of the chi-squared distribution with 1 d.f. leaving probability α in the upper tail.

   The test (3) is in fact the *same* as the two-tailed test of table 6.4. This can be verified (compare appendix tables 6 and 8) by noting that $\chi^2_{\alpha, 1} = z^2_{\alpha/2}$. Therefore, since $Y = z^2$, we see that the critical region ($\{z > z_{\alpha/2}\}$ or $\{z < -z_{\alpha/2}\}$) $= \{Y > \chi^2_{\alpha, 1}\}$, where the former is a rewriting of the critical region of table 6.4 and the latter is the critical region (3).

   For example, to test the hypothesis $H_0 : p_1 = p_2$ of homogeneity for table 10.2 at level $\alpha = .05$, we compute

$$Y = \frac{200 \,(30 \cdot 55 - 70 \cdot 45)^2}{(75)\,(125)\,(100)\,(100)} = \frac{(200)\,(1500)^2}{(75)\,(125)\,(100)\,(100)} = \frac{600}{125} = 4.8$$

From appendix table 8, $\chi^2_{.05, 1} = 3.841$. Hence, since

$$Y = 4.8 > 3.841 = \chi^2_{.05, 1}$$

we assert at the .05 level of significance that there *is* evidence of a difference in attitude between the two sexes; in the general population, women agree with the statement less often than men.

Example 2
In section 6.9 we had the following 2 × 2 contingency table (table 6.5) for two independent samples of 200 consumer attitudes.

TABLE 10.4
Consumer Attitudes to Two New Robot Models

Model \ Attitude	Yes	No	Totals
1	68	132	200
2	52	148	200
Totals	120	280	400

We tested at level $\alpha = .05$ the hypothesis $H_0 : p_1 = p_2$ vs $H_1 :$ $p_1 \neq p_2$ by the test of table 6.4, where $p_i =$ probability of a consumer answering Yes to the question "Would you prefer the new model to the one you now use?"

For this table the test given by (3) yields

$$Y = \frac{400(68 \cdot 148 - 52 \cdot 132)^2}{(120)\,(280)\,(200)\,(200)} = 3.048$$

and since $Y = 3.048 < 3.841 = \chi^2_{.05,\ 1}$, we would *not* reject $H_0 : p_1 = p_2$ at the level of significance .05. The test in section 6.9, which rejects H_0 when $z > 1.96$ or $z < -1.96$, is equivalent to the test (3), which rejects H_0 when $Y > 3.841 = (1.96)^2$.

10.1.2 Test for Independence (One Sample)

When an experiment involving independent trials is performed, and each trial is recorded as having or not having each of 2 traits, a 2×2 contingency table is obtained. The structure of the experiment on each trial is determined by the four probabilities shown below and in table 10.5

$$p_{11} = P(A \text{ and } B) \qquad p_{12} = P(A \text{ and } B')$$
$$p_{21} = P(A' \text{ and } B) \qquad p_{22} = P(A' \text{ and } B')$$

TABLE 10.5
Probabilities for a Single Observation in a 2×2
Contingency Table

Events	B	B'	Sums
A	p_{11}	p_{12}	$p_{1.} = p_{11} + p_{12} = P(A)$
A'	p_{21}	p_{22}	$p_{2.} = p_{21} + p_{22} = P(A')$
Sums	$p_{.1} = p_{11} + p_{21}$ $= P(B)$	$p_{.2} = p_{12} + p_{22}$ $= P(B')$	$1 = $ Total probability

The four cells of table 10.5 constitute a partition of the outcome space of a single trial, so that $p_{11} + p_{12} + p_{21} + p_{22} = 1$.

If we now perform n independent trials of this experiment and record the resulting cell counts

$a = $ number of trials in which $(A$ and $B)$ occurs
$b = $ number of trials in which $(A$ and $B')$ occurs

c = number of trials in which (A' and B) occurs
d = number of trials in which (A' and B') occurs

we obtain the following 2×2 contingency table of counts:

TABLE 10.6
Cell Counts for n Observations in a 2×2
Contingency Table

Events	B	B'	Totals
A	a	b	$n_1 = a + b$
A'	c	d	$n_2 = c + d$
Totals	$m_1 = a + c$	$m_2 = b + d$	n = total sample size

This is again formally the same as table 10.1, but now only n is fixed, while n_1 and n_2 are random variables. For these data we wish to test the hypothesis H_0 that the event A is statistically *independent* of the event B. Consider the following example.

Example 3
A random sample of 200 men, aged 50 to 65, showed the following incidence of diabetes and heart disease:

TABLE 10.7
Diabetes and Heart Disease Cell Counts

Diabetes \ Heart disease	(B) present	(B') absent	Totals
(A) present	16	20	36
(A') absent	32	132	164
Totals	48	152	200

Based on these data, can we claim that for the population in question (50- to 65-year-old males), the occurrence of diabetes and heart disease are dependent events? Here we wish to test the null hypothesis $H_0 : P(B|A) = P(B|A') = P(B)$ (or $P(A|B) = P(A|B') = P(A)$, or $P(A$ and $B) = P(A) \cdot P(B)$) vs $H_1 : H_0$ is not true.

Now, the distribution of a, *given that the first row total is* $n_1 = 36$, is binomial with n_1 trials and success probability $P(B|A)$, since the probability of a single trial yielding a B, given that it is an A, is $P(B|A)$, and we have n_1 such trials. Similarly, the probability distribution of c, *given that the second row total is* $n_2 = 164$, is binomial with n_2 trials and success probability $P(B|A')$. From this point of view we see that the hypothesis H_0 of independence is just that of homogeneity, *given that the row totals are* n_1 *and* n_2. Therefore, given n_1 and n_2, the results of section 10.1.1 show that, under the hypothesis H_0 of the independence of A and B, the probability that (3) holds is approximately α. Since this *conditional* probability is the same for *any* two row totals n_1 and n_2 that are sufficiently large (which they will be with high probability if n is large), the *unconditional* probability of (3) under H_0 is also approximately α. We thereby obtain

An α-level test for independence in a 2 × 2 contingency table:

Null hypothesis: $H_0 : A$ and B independent; that is, $P(B|A) = P(B|A')$ $= P(B)$, or $P(A|B) = P(A|B') = P(A)$, or $P(A$ and $B) = P(A)P(B)$

Alternative hypothesis: A and B not independent

Critical region: Reject H_0 if (3) holds

where $\chi^2_{\alpha, 1}$ is the value of the chi-squared distribution with 1 d.f. leaving probability α in the upper tail.

For example, with the data in table 10.7, suppose that we want to test at level $\alpha = .01$ the null hypothesis H_0 : the occurrence of heart disease is independent of the occurrence of diabetes. Since

$$Y = \frac{200(16 \cdot 132 - 32 \cdot 20)^2}{48 \cdot 152 \cdot 36 \cdot 164} = 10.06 > 6.635 = \chi^2_{.01, 1}$$

we claim that heart disease is *not* independent of diabetes for men aged 50 to 65. The data indicate that diabetics have a higher probability of heart disease.

We note that the test (3) of independence is valid *whether the row totals* n_1 *and* n_2 *are random variables or fixed in advance.* For instance, in table 10.7 we could have chosen one random sample of n_1 men with diabetes and another of n_2 men without diabetes, and carried out the same analysis.

PROBLEMS 10.1

1. Two random samples of 100 freshmen and 100 seniors at the University of Wisconsin, Madison, were asked whether they felt the faculty was too research-oriented. The results were:

Class ╲ Response	Yes	No	Sample sizes
Freshmen	47	53	100
Senior	29	71	100

Based on these results, test the hypothesis that freshmen and seniors have the same attitude toward faculty research, at the level of significance $\alpha = .01$. State the null hypothesis, the critical region, and conclusion of your test.

2. Two treatments for lung cancer gave the following results for two groups of patients. A response is defined as clinical evidence of disease reduction.

Treatment ╲ Result	Response	No response	Sample sizes
T_1	15	53	68
T_2	21	59	80

Test the hypothesis that the two treatments have the same response rate at the level of significance $\alpha = .05$. State the null hypothesis, the critical region, and conclusion of your test.

3. A random sample of 300 voters in Wisconsin was cross-classified by age and voting record in the last gubernatorial election. The results were as follows.

Age ╲ Vote	Democratic candidate	Republican candidate
30 or under	84	53
Over 30	80	83

Test the hypothesis of independence between age and gubernatorial vote in the above 2×2 contingency table, at the level of significance $\alpha = .05$. State the null and alternative hypotheses, the critical region of the test, and the conclusion of the test.

4. A random sample of 137 fish gave the following results when

cross-classified by level of mercury content and length:

Length Mercury content	Longer than 12 inches	Shorter than 12 inches
High	24	10
Low	60	43

Test the hypothesis of independence between level of mercury content and length of fish based on the above 2×2 contingency table at the level of significance $\alpha = .05$. State the null and alternative hypotheses, the critical region of the test, and the conclusion of the test.

5. Explain the differences between the two tests used in problems 1 and 3 above. Why is one a test of homogeneity and one a test of independence?

6. Explain the differences between the two tests used in problems 2 and 4 above. Why is one a test of homogeneity and one a test of independence?

10.2 The Multinomial Distribution. Goodness-of-Fit Tests

10.2.1 The Multinomial Distribution

Consider n independent trials of an experiment for which in each trial there are exactly k distinct possible outcomes, $A_1, \ldots, A_k$. The frequency counts $\{y_1, \ldots, y_k\}$ corresponding to the k outcomes then have what is called a *multinomial distribution*. (The special case $k = 2$ is the binomial distribution, with $A_1 =$ "success," $A_2 =$ "failure," $y_1 = y =$ number of successes, and $y_2 = n - y =$ number of failures.) If we let $p_i = P(A_i)$, for $i = 1, \ldots, k$, then

$$\sum_{i=1}^{k} p_i = \sum_{i=1}^{k} P(A_i) = P(A_1 \text{ or } \ldots \text{ or } A_k) = 1$$

Definition 1
The random variables $\{y_1, \ldots, y_k\}$ have a *multinomial distribution with n trials and cell probabilities* $p_1, \ldots, p_k$ if they arise from the following experimental procedure:

a. n trials are made of an experiment which must have one of k distinct outcomes $A_1 , \ldots , A_k$ on each trial.

b. the trials are independent.

c. the probability of A_i at each trial is $p_i = P(A_i)$; $i = 1 , \ldots , k$, $\sum_{i=1}^{k} p_i = 1$.

d. $y_i =$ number of times in the n trials that outcome A_i occurs.

The probability distribution of $\{y_1 , \ldots , y_k\}$ is then given by the following generalization of the binomial distribution:

$$P(y_1 , \ldots , y_k) = P \text{ \{exactly } y_i \text{ occurrences of } A_i \text{ in } n \text{ trials,}$$

$$\text{for each } i = 1 , \ldots , k\} = \frac{n!}{y_i! \ldots y_k!} \cdot p_1{}^{y_1} \ldots p_k{}^{y_k} \tag{4}$$

where $y_1 , \ldots , y_k$ are any nonnegative integers such that $y_1 + y_2 + \ldots + y_k = n$.

To verify (4), we find first the probability that the following particular sequence of outcomes of the n trials will occur:

$$A_1 \ldots A_1 \quad A_2 \ldots A_2 \quad \ldots \quad A_k \ldots A_k \tag{5}$$
$$y_1 \text{ times} \quad y_2 \text{ times} \quad \ldots \quad y_k \text{ times}$$

Since the trials are independent, the probability of this particular event is

$$[P(A_1) \ldots P(A_1)] \cdot [P(A_2) \ldots P(A_2)] \ldots [P(A_k) \ldots P(A_k)] \tag{6}$$
$$y_1 \text{ terms} \quad\quad y_2 \text{ terms} \quad\quad y_k \text{ terms}$$

$$= p_1{}^{y_1} \cdot p_2{}^{y_2} \ldots p_k{}^{y_k}$$

However, this is not the total probability of obtaining y_1 A_1's, and y_2 A_2's, and $\ldots$, and y_k A_k's, since the sequence of outcomes (5) is only one of many sequences that would do this. To obtain the total number of such sequences we ask: out of the n positions to be filled, in how many ways can we choose y_1 in which to place an A_1, then y_2 out of the remaining $n - y_1$ in which to place an A_2, and so forth? Now, the first of these choices can be made in $\binom{n}{y_1}$ ways, the second in $\binom{n-y_1}{y_2}$ ways, the third in $\binom{n_1 - y_1 - y_2}{y_3}$ ways, and so on, until the last is made in $\binom{y_k}{y_k} = 1$ way. Thus, altogether, we can choose the positions for y_1 A_1's, y_2 A_2's $, \ldots , y_k$ A_k's in the following number of ways:

$$\binom{n}{y_1}\binom{n-y_1}{y_2}\binom{n-y_1-y_2}{y_3}\ldots\binom{y_k}{y_k}$$

$$= \frac{n!}{y_1!(n-y_1)!} \cdot \frac{(n-y_1)!}{y_2!(n-y_1-y_2)!} \cdot \frac{(n-y_1-y_2)!}{y_3!(n-y_1-y_2-y_3)!} \cdots \frac{y_k!}{y_k!0!}$$

$$= \frac{n!}{y_1!\, y_2!\ldots y_k!}$$

Since each of these sequences has the same probability (6), the result (4) follows.

Example 4

A pollster asks three voters whether they prefer candidate 1 (outcome A_1), candidate 2 (outcome A_2), or are undecided (outcome A_3). Suppose that $p_1 = p(A_1) = .5$; $p_2 = P(A_2) = .4$; and $p_3 = P(A_3) = .1$. The probability of observing at least as many choices for candidate 1 as for candidate 2 is as follows.

$$P(y_1 \geq y_2) = P(y_1 = 3) + P(y_1 = 2, y_2 = 0 \text{ or } 1)$$

$$+ P(y_1 = 1, y_2 = 0 \text{ or } 1) + P(y_1 = 0 = y_2)$$

$$= P(3, 0, 0) + P(2, 1, 0) + P(2, 0, 1)$$

$$+ P(1, 1, 1) + P(1, 0, 2) + P(0, 0, 3)$$

$$= (.5)^3 + 3(.5)^2\,(.4) + 3(.5)^2\,(.1)$$

$$+ 6(.5)\,(.4)\,(.1) + 3(.5)\,(.1)^2 + (.1)^3$$

$$= .125 + .300 + .075 + .120 + .015 + .001 = .636$$

Example 5

Four brands $B_1, \ldots, B_4$ of a product are competing in a market. The current probabilities that a randomly chosen customer will prefer each of these brands are $p_1 = P(B_1) = .1$; $p_2 = P(B_2) = .2$; $p_3 = P(B_3) = .3$; and $p_4 = P(B_4) = .4$. If 10 such customers independently buy the product, what is the probability $P(1, 2, 3, 4)$ that exactly 1 will buy brand B_1, 2 will buy brand B_2, 3 brand B_3, and 4 brand B_4?

$$P(1, 2, 3, 4) = \frac{10!}{1!\,2!\,3!\,4!}\,(.1)^1\,(.2)^2\,(.3)^3\,(.4)^4$$

$$= (12,600)\,(.1)\,(.04)\,(.009)\,(.0256)$$

$$= (126 \times 10^2)(9216 \times 10^{-10}) = (1161216) \times 10^{-8} \cong .0116$$

Returning to definition 1, suppose that we consider any *one* of the cell count random variables y_i alone. Then y_i is simply a *binomial* random variable counting the number of trials in which A_i occurs (that is, A_i = "success" and A_i' = not A_i = "failure"). This immediately yields by the formulas for the mean value and variance of the binomial distribution

$$\mu_{y_i} = np_i \qquad \sigma_{y_i}^2 = np_i(1 - p_i) \tag{7}$$

However, the different $y_i's$ are not *independent* binomial variables, since necessarily $\sum_{i=1}^{k} y_i = n$.

We now state an important theorem concerning the multinomial distribution when n is large.

Theorem 1
Let $\{y_1, \ldots, y_k\}$ have a multinomial distribution with cell probabilities $p_1, \ldots, p_k$. Then, for large n, the nonnegative random variable

$$Y = \sum_{i=1}^{k} \frac{(y_i - np_i)^2}{np_i} \tag{8}$$

has approximately a chi-squared distribution with $k - 1$ degrees of freedom. The mean value of Y is exactly

$$\mu_Y = k - 1 \tag{9}$$

and thus depends only on the *number of cells* k, and not on the particular values of the cell probabilities $p_1, \ldots, p_k$.

Equation 9 follows at once from (7), since

$$\mu_y = \sum_{i=1}^{k} \frac{m.v. \ [(y_i - np_i)^2]}{np_i} = \sum_{i=1}^{k} \frac{\sigma_{y_i}^2}{np_i} = \sum_{i=1}^{k} \frac{np_i(1 - p_i)}{np_i}$$

$$= \sum_{i=1}^{k} (1 - p_i) = k - \sum_{i=1}^{k} p_i = k - 1$$

The proof for $k > 2$ that y has an approximately chi-squared distribution with $k - 1$ d.f. involves mathematics beyond the scope of this book. In the special case $k = 2$ (the binomial case) we see that

$$Y = \frac{(y_1 - np_1)^2}{np_1} + \frac{(y_2 - np_2)^2}{np_2} = \frac{(y_1 - np_1)^2}{np_1} \cdot \frac{[(n - y_1) - n(1 - p_1)]^2}{n(1 - p_1)}$$

$$= \frac{(y_1 - np_1)^2}{np_1(1 - p_1)} = z^2, \text{ where } z = \frac{y_1 - np_1}{np_1(1 - p_1)}$$

But by the normal approximation to the binomial distribution, z is approximately standard normal, while by definition 7.1 the square of a standard normal random variable is chi-squared with 1 d.f. Hence we see that $Y = z^2$ above is approximately chi-squared with 1 d.f., which is theorem 1 for $k = 2$.

It is helpful to write (8) in the form

$$Y = \sum_{i=1}^{k} \frac{(y_i - np_1)^2}{np_i} = \sum_{i=1}^{k} \frac{(O_i - E_i)^2}{E_i} \tag{10}$$

where $O_i = y_i$ are the *observed* cell frequencies in the sample of size n, while $E_i = np_i = \mu_{y_i}$ are the corresponding mean or "expected" cell frequencies.

10.2.2 Goodness-of-Fit Tests for the Multinomial Distribution

Using theorem 1, we can now test whether a given set of *observed* cell frequencies $\{y_1, \ldots, y_k\}$ fits an *assumed* multinomial model with specified p_i's; that is, we can test

$$H_0 : p_1, p_2, \ldots, p_k \text{ vs } H_1 : H_0 \text{ is not true} \tag{11}$$

Example 6
In an experiment involving the crossing of two types of peas, Gregor Mendel obtained the results shown below in table 10.8. According to his theory of inheritance the ratios of these frequencies should be 9:3:3:1; that is, the probabilities should be 9/16, 3/16, 3/16, and 1/16.

TABLE 10.8
Mendel's Experiment

Type of pea	Observed freq. $= y_i$	Expected freq. $= np_i$	p_i
Round and yellow	315	312.75	9/16
Round and green	108	104.25	3/16
Wrinkled and yellow	101	104.25	3/16
Wrinkled and green	32	34.75	1/16
Totals	556	556	1

Does table 10.8 tend to contradict Mendel's theoretical model H_0 : $p_1 = 9/16$, $p_2 = 3/16$, $p_3 = 3/16$, $p_4 = 1/16$?

In general, we note that for the Y of (10), a large value is caused by large discrepancies between the observed and "expected" frequencies O_i and E_i. Therefore, it is reasonable to reject H_0 if $y > c$ (the critical region). But Y under H_0 has by theorem 1 an approximately chi-squared distribution with $k - 1$ d.f. when n is large. We therefore choose c from the chi-squared tables and obtain

An α-level goodness-of-fit test for a completely specified multinomial distribution:

Let $\{y_1, \ldots, y_k\}$ be multinomially distributed with n trials.

Null hypothesis : H_0 : the cell probabilities have preassigned values p_1, $p_2, \ldots, p_k$ such that $\sum_{i=1}^{k} p_i = 1$.

Critical region: Reject H_0 if

$$Y = \sum_{i=1}^{k} \frac{(y_i - np_i)^2}{np_i} = \sum_{i=1}^{k} \frac{(O_i - E_i)^2}{E_i} > \chi^2_{\alpha, k-1} \tag{12}$$

where $\chi^2_{\alpha, k-1}$ is the value in the chi-squared distribution with $k - 1$ d.f. leaving probability α in the upper tail.

From table 10.8

$$Y = \frac{(315 - 312.75)^2}{312.75} + \frac{(108 - 104.25)^2}{104.25} + \frac{(101 - 104.25)^2}{104.25}$$

$$+ \frac{(32 - 34.75)^2}{34.75}$$

$$= .0162 + .1349 + .1013 + .2176 = .47$$

Since $\chi^2_{.05, 3} = 7.815$, we see that $Y = .47 < 7.815 = \chi^2_{.05, 3}$ so the test clearly does *not* reject Mendel's hypothesis H_0 at the .05 level of significance.

In this example, the value of $\chi^2_{.90, 3}$ (the value for the chi-squared distribution with 3 d.f. that leaves a probability of .10 *below* it) is .584. Hence, the result $Y \leq .47$ is rather an unlikely event, for even under H_0 it will occur less than 10 percent of the time in repeated samples. When the results of an experiment are "too good" in this sense (that is, give a very *small* value of Y, indicating extremely close agreement of cell counts and their theoretical expectations), one suspects that the investigator may have tampered with the data to make it conform to the theory. For Mendel's data $\chi^2_{.95, 3} = .352$, and hence $Y = .47$, is not unreasonably small when compared to the lower-tail .05 value.

A particular case of the multinomial model is testing whether in an experiment with k possible outcomes the individual outcomes are *equally likely*; $H_0 : p_1 = p_2 = \ldots = p_k = 1/k$. In this case (8) becomes

$$Y = \frac{k}{n} \sum_{i=1}^{k} \left(y_i - \frac{n}{k}\right)^2$$

For example, in 120 tosses of two dice the results were

Face	1	2	3	4	5	6	Totals
Die 1	18	19	23	25	15	20	120
Die 2	11	25	15	29	16	24	120

yielding under the null hypothesis $H_0 : p_1 = p_2 = \ldots = p_6 = 1/6$, $E_i = 120 \cdot 1/6 = 20$

$$Y_1 = \frac{(18-20)^2 + (19-20)^2 + (23-20)^2 + (25-20)^2 + (15-20)^2 + (20-20)^2}{20}$$

$$= 3.2$$

$$Y_2 = \frac{(11-20)^2 + (25-20)^2 + (15-20)^2 + (29-20)^2 + (16-20)^2 + (24-20)^2}{20}$$

$$= 12.2$$

Here $\chi^2_{5,.05} = 11.07$, so at the .05 level of significance the data show that die 2 is biased. A bias for die 1 is not established by the data.

10.2.3 Multinomial Tests with Estimated Parameters

An extension of the results of section 10.2.2 can be made when the cell probabilities $p_1, \ldots, p_k$ are not *completely* specified in advance but depend in a known way on some unknown parameters $\theta_1, \ldots, \theta_q$, with $q < k - 1$. Specifically, suppose the null hypothesis is

$$H_0 : p_i = p_i(\theta_1, \ldots, \theta_q) \qquad \text{for } i = 1, \ldots, k \qquad (13)$$

where the probabilities $p_i(\theta_1, \ldots, \theta_q)$ are prescribed by some theory but the true particular values $\theta_1, \ldots, \theta_q$ are unknown. Then under certain conditions, if one uses estimators $\hat{\theta}_1, \ldots, \hat{\theta}_q$ based on the data for $\theta_1, \ldots, \theta_q$ and substitutes these into (13) to obtain estimates $\hat{p}_i = p_i(\hat{\theta}_1, \ldots, \hat{\theta}_q)$ of the true p_i's, it can be shown that the following theorem holds.

Theorem 2

If the $p_i's$ are in fact given by (13) for some true but unknown values of the q parameters $\theta_1, \ldots, \theta_q$, then for a large n the statistic

$$Y = \sum_{i=1}^{k} \frac{(O_i - E_i)^2}{E_i}$$

with $O_i = y_1$ and $E_i = np(\hat{\theta}_1, \ldots, \hat{\theta}_q)$, $i = 1, \ldots, k$, has approximately a chi-squared distribution with $k - 1 - q$ d.f.

The use and meaning of this theorem will become more evident below. In all the cases given in this book the necessary unstated conditions of theorem 2 are met.

Example 7
According to a genetic theory the offspring of a given mating will fall into one of three groups with the following probabilities:

TABLE 10.9
Cell Probabilities by Genetic Theory

Group	G_1	G_2	G_3
Probability	θ^2	$2\theta(1 - \theta)$	$(1 - \theta)^2$

$$0 < \theta < 1; \ \theta \text{ unknown}$$

Suppose that one has observed the data given in table 10.10 below for $n = 100$ offspring of such a mating, and uses as an estimate of the single unknown parameter θ

$$\hat{\theta} = \frac{2y_1 + y_2}{2n} = \frac{y_1}{n} + \frac{y_2}{2n}$$

TABLE 10.10
Observed and Estimated Cell
Counts for Table 10.9, $n = 100$

Group	G_1	G_2	G_3	Sums
Observed freq. (y_i)	12	56	32	$n = 100$
Estimated freq. (E_i)	$n\hat{\theta}^2$	$n[2\hat{\theta}(1 - \hat{\theta})]$	$n(1 - \hat{\theta})^2$	$n = 100$
E_i when $n = 100$ and $\hat{\theta} = .4$	16	48	36	$n = 100$

For the data of table 10.10, $\hat{\theta} = .12 + .28 = .4$. This estimator is suggested by methods beyond the scope of the present text. However, it is easy to see that $\hat{\theta}$ is unbiased, since

$$\mu_{\hat{\theta}} = m.v. \left(\frac{y_1}{n} + \frac{y_2}{2n} \right) = \frac{1}{n} \mu_{y_1} + \frac{1}{2n} \mu_{y_2}$$

$$= \frac{1}{n}(n\theta^2) + \frac{1}{2n}[n \cdot 2\theta(1 - \theta)] = \theta^2 + \theta(1 - \theta) = \theta$$

Using θ, we obtained the observed and estimated cell frequencies. The last row of this table is calculated by substituting $n = 100$ and $\hat{\theta} = .4$ in the second row of the table. For example, $n\hat{\theta}^2 = 100(.4)^2 = 100(.16) = 16$.

In this example we wish to test the hypothesis $H_0: p_1 = \theta^2$, $p_2 = 2\theta(1 - \theta)$, $p_3 = (1 - \theta)^3$ for some unknown $0 < \theta < 1$.

Under H_0, according to theorem 2, Y will have a chi-squared distribution (approximately) with $k - 1 - q = 3 - 1 - 1 = 1$ d.f. (since $q = 1$ parameter θ is being estimated). Hence, a critical region of level $\alpha = .05$ for testing H_0 is $Y > \chi^2_{.05, 1} = 3.841$. Since

$$Y = \frac{(12 - 16)^2}{16} + \frac{(56 - 48)^2}{48} + \frac{(32 - 36)^2}{36}$$

$$= 1.000 + 1.333 + .444 = 2.777 < 3.841$$

we cannot assert at the .05 level that the data contradict the genetic theory specified by H_0.

PROBLEMS 10.2

1. Use formula 4 to find the probability that if a fair die is tossed six times, each face will come up exactly once.

2. If five patients are treated with a new drug, find the probability of seeing two responses, two no changes, and one progression if the probabilities of "response," "no change," and "progression" are, respectively, .3, .5, and .2. Use equation 4.

3. A pollster asks U.S. voters if they consider themselves Democrats, Republicans, or Independents. If 40 percent of the voters are Democrats, 30 percent Republicans, and 30 percent Independents, what is the probability of getting six Democrats, three Republicans, and one Independent in a random sample of ten voters?

4. In six independent draws from a deck of 52 cards (replaced and reshuffled each time), find the probability of getting exactly two hearts, three clubs, and one spade.

5. A year ago a survey of voters showed that 47 percent answered Yes, 40 percent answered No, and 13 percent answered Undecided when asked "Do you think that the President is doing a good job in foreign policy?" A random sample of 1600 voters asked the same question this year yielded the following results.

Response	Yes	No	Undecided
No. of voters	707	694	199

From the survey of one year ago, find the expected table of frequencies, and test the hypothesis at the level of significance $\alpha = .05$ that the percentages are the same as they were one year ago. State the null and alternative hypotheses, the critical region of the test, and the conclusion of the test.

6. A die is tossed 90 times. The results are

Face	1	2	3	4	5	6
No. of times face appears	12	14	18	21	13	12

Test at the level of significance $\alpha = .05$, H_0 : the die is fair. State the null and alternative hypotheses, the critical region of the test, and the conclusion of the test.

7. In Illinois, according to the 1970 census, the female population over 14 was classified as follows:

Marital status	Single	Married	Widowed	Divorced
Percentage	22.9	60.5	12.6	4.0

Suppose that a random sample of 5000 women in the year 1974 showed the following counts.

Marital status	Single	Married	Widowed	Divorced
Number	1215	2943	618	224

Using these data, test the hypothesis of no change in marital status percentages for females from 1970 to 1974 at the level of significance $\alpha = .05$. Give the null and alternative hypotheses, the table of expected frequencies for 1974 under the hypothesis of no change, the critical region of the test, and the conclusion of the test.

8. Automobile production for 1972 by major U.S. producers was

Manufacturer	A.M.	Chrysler	Ford	G.M.
Percentage	3.2	15.5	27.2	54.1

In a random sample of 3000 sales in Wisconsin for the same year, the results were

Manufacturer	A.M.	Chrysler	Ford	G.M.
No. of sales	127	427	841	1605

Using these data, test at $\alpha = .01$ the hypothesis that the percentages of sales in Wisconsin in 1972 were the same as in the U.S.

Give the null and alternative hypotheses, the table of expected frequencies for the 3000 Wisconsin sales under the null hypothesis, the critical region of the test, and the conclusion of the test.

9. According to genetic theory, the progeny of a certain mating should occur according to the following model.

Group	G_1	G_2	G_3	G_4
Probability	θ^3	$3\theta^2(1-\theta)$	$3\theta(1-\theta)^2$	$(1-\theta)^3$

where $0 < \theta < 1$ is unknown. The following data represent $n = 200$ progeny from such a mating scheme.

Group	G_1	G_2	G_3	G_4
Observed freq.	$y_1 = 12$	$y_2 = 61$	$y_3 = 88$	$y_4 = 39$

Using as an estimator of θ

$$\hat{\theta} = \frac{3y_1 + 2y_2 + y_3}{3n}$$

test the hypothesis H_0 at $\alpha = .05$ that these data fit the above assumed genetic model. Use the method shown in section 10.2.3.

10. Using the genetic model of problem 9, test at level $\alpha = .05$ the hypothesis that the following $n = 400$ progeny follow the model.

Group	G_1	G_2	G_3	G_4
Observed freq.	$y_1 = 41$	$y_2 = 176$	$y_3 = 125$	$y_3 = 58$

10.3 The $r \times c$ Contingency Table

We now extend the results of section 10.1 to two-way contingency tables with r rows and c columns ($r = c = 2$ in section 10.2, yielding the 2×2 contingency table 10.1).

The model is the following: n observations are classified according to two categorical variables. The first variable has r levels, denoted by $A_1, \ldots, A_r$, and the second variable has c levels, denoted by $B_1, \ldots, B_c$. Let $y_{ij} =$ the number of occurrences in which variable 1 is at level i and variable 2 is at level j, with $i = 1, \ldots, r$ and $j = 1, \ldots, c$. The data are arranged as in table 10.11.

TABLE 10.11
The General $r \times c$ Contingency Table

Level of variable 1 \ Level of variable 2	B_1	$\ldots$	B_j	$\ldots$	B_c	Row totals
A_1	y_{11}	$\ldots$	y_{1j}	$\ldots$	y_{1c}	n_1
$\vdots$	$\vdots$	$\vdots$	$\vdots$	$\vdots$	$\vdots$	$\vdots$
A_i	y_{i1}	$\ldots$	y_{ij}	$\ldots$	y_{ic}	n_i
$\vdots$	$\vdots$	$\vdots$	$\vdots$	$\vdots$	$\vdots$	$\vdots$
A_r	y_{r1}	$\ldots$	y_{rj}	$\ldots$	y_{rc}	n_r
Column totals	m_1	$\ldots$	m_j	$\ldots$	m_c	$n = m_1 + \ldots + m_c$ $= n_1 + \ldots + n_r$

As in the case of a 2×2 contingency table, we may wish either to test the *independence* of the categorical variables 1 and 2 or to test the *homogeneity* of the r populations $A_1, \ldots, A_r$. The first case occurs when only n is fixed, and the second when each of $n_1, \ldots, n_r$ is fixed.

10.3.1 A Test of Independence in an $r \times c$ Contingency Table (One Sample)

The test is based on the following
Model for the test of independence:

a. A number n of trials are made and each outcome is classified in two ways, $\{A_1, \ldots, A_r\}$ and $\{B_1, \ldots, B_c\}$. There are thus $r \times c$ possible events (A_i and B_j) at each trial.

b. The n trials are independent.

c. The probability of the event (A_i and B_j) for each single trial is $p_{ij} = P(A_i$ and $B_j)$. The p_{ij} are unknown.

d. y_{ij} = the number of trials in which the event (A_i and B_j) occurs in the n trials = cell frequency in the (i, j)th cell of table 10.11.

This model yields the following table of cell probabilities.

TABLE 10.12
Probabilities for a Single Observation in an $r \times c$ Contingency Table in Testing for Independence

Class.1 \ Class.2	B_1	...	B_j	...	B_c	Row probabilities
A_1	p_{11}	...	p_{1j}	...	p_{1c}	$p_{1.} = P(A_1)$
$\vdots$	$\vdots$	$\vdots$	$\vdots$	$\vdots$	$\vdots$	$\vdots$
A_i	p_{i1}	...	p_{ij}	...	p_{ic}	$p_{i.} = P(A_i)$
$\vdots$	$\vdots$	$\vdots$	$\vdots$	$\vdots$	$\vdots$	$\vdots$
A_r	p_{r1}	...	p_{rj}	...	p_{rc}	$p_{r.} = P(A_r)$
Column probabilities	$p_{.1} = P(B_1)$	...	$p_{.j} = P(B_j)$	...	$p_{.c} = P(B_c)$	1

$$p_{i.} = p_{i1} + \ldots + p_{ic} = P(A_i), \text{ and } P_{.j} = p_{1j} + \ldots + p_{rj} = P(B_j)$$

The null hypothesis here is *independence of the two categorizations*: $H_o : p_{ij} = P(A_i \text{ and } B_j) = P(A_i)P(B_j) = p_{i.} \cdot p_{.j}$ for every $i = 1, \ldots, r$ and $j = 1, \ldots, c$ (hypothesis of independence).

This situation falls under the general scope of theorem 2, all the unknown values $p_{i.}$ and $p_{.j}$ being estimated from the data. Using the *observed sample proportions*

$$\hat{p}_{i.} = \frac{n_i}{n}, \qquad \hat{p}_{.j} = \frac{m_j}{n}$$

as estimates, we obtain

$$E_{ij} = n\hat{p}_{i.}\,\hat{p}_{.j} = \frac{n_i m_j}{n}$$

and hence

$$Y = \sum_{i,j} \frac{\left(y_{ij} - \dfrac{n_i m_j}{n} \right)^2}{\dfrac{n_i m_j}{n}} \tag{14}$$

as the appropriate test statistic. The d.f. here is $k - q - 1$, with $k = rc$ and $q = (r - 1) + (c - 1)$, since the number of unknown parameters being estimated is $r - 1$ for $p_1, \ldots, p_r$ $\left(\sum_{i=1}^{r} p_{i.} = 1 \right)$ and $c - 1$ for

$p_{.1}, \ldots, p_{.c} \left(\sum_{j=1}^{c} p_{.j} = 1 \right)$. Hence, under the hypothesis H_0 of independence, Y will have approximately a chi-squared distribution with
$rc - [(r-1) + (c-1)] - 1 = (r-1)(c-1)$ d.f. We thus obtain
An α-level test for independence in table 10.11:

Null hypothesis : $H_0 : p_{ij} = p_{i.} \cdot p_{.j}$, for each $i = 1, \ldots, r$ and $j = 1, \ldots, c$ (independence of rows and columns)

Critical region : Reject H_0 if

$$Y = \sum_{i,j} \frac{(O_{ij} - E_{ij})^2}{E_{ij}} > \chi^2_{\alpha, (r-1)(c-1)} \tag{15}$$

where $O_{ij} = y_{ij}$, $E_{ij} = (n_i \cdot m_j)/n$, and $\chi^2_{\alpha,(r-1)(c-1)}$ is the value for the
chi-squared distribution with $(r-1) \cdot (c-1)$ d.f. leaving probability
α in the upper tail.

In applying this test we first compute an "expected" frequency
table to obtain the values E_{ij}.

TABLE 10.13
Expected Cell Frequency Table for Table 10.11
Assuming Independence

Classification 1 \ Classification 2	B_1	...	B_j	...	B_c	Row totals
A_1	$\frac{n_1 \cdot m_1}{n}$	...	$\frac{n_1 \cdot m_j}{r}$	...	$\frac{n_1 \cdot m_c}{n}$	n_1
$\vdots$	$\vdots$	$\vdots$	$\vdots$	$\vdots$	$\vdots$	$\vdots$
A_i	$\frac{n_i \cdot m_1}{n}$	...	$\frac{n_i \cdot m_j}{n}$	...	$\frac{n_i \cdot m_c}{n}$	n_i
$\vdots$	$\vdots$	$\vdots$	$\vdots$	$\vdots$	$\vdots$	$\vdots$
A_r	$\frac{n_r \cdot m_1}{n}$	...	$\frac{n_r \cdot m_j}{n}$	...	$\frac{n_r \cdot m_c}{n}$	n_r
Column totals	m_1	...	m_j	...	m_c	n

Example 8
A random sample of 1000 persons was cross-classified with respect
to eye color (brown, blue, other) and height (short, medium, tall). Do

the results below establish dependence between eye color and height at the .01 level of significance?

Eye color \ Height	Short	Medium	Tall	Row totals
Brown	132 (114)	290 (282)	102 (127)	524
Blue	64 (76)	182 (188)	102 (85)	348
Other	22 (28)	67 (69)	39 (31)	128
Column totals	218	539	243	1000

The expected cell frequencies under independence, rounded to the nearest integer, are shown in parentheses; thus

$$E_{11} = \frac{n_1 \cdot m_1}{n} = \frac{524 \cdot 218}{1000} = 114.2 \cong 114, \text{ etc.}$$

By computation

$$Y = \frac{(132 - 114)^2}{114} + \ldots + \frac{(39 - 31)^2}{31} = 16.88$$

Since $(r - 1) \cdot (c - 1) = 2 \cdot 2 = 4$ and $\chi^2_{4,.01} = 13.277$, dependence is indicated for the two factors, height and eye color, for the population under study.

10.3.2 A Test of Homogeneity for r Multinomial Populations

Suppose that corresponding to each of the r rows in table 10.11 we have a multinomial distribution across the c columns with *fixed sample size row totals* $n_1, \ldots, n_c$. The following model is then appropriate.

Model for a test of homogeneity:

a. The ith row $\{y_{i1}, \ldots, y_{ic}\}$ in table 10.11 has a multinomial tribution with n_i trials and cell probabilities $p_{i1}, \ldots, p_{ic}$; $i = 1, \ldots, r$. The event A_i indicates that we are sampling from the ith population.

b. The r samples $\{y_{i1}, \ldots, y_{ic}\}$, $i = 1, \ldots, r$, are mutually independent.

In this model, since the column attributes are exhaustive and mutually exclusive, $\sum_{j=1}^{c} p_{ij} = p_{i1} + \ldots + p_{ic} = 1$ for each $i = 1, \ldots, r$ and, of course, $n_i = \sum_{j=1}^{c} y_{ij}$ for $i = 1, \ldots, r$.

The following table of probabilities illustrates the model for the test of homogeneity.

TABLE 10.14
Probability Model for the Test of Homogeneity in an $r \times c$ Table

Population \ Attribute	B_1	$\ldots$	B_j	$\ldots$	B_c	Sum
A_1	p_{11}	$\ldots$	p_{1j}	$\ldots$	p_{1c}	1
$\vdots$	$\vdots$	$\vdots$	$\vdots$	$\vdots$	$\vdots$	$\vdots$
A_i	p_{i1}	$\ldots$	p_{ij}	$\ldots$	p_{ic}	1
$\vdots$	$\vdots$	$\vdots$	$\vdots$	$\vdots$	$\vdots$	$\vdots$
A_r	p_{r1}	$\ldots$	p_{rj}	$\ldots$	p_{rc}	1

The following example will serve to clarify the concepts illustrated in the general model.

Example 9

A random sample of 100 students was drawn from each of the four college classes, and each student was asked to respond to the statement "The professors at this college are deeply committed to good teaching." The response was either "agree," "neutral," or "disagree."

Table 10.15 (page 328) gives the responses in four possibly distinct multinomial distributions with three cells each. The sample sizes $n_1 = n_2 = n_3 = n_4 = 100$ were fixed by the experimenter, and the samples were mutually independent. Do the data convincingly reject the null hypothesis that the four classes would respond to the question in the same manner; that is, that all four multinomial populations are in fact the same (homogeneous)?

TABLE 10.15
Cell Counts for a 4 × 3 Test of Homogeneity

Class \\ Response	Agree	Neutral	Disagree	Row totals
Freshman	47	18	35	100
Sophmore	60	12	28	100
Junior	68	11	21	100
Senior	73	7	20	100
Column totals	248	48	104	400

In general, the null hypothesis under consideration is that for some set of (unknown) probabilities $p_1, p_2, \ldots, p_c$

$$H_0 : p_{i1} = p_1, \, p_{i2} = p_2, \ldots, p_{ic} = p_c \text{ for each } i = 1, \ldots, r$$

so that the r rows in table 10.11 are in fact independent multinomial samples governed by the *same* (unknown) probabilities $p_1, \ldots, p_c$.

The appropriate test of this hypothesis H_0 of *homogeneity* is formally identical with the test (15) of *independence*, and is given by

An α-level test for homogeneity in table 10.11:

Null hypothesis: $H_0 : p_{i1} = p_1, \ldots, p_{ic} = p_c$ for each $i = 1, \ldots, r$,

where $p_1, \ldots, p_c$ are unspecified but $\sum_{j=1}^{c} p_j = 1$.

Critical region: same as (15).

We verify for the case $r = c = 2$ that the statistic Y defined by (15) does have under H_0 approximately a chi-squared distribution with $(r - 1) \cdot (c - 1)$ d.f. In this case Y reduces to the Y defined by (1), which as we saw has approximately a chi-squared distribution with 1 d.f.. In fact, for $r = c = 2$, setting as in table 10.3

$$y_{11} = a \quad y_{12} = b \quad n_1 = a + b \quad m_1 = a + c$$
$$y_{21} = c \quad y_{22} = d \quad n_2 = c + d \quad m_2 = b + d,$$

the Y defined by (15) can be shown by algebra to be equal to

$$Y = \frac{\left(a - \frac{n_1 m_1}{n}\right)^2}{\frac{n_1 m_1}{n}} + \ldots + \frac{\left(d - \frac{n_2 m_2}{n}\right)^2}{\frac{n_2 m_2}{n}} = \frac{n(ad - bc)^2}{m_1 m_2 n_1 n_2}$$

$$= \text{the } Y \text{ of (1)}$$

Thus the general $r \times c$ test for homogeneity reduces in the 2×2 case to the test considered in section 10.1.1.

In the general case we shall indicate why the large-sample tests for homogeneity and independence are the same. In the model for the test of independence, by the law of large numbers the random row totals will be approximately equal to the constants $np_{i.} = n_i$. Thus under the assumption of *independence* ($p_{ij} = p_{i.} \cdot p_{.j}$) the frequencies across the ith row will be approximately multinomial with n_i trials and with probabilities $P(B_j|A_i) = p_{ij}/p_{i.} = p_{.j}$, the same for all $i = 1, \ldots, r$. But this is just the assumption of *homogeneity*.

We now compute the estimated cell frequency table for the data given in table 10.15, and carry out the test for homogeneity at the level $\alpha = .05$.

TABLE 10.16
Estimated Cell Frequencies for Table 10.15

Class \ Response	Agree	Neutral	Disagree	Row totals
Freshman	62	12	26	100
Sophomore	62	12	26	100
Junior	62	12	26	100
Senior	62	12	26	100
Column totals	248	48	104	400

For example, $E_{11} = \dfrac{n_1 \cdot m_1}{n} = \dfrac{100 \cdot 248}{400} = \dfrac{1}{4}(248) = 62$, and similarly for the other cells.

From table 10.15 of observed frequencies and table 10.16 of estimated frequencies we obtain

$$Y = \frac{(47-62)^2}{62} + \frac{(60-62)^2}{62} + \ldots + \frac{(21-26)^2}{26} + \frac{(20-26)^2}{26}$$
$$= 17.008$$

Now the test (15) of homogeneity in this example with $(r-1)(c-1) = 3 \cdot 2 = 6$ gives

$$Y = 17.008 > 12.592 = \chi^2_{.05, 6}$$

We therefore reject H_0 at level $\alpha = .05$ and assert that the various classes are *not* responding in the same manner. A more favorable impression of professors' devotion to teaching evidently prevails at the upper-class levels.

PROBLEMS 10.3

1. A random sample of 5000 death certificates of males in New York state showed the following results by cause of death and smoking habits.

Cause of death / Smoking habit	Respiratory disease	Heart disease	Other causes
Heavy smoker	116	154	180
Moderate smoker	306	497	797
Nonsmoker	478	849	1623

Test at the level of significance $\alpha = .01$ the independence of cause of death and smoking habit. Give the null hypothesis, the expected frequency table under the null hypothesis, the critical region of the test, and your conclusion.

2. A random sample of 200 professors in the University of Wisconsin system resulted in the following classification by rank and sex.

Rank / Sex	Assistant professor	Associate professor	Professor
Male	46	42	72
Female	24	8	8

Test the hypothesis of independence of sex and rank based on these data at the level of significance $\alpha = .05$. Give the null hypothesis, the expected frequency table under the null hypothesis, the critical region of the test, and your conclusion.

3. A group of 108 patients who had had a kidney transplant operation were randomly assigned two different drugs to prevent rejection of the transplanted kidney. They were observed for two years and the number of rejection episodes (an episode is a threat of rejection requiring treatment) was recorded for each patient.

Drug \ No. of episodes	0	1	2	3 or more	Total
D_1	23	10	9	12	54
D_2	11	6	15	22	54

Test at $\alpha = .05$ the hypothesis that the two drugs have the same distribution of number of rejection episodes. State the null and alternative hypotheses. Give the rejection region and conclusion of your test.

4. Random samples of 1000 freshmen in four-year colleges and 1000 freshmen in two-year colleges gave the following ages.

College \ Age	14–17	18	19	20–21	over 21	Total
Two year	132	249	323	169	127	1000
Four year	170	295	341	123	71	1000

Test the hypothesis that two- and four-year colleges have the same distribution of freshmen by age. Use $\alpha = .01$. State the null and alternative hypotheses. Give the rejection region and conclusion of your test.

5. Explain the difference between problems 1 and 3; why is one a test of independence and one a test of homogeneity?

10.4 Appendix

Example 10

A study is made to determine whether native-born and foreign-born candidates do equally well on an examination for English teacher certification. Let A = native, A' = foreign born, B = pass, and B' = fail. Suppose that the following pass-fail data are obtained for a random sample of n_1 $A's$ and n_2 non-$A's$.

Grade Country	B	B'	Totals
A	a	b	n_1
A'	c	d	n_2
Totals	m_1	m_2	n

Let $H_o : p_1 = p_2$ be the null hypothesis, where

$$p_1 = P(B|A) \qquad p_2 = P(B|A')$$

are the two probabilities of interest (test of homogeneity), n_1 and n_2 being fixed in advance. The chi-squared test rejects H_0 at the .05 level if

$$Y = \frac{n(ad - bc)^2}{m_1 m_2 n_1 n_2}$$

exceeds 3.84, the value for the chi-squared distribution with one degree of freedom that leaves probability .05 to the right.

Suppose in fact that $p_1 \neq p_2$ and that (to simplify the algebra) $n_1 = n_2 = N$, where N is some large number. Then by the law of large numbers

$$a \cong Np_1 \qquad b \cong Nq_1 \qquad (q_1 = 1 - p_1)$$
$$c \cong Np_2 \qquad d \cong Nq_2 \qquad (q_2 = 1 - p_2)$$

so that with high probability

$$Y \cong \frac{2N(N^2 p_1 q_2 - N^2 q_1 p_2)^2}{N(p_1 + p_2) \, N(q_1 + q_2)N^2} = \frac{2N(p_1 - p_2)^2}{(p_1 + p_2)(q_1 + q_2)}$$

since

$$p_1 q_2 - q_1 p_2 = p_1(1 - p_2) - (1 - p_1)p_2 = p_1 - p_2$$

Thus the observed value of Y will almost certainly be approximately equal to the total sample size $2N$ multiplied by the positive constant $(p_1 - p_2)^2/[(p_1 + p_2)(q_1 + q_2)]$. For a sufficiently large N it is therefore almost certain that Y will be found to exceed 3.84 (or any other pre-assigned value).

For example, suppose that in fact one p_i is .49 and the other is .51. Then

$$\frac{(p_1 - p_2)^2}{(p_1 + p_2)(q_1 + q_2)} = \frac{(.02)^2}{1 \cdot 1} = .0004$$

If $N \geq 5000$ then it is almost certain that Y will exceed 3.84, even though the difference $|p_1 - p_2| = .02$ may be regarded as insignificant for all practical purposes.

In cases such as this it would clearly be more informative to find a confidence interval estimate for $p_1 - p_2$, rather than to perform a test of $H_0 : p_1 = p_2$. The appropriate 95% confidence interval for $p_1 - p_2$ is given by formula 6.19 for general n_1 and n_2; it is

$$\hat{p}_1 - \hat{p}_2 \pm 1.96 \sqrt{\frac{\hat{p}_1\hat{q}_1}{n_1} + \frac{\hat{p}_2\hat{q}_2}{n_2}}$$

where $\hat{p}_1 = a/n_1$, $\hat{p}_2 = c/n_2$, $\hat{q}_1 = b/n_1$, $\hat{q}_2 = d/n_2$, and both n_1 and n_2 are large. The width of this interval can never exceed twice the value

$$1.96 \sqrt{\frac{1/4}{n_1} + \frac{1/4}{n_2}} < \sqrt{\frac{1}{n_1} + \frac{1}{n_2}}$$

which for $n_1 = n_2 \geq 5000$ is less than .01.

Example 11
A clinical study is made to investigate whether the use of birth-control pills increases the risk of stroke. Let A = user of pills, A' = nonuser, B = stroke victim, and B' = non-stroke victim. Suppose there are m_1 cases of stroke in which it is known whether the victim used or did not use birth-control pills. The same information is available for a matched control group of m_2 non-B's. The data are displayed in the 2×2 table below.

Pills \\ Stroke	B	B'	Totals
A	a	b	n_1
A'	c	d	n_2
Totals	m_1	m_2	n

Again we are concerned with comparing $p_1 = P(B|A)$ and $p_2 = P(B|A')$, but since here it is the *column* totals m_1, m_2 that are fixed we can only estimate the conditional probabilities

$$
\begin{array}{lll}
P(A|B) & \text{estimated by} & a/m_1 \qquad\qquad (16)\\
P(A'|B) & \text{estimated by} & c/m_1\\
P(A|B') & \text{estimated by} & b/m_2\\
P(A'|B') & \text{estimated by} & d/m_2
\end{array}
$$

How, then, can we say anything about $p_1 = P(B|A)$ and $p_2 = P(B|A')$?

The answer lies in the following fact: by the definition of conditional probability

$$\frac{P(A|B)/P(A'|B)}{P(A|B')/P(A'|B')} = \frac{P(B|A)/P(B'|A)}{P(B|A')/P(B'|A')} \tag{17}$$

since both sides when expressed as unconditional probabilities are easily seen to be equal to

$$\frac{P(A \text{ and } B)P(A' \text{ and } B')}{P(A' \text{ and } B)P(A \text{ and } B')}$$

The right-hand side of (17) is equal to

$$\frac{p_1/(1-p_1)}{p_2/(1-p_2)}$$

while by (16) the left-hand side of (17) can be estimated from the data by

$$\frac{a/c}{b/d} = \frac{ad}{bc}$$

Hence

$$\frac{p_1/(1-p_1)}{p_2/(1-p_2)} \text{ is estimated by } \frac{ad}{bc} \tag{18}$$

the estimation being reliable when both m_1 and m_2 are large.

For example, if the table above is

	B	B'	Totals
A	180	120	300
A'	30	100	130
Totals	210	220	

with $m_1 = 210$ stroke victims and $m_2 = 220$ controls, the estimated value of the "odds ratio" $[p_1/(1-p_1)]/[p_2/(1-p_2)]$ is $ad/bc = 5$. In cases such as this, when both the probabilities p_1 and p_2 are quite small, the odds ratio will be approximately equal to

$$\frac{p_1}{p_2} = \frac{P(B|A)}{P(B|A')} = \text{relative risk of } B \text{ for } A's \text{ and non-}A's$$

Thus we would estimate the probability of stroke for $A's$ to be about five times that for non-A's. Of course, 5 is just a *point estimate* of the odds ratio. A more informative *confidence interval* for the odds ratio is

$$\left(\frac{ad}{bc} \cdot e^{-1.96s} \quad , \quad \frac{ad}{bc} \cdot e^{1.96s}\right)$$

where $e = 2.718 \ldots$ is the familiar mathematical constant, and

$$s = \sqrt{\frac{1}{a} + \frac{1}{b} + \frac{1}{c} + \frac{1}{d}}$$

The coverage probability can be shown to be approximately .95. In the present example

$$s = \sqrt{\frac{1}{180} + \frac{1}{120} + \frac{1}{30} + \frac{1}{100}} \cong .239$$

so that with 95% confidence

$$3.13 = 5 \cdot e^{-.468} < \frac{p_1/(1 - p_1)}{p_2/(1 - p_2)} \approx \frac{p_1}{p_2} < 5 \cdot e^{.468} = 7.98$$

It should be noted that although we can estimate the odds ratio (or relative risk) of B for A's and non-A's from data such as these, it is clearly not possible to estimate separately the values of p_1 and p_2 from such data. The 210 hypothetical stroke victims in the example above surely would represent a very small fraction of the population of all women in the age group under study. Hence, even if $p_2 \cong 5p_1$, when p_1 itself is very small even a five-fold increase in it may represent an acceptable risk.

Distribution-Free Methods

11 Distribution-Free Methods

A method of estimating parameters or testing hypotheses is said to be *distribution-free* if it is valid without any special assumptions concerning the nature of the population from which the sample is drawn. In this chapter we present some distribution-free statistical procedures that are of considerable use. In contrast to them, we recall for example that in chapter 7 the t distribution for small samples assumed a normally distributed population. In chapter 6 the Central Limit Theorem assured us that the methods would be approximately valid even when the underlying population is not normally distributed provided that the samples are large enough. The methods of chapter 6 are therefore "asymptotically" distribution-free, but we must keep in mind that a drastically non-normal population may require a very large sample size before the methods of chapter 6 can be relied on.

The distribution-free methods to be developed here all involve ordering the observations from smallest to largest. An appropriate statistic is then often computed solely from the resulting *ranks* of the data. This will be explained as we proceed.

In section 11.1 we introduce the concept of the *median* of a probability distribution. This, like the mean, measures a "central value" of the distribution, and we give both point and confidence interval estimators for the median in sections 11.2 and 11.3. In sections 11.4 and 11.5 we discuss the problem of comparing two distributions. Section 11.4 treats comparison of paired observations and presents a distribution-free analogue of the paired t test of section 7.6, whereas section 11.5 treats the same problem in the case of two independent samples, and gives an analogue of the unpaired t test. Section 11.6 is devoted to the "rank correlation coefficient", and provides an alternative method of studying the amount of dependence between two variables, as was done in chapter 9 using normal theory.

11.1 The Median of a Distribution and Its Estimation

Definition 1

Let x be a random variable with a continuous probability distribution. The *median* of x, denoted by $\tau = \tau_x$, is that number τ for which

$$P(x \leq \tau) = P(x \geq \tau) = \frac{1}{2} \tag{1}$$

Thus, τ is that value such that "half the population" has an x value that is $\leq \tau$ and the half has an x value that is $\geq \tau$. (See figure 11.1.)

The distribution of a continuous random variable x is said to be *symmetric* about some value b if $P(x \leq b - c) = P(x \geq b + c)$ for every value $c \geq 0$, as in figure 11.2. Clearly, *a random variable* x *that is symmetric about some value* b *will have* b *both as its median* τ *and its mean* μ.

When x has a distribution that is not symmetric, the median τ of x will in general not be equal to the mean μ. In such cases we may be more interested in estimating the median of the distribution than the mean; for a "skewed" distribution such as that shown in figure 11.3 τ may be more informative as a parameter of centrality than μ.

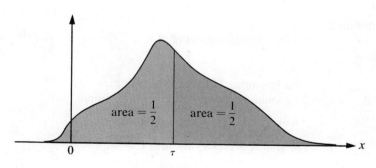

FIGURE 11.1

$P(x \leq \tau) = P(x \geq \tau) = \frac{1}{2}$ when τ is the median of x

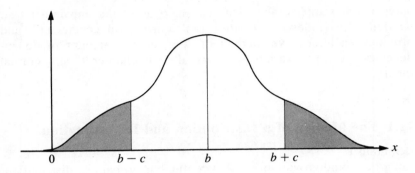

FIGURE 11.2
A symmetric continuous distribution

For example, if x represents the annual income of some large group of people, the median τ of x is that number such that half the people have incomes $\leq \tau$ and half have incomes $\geq \tau$. The mean μ of x gives us no such information, since the value of μ will often be greatly influenced by a small number of people with very large incomes. Moreover, sometimes only the median is capable of experimental determination. For example, in bioassay problems, the median lethal dose of a fly spray is that dose which will kill 50 percent of the flies. The determination of the exact value of the minimum lethal dose for any single fly is impossible.

Let $\{x_1, \ldots, x_n\}$ be a random sample from the distribution of a random variable x. Just as we estimate the mean μ of the distribution of x by the sample mean $\bar{x} = \dfrac{1}{n} \displaystyle\sum_{i=1}^{n} x_i$, a point estimator of μ, we estimate the median τ of the distribution of x by the "sample median", a point estimator of τ.

Definition 2
Let $\{x_1, \ldots, x_n\}$ be a random sample of size n from some distribution. Define

$$x_{(1)} = \text{smallest observation in the sample} \qquad (2)$$
$$x_{(2)} = \text{2nd smallest observation in the sample}$$
$$\vdots$$
$$x_{(i)} = i\text{th smallest observation in the sample}$$
$$\vdots$$
$$x_{(n)} = \text{largest (}n\text{th smallest) observation in the sample}$$

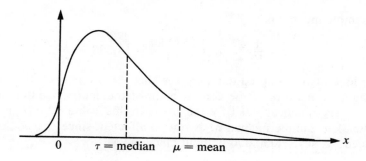

FIGURE 11.3
A skewed distribution

The observed values $x_{(1)} \le x_{(2)} \le \ldots \le x_{(n)}$ are called the *order statistics* of the sample $\{x_1, \ldots, x_n\}$. To obtain them we simply order the n observations from smallest to largest, labeling the smallest $x_{(1)}, \ldots,$ and the largest $x_{(n)}$.

Definition 3
The *sample median M* of $\{x_1, \ldots, x_n\}$ is defined to be the number

$$M = \begin{cases} x_{((n+1)/2)} \text{ if } n \text{ is an } odd \text{ number} \\[2ex] \frac{1}{2}[x_{(n/2)} + x_{((n/2)+1)}] \text{ if } n \text{ is an } even \text{ number} \end{cases} \tag{3}$$

Example 1
A sample of 10 people employed full-time in a city reported the following incomes (in dollars per year):

$x_1 = 9850$	$x_5 = 10{,}670$	$x_9 = 8400$
$x_2 = 7223$	$x_6 = 4274$	$x_{10} = 11{,}200$
$x_3 = 6421$	$x_7 = 8641$	
$x_4 = 20{,}118$	$x_8 = 72{,}087$	

The sample median M for these data is found by ordering the observations and then using (3). Since

$x_{(1)} = 4274$	$x_{(5)} = 8641$	$x_{(8)} = 11{,}200$
$x_{(2)} = 6421$	$x_{(6)} = 9850$	$x_{(9)} = 20{,}018$
$x_{(3)} = 7223$	$x_{(7)} = 10{,}670$	$x_{(10)} = 72{,}087$
$x_{(4)} = 8400$		

and $n = 10$ is an even number, the sample median income is

$$M = \frac{1}{2}[x_{(5)} + x_{(6)}] = 9145.5$$

The sample mean $\bar{x}$ is

$$\bar{x} = \frac{1}{10} \sum_{i=1}^{10} x_i = \frac{158{,}884}{10} = 15{,}888$$

If we look at the ordered data, we see that $\bar{x} = 15{,}888$ is rather misleading as a measure of the central point of the data, since the value of $\bar{x}$ is very much affected by the one extreme value 72,087 in the sample. The sample median M is not so affected, since $x_{(10)}$ could be replaced by, say, 1,000,000 without changing M.

Example 2

A hospital recorded the following monthly numbers of births for a 15-month period: 301, 264, 321, 277, 257, 337, 256, 236, 242, 290, 325, 234, 257, 345, 298.

Ordering the data, we have

$x_{(1)} = 234$	$x_{(4)} = 256$	$x_{(7)} = 264$	$x_{(10)} = 298$	$x_{(13)} = 325$
$x_{(2)} = 236$	$x_{(5)} = 257$	$x_{(8)} = 277$	$x_{(11)} = 301$	$x_{(14)} = 337$
$x_{(3)} = 242$	$x_{(6)} = 257$	$x_{(9)} = 290$	$x_{(12)} = 321$	$x_{(15)} = 345$

Here, since $n = 15$ is an odd number, the sample median is by (3)

$$M = x_{(8)} = 277$$

(As is the case here, the sample median need not be a possible value of the random variable.) The sample mean is

$$\bar{x} = \frac{1}{n} \sum_{i=1}^{n} x_i = \frac{4240}{15} = 282.67$$

with a rather small difference between the sample mean and the sample median in this case.

PROBLEMS 11.1

1. A sample of 10 rockets showed the following times for the first-stage burn (in minutes): 6.2, 8.7, 7.5, 14.1, 6.3, 7.1, 8.1, 7.3, 6.7, 7.0.

   a. Find the median burn time from these data.
   b. Find the mean burn time from these data.
   c. Are (a) and (b) close? Discuss why or why not.

2. A sample of 15 ranches in Texas gave the following acreages:

747	1540	1280	39,700
1642	20,010	720	7220
1900	872	2340	3218
968	1743	1372	

    a. Find the median acreage from these data.

    b. Find the mean acreage from these data.

    c. Are (a) and (b) close? Discuss why or why not.

3. A new process for curing cement resulted in the following compressive strengths (in lbs/sq. inch) for a sample of 24 pieces tested:

9605	5021	3812	7264
4521	5298	7621	5047
6247	6147	4628	6107
3381	8742	9047	12,620
10,647	3605	5798	7147
3910	7018	4340	4129

    a. Find the values of the order statistics of these data.

    b. Find the median for these data.

    c. Is the median value attainable as recorded?

4. A drug developed to reduce ectopic (irregular) heartbeats is given to 30 patients with heart trouble. The following data record the percentage of decrease in mean ectopic heartbeat between the 24-hour periods before and after administration of the drug. (Negative numbers represent an increase.)

53	94	−102	87	72	87
84	39	79	−25	84	69
66	68	96	53	93	77
−30	86	68	41	67	91
87	94	84	72	−12	80

    a. Find the values of the order statistics of these data.

    b. Find the median of these data.

11.2 Confidence Intervals for a Population Median Based on Small Samples

The sample median M is a *point* estimator of the population median τ. It can be shown to be a *consistent* estimator of τ. That is, if the sample size n is sufficiently large there is a high probability that the sample median M will be very close to the population median τ (when the population distribution is continuous). However, as we have seen, a point estimator alone is not of much use without some idea of *how* close it is to the parameter that it estimates. We shall therefore proceed to obtain *confidence intervals* for an unknown population median τ.

    To construct a 100 $(1 - \alpha)\%$ confidence interval for the unknown median τ of a continuous distribution, based on a random sample $\{x_1, \ldots, x_n\}$ from this distribution, we choose in a manner to be specified below two *order statistics* $x_{(r)}$ and $x_{(s)}$ such that

$$P\{x_{(r)} \leq \tau \leq x_{(s)}\} = 1 - \alpha \tag{4}$$

Then the interval from $x_{(r)}$ to $x_{(s)}$, which is random and varies from sample to sample, has a probability $1 - \alpha$ of containing the unknown constant τ, and is therefore a $100(1 - \alpha)\%$ confidence interval for τ. The method of choosing r and s as functions of n and α is as follows.

A $100(1 - \alpha)\%$ confidence interval for the median (small sample). Select an integer r from the binomial table in appendix table 4 such that

$$B\left(r - 1; n, \frac{1}{2}\right) = \sum_{i=0}^{r-1} \binom{n}{i} \frac{1}{2^n} = \frac{\alpha}{2} \tag{5}$$

Then

$$P\{x_{(r)} \leq \tau \leq x_{(n-r+1)}\} = 1 - \alpha \tag{6}$$

An integer r satisfying (5) exactly cannot always be found for an arbitrary preassigned value α. In practice, we choose r to yield an α close to that desired. The following discussion illustrates this.

Suppose that in example 1 we want a confidence interval with a coverage probability of about 90% for the unknown median income τ, so that we would like (5) to be satisfied with $\alpha/2$ about .05. Since $n = 10$ in this example, we have from appendix table 4, $B(2; 10, 1/2) = .055$ and $B(3; 10, 1/2) = .172$. Therefore, if we choose $r = 2$ we get a confidence coefficient $1 - \alpha = 1 - 2(.055) = 1 - .110 = .890$, yielding the 89% confidence interval ($r = 2$ and $n - r + 1 = 9$)

$$x_{(2)} = 6421 \leq \tau \leq 20.018 = x_{(9)}$$

If we were to choose $r = 3$, we would have $1 - \alpha = 1 - 2(.172) = .656$ and the resulting 65.6% confidence interval would be the shorter interval

$$x_{(3)} = 7223 \leq \tau \leq 11.200 = x_{(8)}$$

Verification of (6). We note that the events $A = \{x_{(r)} \leq \tau \leq x_{(s)}\}$ and $B = \{x_{(s)} < \tau\}$ are mutually exclusive for $r < s$, and their union is the event $\{x_{(r)} \leq \tau\}$. Therefore, by the addition property of probability

$$P\{x_{(r)} \leq \tau\} = P\{x_{(r)} \leq \tau \leq x_{(s)}\} + P\{x_{(s)} < \tau\}$$

Since by hypothesis we are sampling from the distribution of a continuous random variable x

$$P\{x_{(r)} \leq \tau \leq x_{(s)}\} = P\{x_{(r)} \leq \tau\} - P\{x_{(s)} \leq \tau\} \tag{7}$$

We now observe that for any integer i

$$P\{x_{(i)} \leq \tau\} = 1 - B\left(i - 1; n, \frac{1}{2}\right) \tag{8}$$

which is the binomial probability of getting $y \geq i$ successes in n trials with success probability $p = 1/2$. In fact,

$$P\{x_{(i)} \leq \tau\} = P(i \text{ or more of } x_1, \ldots, x_n \text{ are } \leq \tau)$$
$$= 1 - P(i - 1 \text{ or fewer of } x_1, \ldots, x_n \text{ are } \leq \tau)$$
$$= 1 - B\left(i - 1; n, \frac{1}{2}\right)$$

The last equality follows by noting that from the definition of the median for a continuous distribution, $P\{x_i \leq \tau\} = 1/2$, and therefore the number y of the sample values $x_1, \ldots, x_n$ that are $\leq \tau$ has a binomial distribution with n trials and $p = 1/2$. Combining (7) with (8) for $i = r$ and $i = s = n - r + 1$, we obtain

$$P\{x_{(r)} \leq \tau \leq x_{(n-r+1)}\} = \left[1 - B\left(r - 1; n, \frac{1}{2}\right)\right] \tag{9}$$

$$- \left[1 - B\left(n - r; n, \frac{1}{2}\right)\right]$$

$$= 1 - 2B\left(r - 1; n, \frac{1}{2}\right)$$

The last equality follows by noting that when $p = 1/2$ in a binomial distribution, the number of successes, y, and the number of failures, $n - y$, have the same probability distribution, so that

$$1 - B\left(n - r; n, \frac{1}{2}\right) = P\{y > n - r\} = P\{n - y > n - r\}$$

$$= P\{y < r\}$$

$$= B\left(r - 1; n, \frac{1}{2}\right)$$

Choosing r to satisfy (5), and substituting into (9), we complete the verification of (6).

The confidence interval (6) is applicable even when the median τ is not unique, as in the case of a *discrete* random variable x, where the median is defined to be *any* value τ for which $P(x \leq \tau) \geq 1/2$ and $P(x \geq \tau) \geq 1/2$ (for example, if $P(x = 0) = P(x = 1) = P(x = 2) = P(x = 3) = 1/4$, then τ is defined to be any number such that $1 \leq \tau \leq 2$).

In fact, it can be shown that for *any* distribution (continuous or discrete)

$$P\{x_{(r)} \leq \tau \leq x_{(n-r+1)}\} \geq 1 - \alpha \tag{10}$$

if (5) holds, so that the interval from $x_{(r)}$ to $x_{(n-r+1)}$ will contain the median τ with probability *at least* $1 - \alpha$ in all cases.

Suppose, for example, that the monthly data on births in example 2 can be assumed to be a random sample from some discrete distribution. Using (10) and (5) we obtain confidence intervals for τ. We find that from appendix table 4, $B(2; 15, 1/2) = .004$ and $B(3; 15, 1/2) = .018$. Therefore, confidence intervals for τ with respective confidence coefficients *at least* $1 - 2(.004) = .992$ and $1 - 2(.018) = .964$ are

$$x_{(2)} \leq \tau \leq x_{(14)}; \text{ i.e., } 236 \leq \tau \leq 337$$

and

$$x_{(3)} \leq \tau \leq x_{(13)}; \text{ i.e., } 242 \leq \tau \leq 325$$

Of course, the higher the confidence coefficient, the wider the corresponding confidence interval.

PROBLEMS 11.2

1. For the data in example 1, section 11.1, find a confidence interval with a coverage probability of about 98% for the unknown median income. State the *exact* confidence coefficient of the resulting interval.

2. For the data in example 2, section 11.1, find a confidence interval with coverage probability about 99% for the unknown median number of monthly births. State the *exact* confidence coefficient obtained.

3. For the data in problem 1, section 11.1, find a $100(1 - \alpha)\%$ confidence interval for the median burn time if: (a) α is about .02; (b) α is about .10. In each case give the *exact* confidence coefficient obtained.

4. For the data in problem 2, section 11.1, find a $100(1 - \alpha)\%$ confidence interval for the median acreage of Texas ranches if: (a) α is about .01; (b) α is about .05. In each case give the *exact* confidence coefficient obtained.

11.3 Large-Sample Confidence Intervals for the Median

Although tables for solving (5) for large n are not available, a normal approximation to the binomial probability in (9) allows us to obtain large-sample ($n > 20$) confidence intervals for an unknown median τ. If y has a binomial distribution with n trials and a success probability $p = 1/2$, then the normal approximation to the binomial distribution gives, with a good degree of accuracy,

$$B\left(r - 1; n, \frac{1}{2}\right) = P\{y \leq r - 1\} = P\{y \leq r - .5\} \tag{11}$$

$$= P\left\{\frac{y - n/2}{\sqrt{n \cdot 1/2 \cdot 1/2}} \leq \frac{r - .5 - n/2}{\sqrt{n \cdot 1/2 \cdot 1/2}}\right\} \cong P\{z \leq z^*\}$$

where

$$z^* = \frac{r - (n + 1)/2}{\sqrt{n}/2}$$

and z is a standard normal random variable. If we choose $z^* = -z_{\alpha/2}$, we obtain

$$B\left(r - 1; n, \frac{1}{2}\right) \cong P\{z \leq -z_{\alpha/2}\} = \frac{\alpha}{2} \text{ for } r = \frac{n + 1}{2} - z_{\alpha/2} \cdot \frac{\sqrt{n}}{2}$$

However, this r need not be an integer, as required in (6). Therefore, we choose r as the largest integer $\leq (n + 1)/2 - z_{\alpha/2} \cdot \sqrt{n}/2$, and obtain an approximately $100(1 - \alpha)\%$ confidence interval by combining (11) with (9). The result is

    An $\cong 100 \cdot (1 - \alpha)\%$ confidence interval for the median (large sample:

    Choose r as the largest integer less than or equal to

$$\frac{n + 1}{2} - z_{\alpha/2} \cdot \frac{\sqrt{n}}{2}$$

where $z_{\alpha/2}$ is the value for the standard normal distribution that leaves probability $\alpha/2$ in the upper tail. Then

$$P\{x_{(r)} \leq \tau \leq x_{(n-r+1)}\} \cong 1 - \alpha \tag{12}$$

That is, the interval $x_{(r)}$ to $x_{(n-r+1)}$, including the end points, is an (approximately) $100(1 - \alpha)\%$ confidence interval for the population median τ.

Example 3

A random sample of $n = 36$ monthly rents for one-bedroom apartments in Houston, Texas, yielded (in 1973 dollars)

120	116	90	160	100	160
210	225	175	215	215	70
195	168	260	410	170	104
85	140	180	125	114	195
173	275	325	150	335	140
155	130	80	159	120	80

Suppose that we wish to estimate τ, the median monthly rent, by a 95% confidence interval. Here, $\alpha = .05$ and $z_{\alpha/2} = 1.96$, so that

$$\frac{n+1}{2} - z_{\alpha/2} \cdot \frac{\sqrt{n}}{2} = \frac{37}{2} - \frac{(1.96)(6)}{2} = 12.62$$

and $r = 12$ is the largest integer ≤ 12.62. The $\cong 95\%$ confidence interval (12) thus becomes

$$x_{(12)} \leq \tau \leq x_{(25)}$$

Ordering the data, we obtain

70	104	130	160	$180 = x_{(25)}$	225
80	114	140	160	195	260
80	116	140	168	195	275
85	120	150	170	210	325
90	120	155	173	215	335
100	$125 = x_{(12)}$	159	175	215	410

so the $\cong 95\%$ confidence interval for the median monthly rent is $125 \leq \tau \leq 180$.

Note:
  a. When $n > 20$ the approximation (12) is quite accurate.
  b. The interval (12) can be used for either discrete or continuous data. For discrete distributions the confidence interval statement (12) holds with probability *at least* $1 - \alpha$.

PROBLEMS 11.3

1. For the data in example 3, find an (approximately) 90% confidence interval for the median monthly rent using (12).

2. For the data in example 3, find an (approximately) 99% confidence interval for the median monthly rent using (12).

3. For the data in problem 3, section 11.1, find an (approximately) $100(1 - \alpha)\%$ confidence interval for the median compressive strength if (a) $\alpha = .01$; (b) $\alpha = .10$.

4. For the data in problem 4, section 11.1, find an (approximately) $100(1 - \alpha)\%$ confidence interval for the median percentage decrease in ectopic heartbeat if (a) $\alpha = .05$; (b) $\alpha = .01$.

11.4 Distribution-Free Comparison of Paired Data. The Wilcoxon Test for Paired Data

In section 4.7 we discussed the "sign test," a rather crude method for comparing two populations based on paired observations. The null hypothesis was $H_0 : P(x > y) = P(x < y)$ for a pair of random variables (x, y) from a sample $\{(x_1, y_1), \ldots, (x_n, y_n)\}$ of n untied pairs. The sign test is in fact a test of the null hypothesis $H_0 : \tau_d = 0$ versus $H_1 : \tau_d \neq 0$, where τ_d is the *median of the distribution of the difference* $d = x - y$, from which $\{d_1, \ldots, d_n\}$ is a random sample. We shall develop here a test for this hypothesis, the *one-sample Wilcoxon test*, in which we take into account not only the *signs* of the $d_i = x_i - y_i$ but also their *relative magnitudes*.

Let $\{(x_1, y_1), \ldots, (x_n, y_n)\}$ be n pairs of observations, with differences $d_i = x_i - y_i$. We suppose that all ties $x_i = y_i$ (if any) have been eliminated from the original data, so that each d_i is either > 0 or < 0.

We now make the following basic assumption: *The* $d_i = x_i - y_i$ *are a random sample from some continuous distribution which is symmetric (about its median,* τ_d).

Suppose we now wish to test

$$H_0 : \tau_d = 0 \text{ vs } H_1 : \tau_d \neq 0$$

If $\tau_d > 0$, then a randomly chosen x value has a greater than 50 percent chance of being larger than the corresponding y value. To see this, we note that $\tau_d > 0$ implies that

$$P(x < y) = P(d < 0) < P(d \leq \tau_d) = \frac{1}{2}$$

so that $P(x < y) < 1/2$. A similar argument shows that $P(x > y) > 1/2$ if $\tau_d < 0$. Thus, testing H_0 vs H_1 is equivalent to asking whether one of the two random variables x, y tends to have larger values than the other. Alternatively, since a symmetric distribution will have its mean equal to its median, $\tau_d = \mu_{x-y} = \mu_x - \mu_y$. Hence a test of H_0 vs H_1 may be regarded as testing

$$H_0 : \mu_x = \mu_y \text{ vs } H_1 : \mu_x \neq \mu_y \tag{13}$$

We see, then, that the Wilcoxon test can be used to test the same hypothesis as the paired t test of section 7.6 without assuming that the distribution of $x - y$ is *normal* but merely that it is *symmetric*. It may be used instead of the paired t test whenever one cannot make the assumption of approximate normality required for the latter, since the only assumption for the Wilcoxon test is that just given.

We now describe the Wilcoxon test. We begin by taking the absolute values of the differences $|d_i|$, $i = 1, \ldots, n$, and ordering them from smallest to largest. Define the rank of the smallest $|d_i|$ to be 1, the rank of the second smallest to be 2, . . . , the rank of the largest (nth smallest) to be n. Then for each d_i we have a corresponding *rank* R_i, given for each $i = 1, \ldots, n$ by

$$R_i = k \text{ if } |d_i| \text{ is the } k\text{th smallest of } |d_1|, \ldots, |d_n| \qquad (14)$$

If two (or more) of the $|d_i|$ have the same value, we assign the same rank to both (or all) such observations by averaging the ranks. For instance, if two of the $|d_i|$ are equal and should be assigned, say ranks 6 and 7, then each is assigned rank 6.5. To clarify these ideas, consider the following example.

Example 4

A pharmaceutical firm wishes to test the effect of a drug on pulse rate. A random sample of 12 people is drawn, and the pulse rate of each person is measured before and after administration of the drug. The results, with the ranks of the absolute differences (the column labeled U_i will be explained later), are as follows.

TABLE 11.1
Data for Paired Comparison of Pulse Rates

Subject	Rate before drug (x_i)	Rate after drug (y_i)	$d_i = x_i - y_i$	$\|d_i\|$	R_i	U_i
1	72.0	74.8	−2.8	2.8	6.5	0
2	75.2	78.1	−2.9	2.9	8	0
3	62.0	65.3	−3.3	3.3	9	0
4	71.5	70.0	1.5	1.5	4	4
5	69.7	69.5	.2	.2	1	1
6	78.6	80.4	−1.8	1.8	5	0
7	63.8	61.0	2.8	2.8	6.5	6.5
8	70.0	75.2	−5.2	5.2	11	0
9	71.0	76.4	−5.4	5.4	12	0
10	73.8	74.2	− .4	.4	3	0
11	63.2	67.0	−3.8	3.8	10	0
12	78.0	78.3	− .3	.3	2	0

The data here are naturally paired (before-after test), *thus eliminating the disturbing effect of person-to-person variability in pulse rate.* Based on these data, can the firm claim at level $\alpha = .05$ that the drug has an effect on pulse rate?
Define

$$U_i = \begin{cases} 0 \text{ if } d_i = x_i - y_i < 0 \\ R_i \text{ if } d_i = x_i - y_i > 0 \end{cases} \tag{15}$$

and form the sum

$$T^+ = U_1 + \ldots + U_n \tag{16}$$

which is the sum of the ranks of the *positive* d_i's. Either very large or very small values of T^+ are unlikely under H_0 and thus tend to support H_1. To see this, we note that a large value of T^+ arises when many U_i's are relatively large. Thus, a large value of T^+ tends to support the hypothesis that $P(x > y) = P(d > 0) > 1/2$; in other words, that $\tau_d < 0$. Similarly, a small value of T^+ supports the hypothesis that $\tau_d > 0$. The critical region R of our test will therefore be taken as

Reject H_0 if $T^+ \le c_1$ or $T^+ \ge c_2$

for some suitably chosen integers c_1 and c_2. In order to determine c_1 and c_2, we use appendix table 11, which gives the lower-tail probabilities $P(T^+ \le c)$ computed when $\tau_d = 0$ (under H_0) for various values of n. For example, when $n = 6$

c	0	1	2	3	4
$P(T^+ \le c)$	.0156	.0313	.0469	.0781	.1094

It can be seen by symmetry that we need tabulate only the lower-tail probabilities, since the upper-tail probabilities can be obtained from the fact that if we denote by T^- the sum of the ranks of the negative d_i's then $T^+ + T^- = 1 + 2 + \ldots + n = n(n + 1)/2$. Hence, since under H_0 the distribution of T^- is the same as that of T^+, $P\{T^+ \le c\} = P\{n(n + 1)/2 - T^- \le c\} = P\{T^- \ge n(n + 1)/2 - c\} = P\{T^+ \ge n(n + 1)/2 - c\}$. Therefore, a test of $H_0 : \tau_d = 0$ with the critical region: reject H_0 if $T^+ \le c$ or $T^+ \ge n(n + 1)/2 - c$, will be a test of level $2P\{T^+ \le c\}$. Table 11.1 has the U_i values for example 4 in the last column. From this we obtain

$$T^+ = \sum_{i=1}^{12} U_i = R_4 + R_5 + R_7 = 4 + 1 + 6.5 = 11.5$$

Since from appendix table 11 for $n = 12$

$$P(T^+ \le 14) = .0261$$

we see that a test of level $\alpha = 2(.0261) = .0522$ (approximating the desired level of .05) is given by

Reject H_0 in favor of H_1 if $T^+ \le 14$ or $T^+ \ge 64$

since $n(n+1)/2 - 14 = (12)(13)/2 - 14 = 78 - 14 = 64$. Therefore, with $T^+ = 11.5$ the conclusion at level $\alpha = .0522$ is that the drug *does* affect pulse rate. In the data given in table 11.1 most of the differences d_i are negative, suggesting that the median difference τ_d is < 0 and that the drug has a tendency to *raise* the pulse rate ($d_i = x_i - y_i =$ before— after).

The test just described is a two-tailed test. One-tailed tests of $H_0 : \tau_d \le 0$ versus $H_1 : \tau_d > 0$ or of $H_0 : \tau_d \ge 0$ versus $H_1 : \tau_d > 0$ can also be given by using upper- and lower-tail probabilities only. The results are summarized in table 11.2 below, where $n =$ the size of the sample, eliminating ties, and T^+ is defined by (16). The value c_α satisfying $P\{T^+ \le c_\alpha\} = \alpha$ is taken from appendix table 11.

Table 11.2 also contains a large-sample approximate test, based on the statistic T^+, that can be used when $n > 20$. It is shown below that if $\tau_d = 0$ then $m.v.(T^+) = n(n+1)/4$ and $var(T^+) = n(n+1)(2n+1)/24$. A generalization of the Central Limit Theorem then shows that under H_0 the standardized random variable

$$z = \frac{T^+ - \mu_{T+}}{\sqrt{\text{Var}(T^+)}} = \frac{T^+ - n(n+1)/4}{\sqrt{\dfrac{n(n+1)(2n+1)}{24}}} \tag{17}$$

is approximately standard normal. Therefore, we can test $H_0 : \tau_d = 0$ versus $H_1 : \tau_d \neq 0$ by the two-tailed α-level test: reject H_0 if $z > z_{\alpha/2}$ or $z < -z_{\alpha/2}$, where z is given by (17). This test, along with the corresponding one-tailed tests and small-sample tests, is called the *Wilcoxon signed-rank test for paired data* and is outlined in table 11.2.

Example 5

A physiologist, wishing to determine if that lack of sleep increases reaction time, records for a random sample of 25 adults their reaction times to a visual stimulus, first at 8.00 A.M. one morning, and again after 36 hours of deprivation of sleep. Based on the results given in table 11.3, can the physiologist say at level $\alpha = .05$ that lack of sleep increases reaction time? Here we are testing $H_0 : \tau_d \ge 0$ versus $H_1 : \tau_d < 0$, based on a sample of $n = 24$, since there is one pair that we omit because of a tie.

TABLE 11.2
Wilcoxon Signed-Rank Test for Paired Data $d = x - y$

H_0	H_1	Critical region: reject H_0 if
$\tau_d = 0$ (or $\mu_x = \mu_y$)	$\tau_d \neq 0$ (or $\mu_x \neq \mu_y$)	$T^+ \leq c_{\alpha/2}$ or $T^+ \geq \dfrac{n(n+1)}{2} - c_{\alpha/2}$ (if $n \leq 20$) $z < -z_{\alpha/2}$ or $z > z_{\alpha/2}$ (if $n > 20$)
$\tau_d \geq 0$ (or $\mu_x \geq \mu_y$)	$\tau_d < 0$ (or $\mu_x < \mu_y$)	$T^+ \leq c_\alpha$ (if $n \leq 20$) $z < -z_\alpha$ (if $n > 20$)
$\tau_d \leq 0$ (or $\mu_x \leq \mu_y$)	$\tau_d > 0$ (or $\mu_x > \mu_y$)	$T^+ \geq \dfrac{n(n+1)}{2} - c_\alpha$ (if $n \leq 20$) $z > z_a$ (if $n > 20$)

TABLE 11.3
Reaction Times (in seconds) for Example 5

Subject	First reaction time (x_i)	Second reaction time (y_i)	$d_i = x_i - y_i$	$\lvert d_i \rvert$	R_i	U_i
1	2.8	3.6	− .8	.8	20	0
2	3.7	3.0	.7	.7	17.5	17.5
3	5.1	4.9	.2	.2	3.5	3.5
4	1.6	2.0	− .4	.4	11	0
5	2.7	2.7	0	0	omit	omit
6	3.1	3.2	− .1	.1	1.5	0
7	4.6	5.0	− .4	.4	11	0
8	4.7	5.5	− .8	.8	20	0
9	3.2	3.8	− .6	.6	15.5	0
10	1.5	2.3	− .8	.8	20	0
11	3.2	4.1	− .9	.9	22	0
12	3.4	3.1	.3	.3	6.5	6.5
13	2.3	2.0	.3	.3	6.5	6.5
14	2.7	2.3	.4	.4	11	11
15	3.7	4.8	−1.1	1.1	24	0
16	5.0	5.3	− .3	.3	6.5	0
17	4.3	4.8	− .5	.5	14	0
18	3.7	4.3	− .6	.6	15.5	0
19	2.7	2.6	.1	.1	1.5	1.5
20	1.4	1.8	− .4	.4	11	0
21	3.0	4.0	−1.0	1.0	23	0
22	2.2	2.4	− .2	.2	3.5	0
23	4.1	4.5	− .4	.4	11	0
24	3.1	2.4	.7	.7	17.5	17.5
25	2.2	2.5	− .3	.3	6.5	0

For table 11.3,

$$T^+ = 17.5 + 3.5 + 6.5 + 6.5 + 11 + 1.5 + 17.5 = 62$$

The critical region for the test as given by table 11.2 with $n = 24$ is: Reject H_0 if $z < -z_{.05} = 1.64$, where

$$z = \frac{62 - \dfrac{(24)(25)}{4}}{\sqrt{\dfrac{24 \cdot 25 \cdot 49}{24}}} = \frac{-88}{35} = -2.51$$

Since $z = -2.51 < -1.64$, we reject H_0 and conclude that the median of the difference (or the difference of the means) is negative; that is, lack of sleep increases reaction time.

We close this section by deriving the formulas for the mean and variance of T^+ used in (17).

It is simple in principle to obtain the probability distribution of T^+ under the null hypothesis H_0 that the distribution of the d_i is in fact symmetric about 0. Since $R_1, \ldots, R_n$ is just a permutation of the integers $1, \ldots, n$, and since under H_0 each d_i is equally likely to be positive or negative, independently of the other d_i's, it follows that T^+ can be written in the form

$$T^+ = 1 \cdot t_1 + 2 \cdot t_2 + \ldots + n \cdot t_n$$

where the t_k are independent random variables such that

$$P(t_k = 1) = P(t_k = 0) = 1/2$$

Here $t_k = 1$ if the $|d_i|$ of rank k is such that $d_i > 0$, and $t_k = 0$ if the $|d_i|$ of rank k is such that $d_i < 0$. Since $\mu_{t_k} = 1/2$ and $\sigma_{t_k}^2 = 1/4$ (binomial with $n = 1$ and $p = 1/2$), it follows by using algebraic formulas for $1 + 2 + \ldots + n$ and $1^2 + 2^2 + \ldots + n^2$ that

$$\mu_{T^+} = \frac{1}{2}(1 + 2 + \ldots + n) = \frac{n(n+1)}{4} \tag{18}$$

and

$$\sigma_{T^+}^2 = \frac{1}{4}(1^2 + 2^2 + \ldots + n^2) = \frac{n(n+1)(2n+1)}{24} \tag{19}$$

The entire probability distribution of T^+ for a small n can be obtained by direct enumeration. For example, when $n = 3$ we have the following possibilities.

t_1	t_2	t_3	T^+	$(T^+)^2$
1	1	1	6	36
0	1	1	5	25
1	0	1	4	16
1	1	0	3	9
0	0	1	3	9
0	1	0	2	4
1	0	0	1	1
0	0	0	0	0
		sum	24	100

$$\mu_{T+} = \frac{24}{8} = 3, \ \mu_{(T+)^2} = \frac{100}{8} = \frac{25}{2}, \ \sigma^2_{T+} = \frac{25}{2} - 9 = \frac{7}{2}$$

$$P(T^+ \leq 0) = \frac{1}{8} \qquad\qquad P(T^+ \leq 4) = \frac{6}{8}$$

$$P(T^+ \leq 1) = \frac{2}{8} \qquad\qquad P(T^+ \leq 5) = \frac{7}{8}$$

$$P(T^+ \leq 2) = \frac{3}{8} \qquad\qquad P(T^+ \leq 6) = 1$$

$$P(T^+ \leq 3) = \frac{5}{8}$$

PROBLEMS 11.4

1. A consumers group in Detroit wished to determine whether or not a "typical" market basket of 20 items had changed in price from January 4, 1974, to April 5, 1974. To do this they sampled twelve supermarkets and recorded the following costs for the market basket on the two dates in question.

Supermarket	Jan. 4, 1974	April 5, 1974
1	15.82	16.07
2	17.60	17.75
3	20.31	20.60
4	16.87	17.62
5	16.49	17.38
6	17.69	17.42
7	18.23	18.62
8	18.28	19.10
9	17.31	17.64
10	19.05	18.80

Use the above data to test at level $\alpha = .05$ the hypothesis H_0: the mean market cost has not changed in the three-month period.

a. State the alternative hypothesis of the test.
b. State the critical region of the test.
c. What conclusion would you draw from the above data?

2. To determine whether Berkeley students spend less time studying in their sophomore year than in their freshman year, the weekly study times of a random sample of 15 full-time students were monitored for the two years. The results in average number of study hours per week were as follows.

Student	1	2	3	4	5	6	7	8
Fresh. yr	31.7	26.9	26.5	19.6	40.8	32.3	27.8	29.2
Soph. yr	29.1	28.4	27.0	17.8	37.2	28.4	27.0	31.2

Student	9	10	11	12	13	14	15
Fresh. yr	17.8	27.3	34.1	43.6	30.0	22.5	36.7
Soph. yr	21.5	24.1	29.3	35.7	31.7	20.7	34.6

a. State the null and alternative hypotheses of the test.
b. State the critical region of the test for $\alpha = .05$.
c. What conclusion would you draw from the above data at level $\alpha = .05$?

3. The seniors in the Milwaukee public school system were given nationally standardized achievement tests (scores 0 to 100, 50 being the national median). The results for two different scores for a sample of 25 students were

Student	1	2	3	4	5	6	7	8	9	10	11	12	13
Verbal score	41	32	68	87	75	53	94	18	36	49	63	55	43
Quant. score	53	41	63	90	60	62	82	29	39	36	58	67	40

Student	14	15	16	17	18	19	20	21	22	23	24	25
Verbal score	48	61	71	52	49	29	68	37	57	84	42	77
Quant. score	48	47	87	43	78	22	60	53	48	70	31	91

Based on these data, can one claim that there is a significant difference in the mean scores of verbal and quantitative tests among seniors in the Milwaukee public school system? Use an $\alpha = .05$ test.

a. State the null and alternative hypotheses.
b. State the critical region of the test.
c. Give your conclusion for these data.

4. A random sample of 30 rats were timed in two consecutive trials (I and II) of a simple maze test with a food reward at the end. Test the hypothesis at level $\alpha = .02$ that the second trial time has a lower mean value than the first trial time (in other words, that rats learn). The times (in seconds) for each rat are given below.

Rat	1	2	3	4	5	6	7	8	9	10	11	12	13	14	15
I	43	107	63	48	69	57	83	74	93	71	63	45	57	76	69
II	51	91	64	38	73	52	89	59	104	62	60	52	42	62	42

Rat	16	17	18	19	20	21	22	23	24	25	26	27	28	29	30
I	68	43	59	71	67	42	81	60	112	53	47	61	94	52	63
II	51	37	63	62	67	56	70	47	86	74	40	67	88	54	43

a. State the null and alternative hypotheses.
b. State the critical region of the test.
c. What conclusion would you draw from these data?

5. Redo problem 1, section 7.6, with the method of this section.

6. Redo problem 2, section 7.6, with the method of this section.

11.5 Distribution-Free Comparison of Two Independent Samples. The Two-Sample Wilcoxon Test

If we have independent samples from each of two populations we may use a t test (see page 217 of section 7.5) of equality of the population means. The assumptions required for this test are that the distributions of the underlying variables are nearly normal and have the same variance. We now give a distribution-free procedure for comparing two populations which is based on independent random samples from each population and which is valid under much weaker assumptions (see B_1–B_3 below) than the t test. It is only slightly less efficient than the t test even when the distributions *are* normal with the same variance.

In comparing the "central values" of two populations, a possible approach is to *combine the samples* from the two populations and see if *in the combined sample* the observations from one of the populations tend to be larger than those from the other. One method of doing this is to order the observations in the combined sample from least to greatest, and see if the sum of the *ranks* of the observations from one of the populations is either very large or very small, indicating that this population tends to have larger or smaller values than the other. This is the intuitive basis for the test to be proposed.

TABLE 11.4
Data for the Two-Sample Wilcoxon Test

Population	Sample size	Sample values
1	m	$x_1, x_2, \ldots, x_m$
2	n	$y_1, y_2, \ldots, y_n$

More precisely, suppose we have independent random samples from two populations. We make the following
Assumptions for the test:

(B_1) The two random samples are independent of each other.

(B_2) Each of the two underlying probability distributions from which we are sampling is that of a continuous random variable.

(B_3) The two distributions are identical in shape, but may have different location parameters (for example, means μ_x and μ_y).

Now suppose we wish to test H_0: the two distributions are identical, $\mu_x = \mu_y$, versus H_1: the two distributions are not identical, $\mu_x \neq \mu_y$.

Under H_1, the graph of the distributions of x and y might, for example, resemble the one shown in figure 11.4.

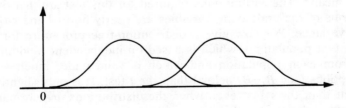

FIGURE 11.4
Two distributions that are identical except for their location parameters

Under H_0, the combined sample $\{x_1, \ldots, x_m, y_1, \ldots, y_n\}$ is just a random sample of size $n + m$ from a single population (recall that the two samples are independent of each other by B_1). As such, if we order these $m + n$ observations from smallest to largest, we would expect under H_0 to find the m ranks of the x_i's *randomly located* among the numbers $1, 2, \ldots, m + n$. However, if H_0 is not true, the ranks of the x_i would tend to be high (if $\mu_x > \mu_y$) or low (if $\mu_x < \mu_y$). The proposed test of H_0 vs H_1 will be to reject H_0 if the sum of the ranks of the x_i's in the combined sample is either *too large* or *too small*.

Specifically, let $R(x_i)$ be the rank of x_i, $i = 1, \ldots, m$, in the combined sample $\{x_1, \ldots, x_m, y_1, \ldots, y_n\}$. (For example, if x_1 is the 15th from the smallest of the combined sample, $R(x_1) = 15$, and if x_5 is the smallest of the combined sample, $R(x_5) = 1$.) If two observations are tied in the combined sample their ranks are taken as the average of their combined ranks. Although ties are theoretically impossible for continuous observations, they will occur in a set of observations that are measured only to a certain degree of precision; thus 6.8214 and 6.8208 rounded to three decimal places both become 6.821.

Using the ranks of the x's in the combined sample, we form the *sum of these ranks*

$$T_x = R(x_1) + \ldots + R(x_m) \tag{20}$$

and use T_x as our test statistic.

By the intuitive reasoning above, a very small or a very large value of T_x tends to support H_1 over H_0, since under H_1 the values (and hence the ranks) of the x's are distributed unlike those of the y's, contrary to what would occur under H_0.

Example 6

A physical anthropologist has taken two samples of $m = 6$ and $n = 8$ female skeletons from two different sites of prehistoric North American Indian tribes, and wishes to decide whether female skeletal heights are identically distributed for the two tribes. The sample values for the skeletal heights (in inches) are given below.

Tribe 1 (m): 58.2, 59.7, 60.4, 56.4, 60.0, 61.4

Tribe 2 (n): 63.1, 62.2, 59.3, 66.4, 64.3, 60.2, 60.7, 64.6

If we combine the data, order the total combined sample, and compute T_x, we obtain the following table.

TABLE 11.5
Ranks of Combined Samples for Example 6

Observation	✓ if an x	✓ if a y	Rank
56.4	✓		$1 = R(x_4)$
58.2	✓		$2 = R(x_1)$
59.3		✓	3
59.7	✓		$4 = R(x_2)$
60.0	✓		$5 = R(x_5)$
60.2		✓	6
60.4	✓		$7 = R(x_3)$
60.7		✓	8
61.4	✓		$9 = R(x_6)$
62.2		✓	10
63.1		✓	11
64.3		✓	12
64.6		✓	13
66.4		✓	14

Here, $T_x = 1 + 2 + 4 + 5 + 7 + 9 = 28$. The question now arises: Is a value $T_x \leq 28$ likely or unlikely under H_0? It appears small from looking at the data of table 11.5 but is it unreasonably small; that is, is $T_x \leq 28$ very unlikely under H_0?

To answer this question one needs a table of $P\{T_x \leq c\}$ for various values of m and n under H_0. We give in appendix table 12 certain pairs of critical values (c_1, c_2) and probabilities p such that under H_0

$$P\{T_x \leq c_1\} = P\{T_x \geq c_2\} = p \tag{21}$$

for various values of m and n. The values of p given in the two-part table are those for which p is closest to .01 and .05. For example, with $m = 7$ and $n = 10$, we see from the first of the two tables that

$$(c_1, c_2, p) = \frac{(39, 87, .0093)}{(40, 86, .0125)}$$

so for $m = 7$ and $n = 10$, when H_0 is true

$$P\{T_x \leq 39\} = P\{T_x \geq 87\} = .0093$$
$$P\{T_x \leq 40\} = P\{T_x \geq 86\} = .0125$$

Therefore, in the combined sample of $m = 7$ and $n = 10$ observations, under H_0 a rank sum $T_x \leq 39$ (or $T_x \geq 87$) is quite unlikely, and will happen only with probability .0093.

With appendix table 12 at hand, we can now devise a test of H_0: the distributions are identical vs H_1: the distributions are different.

First, we choose a desired level of significance α for our test, and compute the statistic $T_x = \sum_{i=1}^{m} R(x_i)$. Since either a very small or a very large value of T_x tends to support H_1 over H_0, we find in appendix table 12 the values of c_1 and c_2 such that under H_0

$$P\{T_x \leq c_1\} = P\{T_x \geq c_2\} = p \cong \alpha/2$$

Then the critical region R of the test, which comprises those values of T_x for which $T_x \leq c_1$ or $T_x \geq c_2$, will have a total probability under H_0 of

$$P\{T_x \leq c_1\} + P\{T_x \geq c_2\} = 2p \cong \alpha$$

yielding an approximately α-level test of H_0. (It will have the exact level $2p$.)

We illustrate the method for table 11.5. Here we decide to use a two-sided test of level $\alpha \cong .02$, since we are interested in whether there is a difference in the mean skeletal heights of the two tribes, no matter what direction that difference takes, $\mu_x < \mu_y$ or $\mu_x > \mu_y$. Now, from the table labeled $\alpha = .02$ (two-sided) in appendix table 12, we have for $m = 6$ and $n = 8$

$$P\{T_x \leq 27\} = P\{T_x \geq 63\} = .0100$$
$$P\{T_x \leq 28\} = P\{T_x \geq 62\} = .0147$$

Therefore, at level $2p = 2(.0147) = .0294$ we would reject H_0 (accept H_1) if $T_x \leq 28$ or $T_x \geq 62$. Since $T_x = 28$ for this example, we reject H_0 at level .0294, the data indicating that the mean height for tribe 1 is less than that for tribe 2. If we insist on level $p = 2(.01) = .02$, the test would not reject H_0, since then the rejection region would be $T_x \leq 27$ or $T_x \geq 63$.

One-sided tests may also be used. For example, if we wish to test $H_0 : \mu_x \leq \mu_y$ vs $H_1 : \mu_x > \mu_y$ at level α, we use the critical region: Reject H_0 if $T_x \geq c_2$, where $P\{T_x \geq c_2\} = p$ is taken from appendix table 12 to be $\cong \alpha$. (We use this critical region because a large T_x occurs when the x values are large in comparison to the y values in the combined sample, tending to support $H_1 : \mu_x > \mu_y$.)

Similar one-sided tests are available. The results are summarized in table 11.6 below, where $T_x = \sum_{i=1}^{m} R(x_i)$, $R(x_i)$ is the rank of x_i in the combined sample,

$$\mu_{T_x} = \frac{m(m+n+1)}{2} \tag{22}$$

and

$$\sigma_{T_x}^2 = \frac{mn(m+n+1)}{12} \tag{23}$$

(the mean value and variance of T_x under H_0, as shown below).

The large sample tests in table 11.6 are based on the fact that

$$z = \frac{T_x - \mu_{T_x}}{\sigma_{T_x}} \tag{24}$$

is approximately standard normal. This is a generalized version of the Central Limit Theorem for the dependent random variables that occur in random sampling without replacement from a finite population.

TABLE 11.6
The Wilcoxon Test of Level α (Independent Samples from Two Populations)

H_0	H_1	Critical region: reject H_0 (accept H_1) if
The two distributions are identical: $\mu_x = \mu_y$	$\mu_x \neq \mu_y$	$T_x \leq c_1$ or $T_x \geq c_2$, where (i) if m and n are ≤ 20, c_1 and c_2 are chosen from appendix table 12 with $P(T_x \leq c_1) = P(T_x \geq c_2) = p \cong \alpha/2$ (ii) if m or n is $> 2c$ $c_1 = \mu_{T_x} - z_{\alpha/2}\sigma_{T_x}$ and $c_2 = \mu_{T_x} + z_{\alpha/2}\sigma_{T_x}$
$\mu_x \geq \mu_y$	$\mu_x < \mu_y$	$T_x \leq c_1$, where (i) if m and n are ≤ 20, c_1 is chosen from appendix table 12 with $P(T_x < c_1) = p \cong \alpha$. (ii) if m or n is > 20, $c_1 = \mu_{T_x} - z_\alpha \sigma_{T_x}$
$\mu_x \leq \mu_y$	$\mu_x > \mu_y$	$T_x \geq c_2$, where (i) if m and n are ≤ 20, c_2 is chosen from appendix table 12 with $P(T_x \geq c_2) = p \cong \alpha$ (ii) if m or n is > 20, $c_2 = \mu_{T_x} + z_\alpha \sigma_{T_x}$

If there are ties among the data in the combined sample, then the ranks assigned to these observations are the average of the ranks for the tied observations. For example, if in the combined sample two observations are tied with, say, ranks 7 and 8, then each should be given rank $7.5 = 1/2(7 + 8)$. If there are only a moderate number of ties in the data, the test is still valid.

Example 7

An agronomist wishes to check whether a fertilizer increases the yield of cherry trees. A random sample of $m = 10$ fertilized and $n = 25$ unfertilized trees gives the following yields.

TABLE 11.7
Yields of Cherry Trees (in pints)

Fertilized trees (x_i)		Unfertilized trees (y_i)				
40	61	58	30	21	36	40
55	37	24	59	44	42	23
66	54	19	62	45	52	37
43	41	34	28	38	40	30
26	49	35	50	48	47	32

If the agronomist can claim at level .05 that the fertilizer improves yield, he intends to recommend the new fertilizer to the Cherry Growers Association of his state.

Here, he wishes to test $H_0 : \mu_x \le \mu_y$ versus $H_1 : \mu_x > \mu_y$, since if $\mu_x \le \mu_y$ he wants the probability of claiming $\mu_x > \mu_y$ to be at most $\alpha = .05$. The large sample test given by table 11.6 has the critical region

$$\text{Reject } H_0 \text{ in favor of } H_1 \text{ if } T_x \ge 225.05$$

since

$$c_2 = \mu_{T_x} + z_{.05}\, \sigma_{T_x}$$
$$= \frac{10(10 + 25 + 1)}{2} + 1.645 \sqrt{\frac{10(25)(10 + 25 + 1)}{12}}$$
$$= 180 + 1.645\sqrt{750} = 180 + (1.645)(27.386)$$
$$= 180 + 45.05 = 225.05.$$

We now order the data in table 11.6, compute T_x, and carry out the test. The ranks corresponding to the x_i's are starred.

Observation	✓ if x	✓ if y	Rank	Observation	✓ if x	✓ if y	Rank
19		✓	1	41	✓		19*
21		✓	2	42		✓	20
23		✓	3	43	✓		21*
24		✓	4	44		✓	22
26	✓		5*	45		✓	23
28		✓	6	47		✓	24
30		✓	7.5	48		✓	25
30		✓	7.5	49	✓		26*
32		✓	9	50		✓	27
34		✓	11	52		✓	28
35		✓	11	54	✓		29*
36		✓	12	55	✓		30*
37	✓		13.5*	58		✓	31
37		✓	13.5	59		✓	32
38		✓	15	61	✓		33*
40		✓	17	62		✓	34
40		✓	17	66	✓		35*
40	✓		17*				

$$T_x = \sum_{i=1}^{m} R(x_i) = 5 + 13.5 + 17 + 19 + 21 + 26 + 29 + 30 + 33 + 35$$
$$= 228.5 > 225.05 = c_2$$

The agronomist therefore claims that the fertilizer increases yield ($\mu_x > \mu_y$), and recommends its use to the Cherry Growers Association.

Derivation of (22) and (23)
When H_0 is true, the ranks of the x_i's among the combined samples may be imagined as a single random sample without replacement from the integers $1, 2, \ldots, N$, where $N = m + n$ is the combined sample size. Thus, T_x is distributed like the sum of the numbers obtained in drawing m chips at random without replacement from a bowl containing N chips numbered $1, 2, \ldots, N$. The mean value and variance of T_x can be shown to be given by (22) and (23).

Note that under H_0 we can find the *exact* distribution of T_x for small m and n by direct enumeration. There are $\binom{m+n}{m}$ equally likely ways of choosing m out of the ranks $1, 2, \ldots, m + n$. Thus, for $m = 2$ and $n = 3$

$$T_x = 9 = 4 + 5 \qquad \text{with probability } \frac{1}{\binom{5}{2}} = \frac{2!3!}{5!} = .1$$

$$
\begin{aligned}
T_x &= 8 = 3 + 5 &&= .1 \\
T_x &= 7 = 2 + 5 = 3 + 4 &&= .2 \\
T_x &= 6 = 1 + 5 = 2 + 4 &&= .2 \\
T_x &= 5 = 4 + 1 = 3 + 2 &&= .2 \\
T_x &= 4 = 3 + 1 &&= .1 \\
T_x &= 3 = 2 + 1 &&= .1 \\
&&&\overline{\hphantom{=}\text{sum} = 1}
\end{aligned}
$$

For example, $P\{T_x \le 5\} = P\{T_x \ge 7\} = .4$ in this case.

PROBLEMS 11.5

1. Two brands of sugar-free cola were compared for calorie content per gallon. The following data resulted from tests on a random sample of 10 gallons of each brand. Based on these data, use an (approximate) $\alpha = .10$ level test to determine whether or not there is a difference between the brands.

Calorie content (gallon bottles)

Brand 1	14	15	11	12	12	16	14	11	13	12
Brand 2	11	12	12	10	14	10	12	12	12	10

   a. State the null and alternative hypotheses of the test.
   b. State the critical region and give the exact significance level of the test.
   c. What is the conclusion of the test?

2. The Food and Drug Administration wishes to test a drug manufacturer's claim that a new drug lowers the dystolic blood pressure in high-blood-pressure patients. Ten pairs of patients with high blood pressure were randomly assigned to a control group (receives no treatment) and an experimental group (receives the drug). The following readings show the decrease in blood pressure over a month (a negative value represents an increase). Since one patient in the control group dropped out of the study before the

end of the month, there are only 9 readings in the control group. Based on these data test the drug manufacturer's claim at level $\alpha = .05$ (approximately).

Decrease in dystolic blood pressure

Control group: 7, −4, 2, 6, −10, 8, −7, 0, 13
Experimental group: 8, 12, 11, −2, 9, 18, 15, 5, −3, 13

  a. State the null and alternative hypotheses of the test.
  b. State the critical region of the test and give the exact significance level of the test.
  c. What is the conclusion of the test?

3. Redo problem 7, section 7.5 by the method of this section. State the *exact* level of the approximate $\alpha = .02$ test.

4. Redo problem 8 of section 7.5 by the method of this section. State the *exact* level of the approximate $\alpha = .05$ test.

5. A Chicago traffic engineer wants to see if changing the stoplight pattern on a two-mile stretch of State Street will alter the driving time during rush hour. He takes a random sample of 20 traveling times before the change and 25 traveling times after. Using the resulting recorded times (in minutes) below, can the traffic engineer claim that the change lowered the mean driving times? Use $\alpha = .05$.

Driving Times

Before change				After change				
7.8	5.7	4.9	7.2	6.4	7.2	3.9	5.2	4.7
5.2	6.8	6.0	5.7	5.9	6.3	5.8	8.1	3.6
6.3	7.4	5.4	6.9	4.8	5.7	7.0	4.2	6.0
4.1	8.3	8.1	9.4	3.8	6.7	4.1	5.0	4.5
8.2	6.4	5.5	6.8	5.2	4.3	8.6	7.7	5.5

  a. State the null and alternative hypotheses of the test.
  b. State the critical region of the test.
  c. State the conclusion of the test.

6. Sixty laying hens were randomly divided into two groups. For two months one group was given a standard diet, while the second group was given a standard diet plus a dietary supplement claimed to increase egg production. The egg production for the two-month period is given below. Is the diet-supplement manufacturer's claim justified at level $\alpha = .01$? One chicken on the standard diet died, leaving only 24 observations in that group.

Egg Production

Standard diet					Supplemented diet				
47	59	46	52	47	54	60	62	47	44
41	62	49	50	41	40	49	61	65	57
53	54	51	57	65	52	66	60	58	52
61	55	48	38	58	63	49	67	55	54
50	60	53	45		48	55	44	60	59

a. State the null and alternative hypotheses of the test.
b. State the critical region of the test.
c. State the conclusion of the test.

7. a. Redo problem 6 for $\alpha = .05$.
   b. Using the data in problem 6, carry out a t test at level $\alpha = .05$ for the same hypotheses as in problem 6. (See section 7.5.)
   c. Are the conclusions different in (a) and (b)? Explain any discrepancies.

11.6 The Rank Correlation Coefficient and Tests of Independence

In chapter 9 we saw that for n data pairs $(x_1, y_1), \ldots, (x_n, y_n)$, the correlation coefficient

$$r = \frac{\sum\limits_{i=1}^{n} (x_i - \bar{x})(y_i - \bar{y})}{\sqrt{\sum\limits_{i=1}^{n} (x_i - \bar{x})^2 \cdot \sum\limits_{i=1}^{n} (y_i - \bar{y})^2}} \tag{25}$$

is used to measure the amount of linear relationship between x and y. In this section, we introduce Spearman's *rank correlation coefficient*. This is simply the correlation coefficient r computed for the *ranks* of the data.

Let $\{(x_1, y_1), \ldots, (x_n, y_n)\}$ be a set of n pairs of data taken on two variables x and y for each of n subjects. We form the two sets of ranks $\{R(x_1), \ldots, R(x_n)\}$ and $\{R(y_1), \ldots, R(y_n)\}$, where for $i = 1, \ldots, n$

$$R(x_i) = \text{rank of } x_i \text{ among the observations } x_1, \ldots, x_n$$

and

$$R(y_i) = \text{rank of } y_i \text{ among the observations } y_1, \ldots, y_n$$

For example, if x_5 is the 8th from the smallest observation among $x_1, \ldots, x_{10}$, then $R(x_5) = 8$. Observe that $R(x_i)$ and $R(y_i)$ are integers between 1 and n.

Now, suppose that the x and y variables being measured are *dependent*, in the sense, say, that large values of y tend to go with large values of x. If this is so, we would usually have a large value of $R(y_i)$ when $R(x_i)$ is large, and hence a large (close to $+1$) value for their correlation coefficient. Similarly, small values (close to -1) of this correlation coefficient would indicate that large values of the x variable tend to go with small values of the y variable.

If we compute the correlation coefficient r for the pairs of ranks $\{(R(x_1), R(y_1)), \ldots, (R(x_n), R(y_n))\}$, using (25) with x_i replaced by $R(x_i)$ and y_i replaced by $R(y_i)$, we obtain

Definition 4

For the n pairs of observation $\{(x_1, y_1), \ldots, (x_n, y_n)\}$, Spearman's *rank correlation coefficient* is the number

$$R = \frac{\sum_{i=1}^{n} \left[R(x_i) - \frac{n+1}{2} \right]\left[R(y_i) - \frac{n+1}{2} \right]}{n(n^2 - 1)/12} = 1 - \frac{6D}{n(n^2 - 1)} \quad (26)$$

where

$$D = \sum_{i=1}^{n} d_i^2, \quad d_i = R(x_i) - R(y_i) \quad (27)$$

We omit the algebraic details of verifying that the two expressions for R in (26) are in fact equal. We note

a. If $R(x_i) = R(y_i)$ for every $i = 1, \ldots, n$, then each $d_i = 0$ and hence $D = 0$ and $R = +1$. Similarly,

b. $R = -1$ if $R(x_i) = n + 1 - R(y_i)$ for each $i = 1, \ldots, n$.

c. (a) and (b) suggest that if $R(y_i)$ generally increases with $R(x_i)$ then R will be close to $+1$, and if $R(y_i)$ generally decreases as $R(x_i)$ increases then R will be close to -1. Such is the case.

Suppose now that we wish to test whether or not the $y_1, \ldots, y_n$ observations are independent of the corresponding $x_1, \ldots, x_n$ values. For convenience we renumber the n subjects measured so that $R(x_1) = 1$, $R(x_2) = 2, \ldots, R(x_n) = n$. Then the ranks of the y_i's, $R(y_i)$, $\ldots, R(y_n)$, will be some rearrangement of·the integers $1, \ldots, n$. If in fact the x and y measurements on each subject are independent, all the $n!$ such arrangements $R(y_1), \ldots, R(y_n)$ will be *equally likely*. We shall take as our hypotheses

$$H_0 : x, y \text{ are independent vs } H_1 : x, y \text{ are dependent}$$

As we saw, a two-sided test of H_0 vs H_1 should reject H_0 if R is very large (near $+1$) or very small (near -1). Therefore, we take as our critical region $[\{R \le r_1\}$ or $\{R \ge r_2\}]$. It can be shown that the distribution of R under H_0 is symmetric about zero, so that $\mu_R = 0$ under H_0. This suggests taking $r_1 = -r$ and $r_2 = r$ for some $r > 0$. Under H_0, appendix table 13 gives the values r_α such that

$$P\{R \ge r_\alpha\} \cong \alpha$$

for various values of α and $n = 2, \ldots, 30$. Therefore, we obtain an α-level test of H_0 by choosing our critical region as

$$\text{Reject } H_0 \text{ if } R \ge r_{\alpha/2} \text{ or } R \le -r_{\alpha/2}$$

with a probability under H_0 of $P\{R \ge r_{\alpha/2}\} + P\{R \le -r_{\alpha/2}\} \cong \alpha/2 + \alpha/2 = \alpha$.

We obtain one-sided tests of H_0 by using only the upper tail $\{R \ge r_\alpha\}$ or lower tail $\{R \le -r_\alpha\}$ as the critical region. These tests are summarized in table 11.8 below.

Let $\{(x_1, y_1), \ldots, (x_n, y_n)\}$ be n pairs of observations of two random variables x, y. Let $R(x_i)$, $R(y_i)$ be the ranks of the x_i and y_i, respectively, $i = 1, \ldots, n$. Let $d_i = R(x_i) - R(y_i)$, and compute $D = \sum_{i=1}^{n} d_i^2$. In the table, r_α is that value from appendix table 13 that for the given n satisfies $P\{R \ge r_\alpha\} \cong \alpha$, and z_α is the value of the standard normal distribution that leaves probability α above it.

TABLE 11.8
α-Level Tests Based on the Rank Correlation Coefficient R

H_0	H_1	Critical region: reject H_0 (accept H_1) if
x, y, independent	x, y dependent	$R \le r_{\alpha/2}$ or $R \ge r_{\alpha/2}$ ($n \le 30$) $z < -z_{\alpha/2}$ or $z > z_{\alpha/2}$ ($n > 30$) where $z = R\sqrt{n-1}$
$\mu_R \le 0$	$\mu_R > 0$	$R \ge r_\alpha$ ($n \le 30$) $z = R\sqrt{n-1} \ge z_\alpha$ ($n > 30$)
$\mu_R \ge 0$	$\mu_R < 0$	$R \le -r_\alpha$ ($n \le 30$) $z = R\sqrt{n-1} < -z_\alpha$ ($n > 30$)

We remark that R is frequently used when there are in fact no quantitative x and y values to be ranked, but only the *ranks themselves*. Thus, suppose that two different judges are asked to rank n

wines in order of excellence. If judge 1 ranks them in increasing order as $1, 2, \ldots, n$, while judge 2 ranks them as $R_1, R_2, \ldots, R_n$ (a permutation of $1, 2, \ldots, n$), then Spearman's rank correlation coefficient (26) is

$$R = 1 - \frac{6D}{n(n^2 - 1)}, \text{ where now } D = \sum_{i=1}^{n} (i - R_i)^2$$

For example, if $n = 5$ and the rankings are

Rank by judge 1	1	2	3	4	5
Rank by judge 2	1	2	4	3	5

then $D = 0^2 + 0^2 + 1^2 + 1^2 + 0^2 = 2$ and $R = 1 - 6.2/5.24 = .90$. Of the $5! = 120$ possible rankings by judge 2, only 5 (which?) produce a value of $R \geq .90$, so we can assert at the level $\alpha = 5/120 = .042$ that there is more than a random amount of agreement between the two judges.

Also included in table 11.8 are the corresponding large sample tests for $n > 30$. These tests are based on the fact that under H_0 it may be shown that

$$\mu_R = 0, \ \sigma_R^2 = \frac{1}{n - 1} \tag{28}$$

and that the statistic

$$z = R\sqrt{n - 1} \tag{29}$$

has an approximately standard normal distribution when H_0 is true.

Example 8
Lotteries were held on December 2, 1969, and March 8, 1973, to determine the order of draft into the army. The lotteries were supposed to be conducted in such a way that the birth date of a person (1 to 366 for the 1969 lottery, in which February 29 was included; 1 to 365 for 1973) was independent of his draft lottery number. To see if the lotteries met this criterion one could perform a two-tailed test for the pairs of ranks $[R(x_i) = i, R(y_i)]$, $i = 1, \ldots, n$, where $R(x_i) =$ rank of the birth data (January $1 = 1$, and so on) and $R(y_i) =$ observed draft lottery number (order of draft). We shall present the results of such an analysis at the end of this section.

To simplify the computations we group the data by months and form the following table of *average* draft lottery numbers for the twelve months, putting $y_i =$ average draft number for month i.

TABLE 11.9
Average Monthly Draft Lottery Numbers for
1969 and 1973

Monthly average	Jan.	Feb.	Mar.	April	May	June
1969	205.8	203.0	225.8	203.7	208.0	191.0
1973	198.5	180.2	174.9	185.1	198.0	202.5

Monthly average	July	Aug.	Sept.	Oct.	Nov.	Dec.
1969	181.5	173.5	175.3	182.5	418.7	212.5
1973	172.5	169.0	197.8	160.2	181.6	176.4

If we now rank the months from 1 to 12, $R(x_i) = i$, $i = 1, \ldots,$ 12, and similarly rank the observations y_i, we obtain the grouped data

1969

$R(x_i)$ (month)	1	2	3	4	5	6	7	8	9	10	11	12
$R(y_i)$ (average)	10	8	12	9	11	7	5	4	3	6	2	1
d_i^2	81	64	81	25	36	1	4	16	36	16	81	121

sum of $d_i^2 = D = 562$

1973

$R(x_i)$ (monthly)	1	2	3	4	5	6	7	8	9	10	11	12
$R(y_i)$ (average)	11	6	4	8	10	12	3	2	9	1	7	5
d_i^2	100	16	1	16	25	36	16	36	0	81	16	49

sum of $d_i^2 = D = 392$

Computing R for both years we have, since $n = 12$

$$(1969) \quad R = 1 - \frac{6(562)}{12(143)} = 1 - \frac{3372}{1716} = 1 - 1.965 = -.965$$

$$(1973) \quad R = 1 - \frac{6(392)}{12(143)} = 1 - \frac{2362}{1716} = 1 - 1.37 = -.37$$

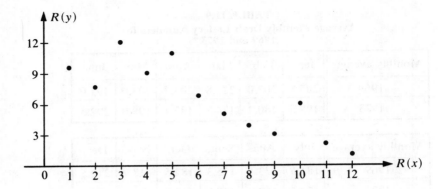

If we now use a two-sided test of level $\alpha = .002$, we have from appendix table 13, $r_{.001} = .8182$ for $n = 12$. The critical region as given by table 11.8 in this case is

$$\text{Reject } H_0 \text{ if } R \geq .8182 \text{ or } R \leq -.8182$$

We would therefore reject H_0 for 1969, where $R = -.965$, but not for 1973, where $R = -.37$. In 1969 the lottery numbers were strongly negatively correlated with the birth dates, while this was not the case in 1973. The scattergram of the ranked data for 1969 is shown above.

Because of the apparent tendency for high birth date months to go with low draft lottery numbers, several court cases were instituted accusing the Selective Service System of holding an invalid, that is, nonrandom, lottery in 1969.

Using all the data for 366 days in the 1969 lottery and 365 days in the 1973 lottery, the results are

$$(1969) \; R = -.2314 \text{ and } z = R\sqrt{n-1} = -4.42$$

$$(1973) \; R = -.0410 \text{ and } z = R\sqrt{n-1} = -0.783$$

The large-sample test at the same level $\alpha = .002$ has the rejection region: Reject H_0 if $z \leq -3.09$ or $z \geq 3.09$ (since $z_{.001} = 3.09$), and again we would reject H_0 for 1969, but not for 1973.

PROBLEMS 11.6

1. The rankings of 15 graduate students in two semesters of a year's statistics course are as follows:

Sem. 1	1	2	3	4	5	6	7	8	9	10	11	12	13	14	15
Sem. 2	1	6	2	10	9	4	7	11	14	5	3	8	12	15	13

   a. Compute Spearman's rank correlation coefficient R for these data.
   b. Test at level $\alpha = .05$ whether or not the two semesters' rankings are independent.
   c. Plot a scattergram of the ranks.

2. The following rankings were given by two judges to 10 paintings in an art show.

Judge 1	1	2	3	4	5	6	7	8	9	10
Judge 2	7	5	3	6	1	2	10	4	8	9

   a. Compute Spearman's rank correlation coefficient R for these data.
   b. Test at level $\alpha = .10$ whether or not the rankings of the two judges are independent.
   c. Plot a scattergram of the ranks.

3. The following data give the 1960 and 1970 populations (in units of 100,000) of the 12 largest U.S. cities in 1970 (U.S. Census Bureau).

City	1970	1960
New York	7896	7782
Chicago	3369	3550
Los Angeles	2810	2479
Philadelphia	1950	2003
Detroit	1514	1670
Houston	1233	938
Baltimore	906	939
Dallas	844	680
Washington	757	764
Cleveland	751	876
Indianapolis	746	476
Milwaukee	717	741

   a. Compute Spearman's rank correlation coefficient for these data.
   b. Test at level $\alpha = .01$ the hypothesis $\mu_R \leq 0$ versus the alternative $\mu_R > 0$. State your conclusion.
   c. Is your conclusion in (b) surprising or to be expected? Why?
   d. Plot a scattergram of the ranks.

4. The following data give the number of motor vehicles per 1000 population and the number of motor vehicle accident deaths per

100,000 population for 14 countries in 1969 (National Highway Traffic Safety Administration).

Country	Motor vehicles (per 1000)	Motor vehicle deaths (per 100,000)
United States	530	27
Canada	400	27
Australia	390	31
France	390	34
New Zealand	390	21
Denmark	370	24
Netherlands	360	24
Belgium	280	80
Norway	270	14
West Germany	270	28
Austria	260	31
United Kingdom	260	14
Italy	250	20
Japan	240	21

a. Compute Spearman's rank correlation coefficient R for these data. (In case of ties, say, at ranks 3 and 4, each entry gets rank 3.5.)

b. Test at level $\alpha = .05$ $H_0 : \mu_R \leq 0$ against the alternative $\mu_R > 0$. State and interpret your conclusion.

c. Plot a scattergram of the ranks.

5. The following data are the ranks in class and reading grade-level scores for a class of 33 Van Hise (Madison, Wis.) eighth-grade students.

Class rank	1	2	3	4	5	6	7	8	9	10	11
Grade level	10.1	11.4	9.8	8.8	12.0	10.7	9.7	11.1	9.6	10.3	10.0

Class rank	12	13	14	15	16	17	18	19	20	21	22
Grade level	9.0	8.7	9.3	10.2	8.6	7.8	8.7	7.6	9.1	8.2	8.4

Class rank	23	24	25	26	27	28	29	30	31	32	33
Grade level	8.5	7.4	6.8	8.3	7.2	6.9	7.9	6.0	7.5	8.0	6.4

a. Compute Spearman's rank correlation coefficient R for these data.

b. Use the statistic (29) to test at level $\alpha = .01$ the null hypothesis $\mu_R \leq 0$ versus the alternative $\mu_R > 0$. State and interpret your conclusion.

6. The following are the ages at inauguration and at death of 35 U.S. Presidents.

President	Age at inaug.	Age at death	President	Age at inaug.	Age at death
Washington	57	67	Hayes	54	70
J. Adams	61	90	Garfield	49	49
Jefferson	57	83	Arthur	50	56
Madison	57	85	Cleveland	47	71
Monroe	58	73	B. Harrison	55	67
J.Q. Adams	57	80	McKinley	54	58
Jackson	61	78	T. Roosevelt	42	60
Van Buren	54	79	Taft	51	72
W. Harrison	68	68	Wilson	56	67
Tyler	51	71	Harding	55	57
Polk	49	53	Coolidge	51	60
Taylor	64	65	Hoover	54	90
Fillmore	50	74	F. Roosevelt	51	63
Pierce	48	64	Truman	60	88
Buchanan	65	77	Eisenhower	62	78
Lincoln	52	56	Kennedy	43	46
A. Johnson	56	66	L. Johnson	55	64
Grant	46	63			

a. Compute Spearman's rank correlation coefficient R for these data.

b. Use the statistic (29) to test at level $\alpha = .01$ the null hypothesis $\mu_R \leq 0$ versus the alternative $\mu_R > 0$. State and interpret your conclusion.

Appendix

Statistical Tables

Short Answers to Odd-Numbered Problems

APPENDIX TABLE 1

Squares and Square Roots

n	n^2	$\sqrt{n}$	$\sqrt{10n}$	n	n^2	$\sqrt{n}$	$\sqrt{10n}$
1.0	1.00	1.000	3.162	5.5	30.25	2.345	7.416
1.1	1.21	1.049	3.317	5.6	31.36	2.366	7.483
1.2	1.44	1.095	3.464	5.7	32.49	2.387	7.550
1.3	1.69	1.140	3.606	5.8	33.64	2.408	7.616
1.4	1.96	1.183	3.742	5.9	34.81	2.429	7.681
1.5	2.25	1.225	3.873	6.0	36.00	2.449	7.746
1.6	2.56	1.265	4.000	6.1	37.21	2.470	7.810
1.7	2.89	1.304	4.123	6.2	38.44	2.490	7.874
1.8	3.24	1.342	4.243	6.3	39.69	2.510	7.937
1.9	3.61	1.378	4.359	6.4	40.96	2.530	8.000
2.0	4.00	1.414	4.472	6.5	42.25	2.550	8.062
2.1	4.41	1.449	4.583	6.6	43.56	2.569	8.124
2.2	4.84	1.483	4.690	6.7	44.89	2.588	8.185
2.3	5.29	1.517	4.796	6.8	46.24	2.608	8.246
2.4	5.76	1.549	4.899	6.9	47.61	2.627	8.307
2.5	6.25	1.581	5.000	7.0	49.00	2.646	8.367
2.6	6.76	1.612	5.099	7.1	50.41	2.665	8.426
2.7	7.29	1.643	5.196	7.2	51.84	2.683	8.485
2.8	7.84	1.673	5.292	7.3	53.29	2.702	8.544
2.9	8.41	1.703	5.385	7.4	54.76	2.720	8.602
3.0	9.00	1.732	5.477	7.5	56.25	2.739	8.660
3.1	9.61	1.761	5.568	7.6	57.76	2.757	8.718
3.2	10.24	1.789	5.657	7.7	59.29	2.775	8.775
3.3	10.89	1.817	5.745	7.8	60.84	2.793	8.832
3.4	11.56	1.844	5.831	7.9	62.41	2.811	8.888
3.5	12.25	1.871	5.916	8.0	64.00	2.828	8.944
3.6	12.96	1.897	6.000	8.1	65.61	2.846	9.000
3.7	13.69	1.924	6.083	8.2	67.24	2.864	9.055
3.8	14.44	1.949	6.164	8.3	68.89	2.881	9.110
3.9	15.21	1.975	6.245	8.4	70.56	2.898	9.165
4.0	16.00	2.000	6.325	8.5	72.25	2.915	9.220
4.1	16.81	2.025	6.403	8.6	73.96	2.933	9.274
4.2	17.64	2.049	6.481	8.7	75.69	2.950	9.327
4.3	18.49	2.074	6.557	8.8	77.44	2.966	9.381
4.4	19.36	2.098	6.633	8.9	79.21	2.983	9.434
4.5	20.25	2.121	6.708	9.0	81.00	3.000	9.487
4.6	21.16	2.145	6.782	9.1	82.81	3.017	9.539
4.7	22.09	2.168	6.856	9.2	84.64	3.033	9.592
4.8	23.04	2.191	6.928	9.3	86.49	3.050	9.644
4.9	24.01	2.214	7.000	9.4	88.36	3.066	9.695
5.0	25.00	2.236	7.071	9.5	90.25	3.082	9.747
5.1	26.01	2.258	7.141	9.6	92.16	3.098	9.798
5.2	27.04	2.280	7.211	9.7	94.09	3.114	9.849
5.3	28.09	2.302	7.280	9.8	96.04	3.130	9.899
5.4	29.16	2.324	7.348	9.9	98.01	3.146	9.950

APPENDIX TABLE 2

Binomial Coefficients $\dfrac{n!}{i!(n-i)!}$

n \ i	2	3	4	5	6	7	8	9	10
2	1								
3	3	1							
4	6	4	1						
5	10	10	5	1					
6	15	20	15	6	1				
7	21	35	35	21	7	1			
8	28	56	70	56	28	8	1		
9	36	84	126	126	84	36	9	1	
10	45	120	210	252	210	120	45	10	1
11	55	165	330	462	462	330	165	55	11
12	66	220	495	792	924	792	495	220	66
13	78	286	715	1287	1716	1716	1287	715	286
14	91	364	1001	2002	3003	3432	3003	2002	1001
15	105	455	1365	3003	5005	6435	6435	5005	3003
16	120	560	1820	4368	8008	11440	12870	11440	8008
17	136	680	2380	6188	12376	19448	24310	24310	19448
18	153	816	3060	8568	18564	31824	43758	48620	43758
19	171	969	3876	11628	27132	50388	75582	92378	92378
20	190	1140	4845	15504	38760	77520	125970	167960	184756

APPENDIX TABLE 3

Random Numbers

Col. Line	(1)	(2)	(3)	(4)	(5)	(6)	(7)	(8)	(9)	(10)	(11)	(12)	(13)	(14)
1	10480	15011	01536	02011	81647	91646	69179	14194	62590	36207	20969	99570	91291	90700
2	22368	46573	25595	85393	30995	89198	27982	53402	93965	34095	52666	19174	39615	99505
3	24130	48360	22527	97265	76393	64809	15179	24830	49340	32081	30680	19655	63348	58629
4	42167	93093	06243	61680	07856	16376	39440	53537	71341	57004	00849	74917	97758	16379
5	37570	39975	81837	16656	06121	91782	60468	81305	49684	60672	14110	06927	01263	54613
6	77921	06907	11008	42751	27756	53498	18602	70659	90655	15053	21916	81825	44394	42880
7	99562	72905	56420	69994	98872	31016	71194	18738	44013	48840	63213	21069	10634	12952
8	96301	91977	05463	07972	18876	20922	94595	56869	69014	60045	18425	84903	42508	32307
9	89579	14342	63661	10281	17453	18103	57740	84378	25331	12566	58678	44947	05585	56941
10	85475	36857	43342	53988	53060	59533	38867	62300	08158	17983	16439	11458	18593	64952
11	28918	69578	88231	33276	70997	79936	56865	05859	90106	31595	01547	85590	91610	78188
12	63553	40961	48235	03427	49626	69445	18663	72695	52180	20847	12234	90511	33703	90322
13	09429	93969	52636	92737	88974	33488	36320	17617	30015	08272	84115	27156	30613	74952
14	10365	61129	87529	85689	48237	52267	67689	93394	01511	26358	85104	20285	29975	89868
15	07119	97336	71048	08178	77233	13916	47564	81056	97735	85977	29372	74461	28551	90707
16	51085	12765	51821	51259	77452	16308	60756	92144	49442	53900	70960	63990	75601	40719
17	02368	21382	52404	60268	89368	19885	55322	44819	01188	65255	64835	44919	05944	55157
18	01011	54092	33362	94904	31273	04146	18594	29852	71585	85030	51132	01915	92747	64951
19	52162	53916	46369	58586	23216	14513	83149	98736	23495	64350	94738	17752	35156	35749
20	07056	97628	33787	09998	42698	06691	76988	13602	51851	46104	83916	19500	25625	58104
21	48663	91245	85828	14346	09172	30168	90229	04734	59193	22178	30421	61666	99904	32812
22	54164	58492	22421	74103	47070	25306	76468	26384	58151	06646	21524	15227	96909	44592
23	32639	32363	05597	24200	13363	38005	94342	28728	35806	06912	17012	64161	18296	22851

	(1)	(2)	(3)	(4)	(5)	(6)	(7)	(8)	(9)	(10)	(11)	(12)	(13)	(14)
24	29334	27001	87637	87308	58731	00256	45834	15398	46557	41135	10367	07684	36188	18510
25	02488	33062	28834	07351	19731	92420	60952	61280	50001	67658	32586	86679	50720	94953
26	81525	72295	04839	96423	24878	82651	66566	14778	76797	14780	13300	87074	79666	95725
27	29676	20591	68086	26432	46901	20849	89768	81536	86645	12659	92259	57102	80428	25280
28	00742	57392	39064	66432	84673	40027	32832	61362	98947	96067	64760	64584	96096	98253
29	05366	04213	25669	26422	44407	44048	37937	63904	45766	66134	75470	66520	34693	90449
30	91921	26418	64117	94305	26766	25940	39972	22209	71500	64568	91402	42416	07844	69618
31	00582	04711	87917	77341	42206	35126	74087	99547	81817	42607	43808	76655	62028	76630
32	00725	69884	62797	56170	86324	88072	76222	36086	84637	93161	76038	65855	77919	88006
33	69011	65797	95876	55293	18988	27354	26575	08625	40801	59920	29841	80150	12777	48501
34	25976	57948	29888	88604	67917	48708	18912	82271	65424	69774	33611	54262	85963	03547
35	09763	83473	73577	12908	30883	18317	28290	35797	05998	41688	34952	37888	38917	88050
36	91567	42595	27958	30134	04024	86385	29880	99730	55536	84855	29080	09250	79656	73211
37	17955	56349	90999	49127	20044	59931	06115	20542	18059	02008	73708	83517	36103	42791
38	46503	18584	18845	49618	02304	51038	20655	58727	28168	15475	56942	53389	20562	87338
39	92157	89634	94824	78171	84610	82834	09922	25417	44137	48413	25555	21246	35509	20468
40	14577	62765	35605	81263	39667	47358	56873	56307	61607	49518	89656	20103	77490	18062
41	98427	07523	33362	64270	01638	92477	66969	98420	04880	45585	46565	04102	46880	45709
42	34914	63976	88720	82765	34476	17032	87589	40836	32427	70002	70663	88863	77775	69348
43	70060	28277	39475	46473	23219	53416	94970	25832	69975	94884	19661	72828	00102	66794
44	53976	54914	06990	67245	68350	82948	11398	42878	80287	88267	47363	46634	06541	97809
45	76072	29515	40980	07391	58745	25774	22987	80059	39911	96189	41151	14222	60697	59583
46	90725	52210	83974	29992	65831	38857	50490	83765	55657	14361	31720	57375	56228	41546
47	64364	67412	33339	31926	14883	24413	59744	92351	97473	89286	35931	04110	23726	51900
48	08962	00358	31662	25388	61642	34072	81249	35648	56891	69352	48373	45578	88547	81788
49	95012	68379	93526	70765	10593	04542	76463	54328	02349	17247	28865	14777	62730	92277
50	15664	10493	20492	38391	91132	21999	59516	81652	27195	48223	46751	22923	32261	85653

APPENDIX TABLE 3 (Continued)

Col. Line	(1)	(2)	(3)	(4)	(5)	(6)	(7)	(8)	(9)	(10)	(11)	(12)	(13)	(14)
51	16408	81899	04153	53381	79401	21438	83035	92350	36693	31238	59649	91754	72772	02338
52	18629	81953	05520	91962	04739	13092	97662	24822	94730	06496	35090	04822	86772	98289
53	73115	35101	47498	87637	99016	71060	88824	71013	18735	20286	23153	72924	35165	43040
54	57491	16703	23167	49323	45021	33132	12544	41035	80780	45393	44812	12515	98931	91202
55	30405	83946	23792	14422	15059	45799	22716	19792	09983	74353	68668	30429	70735	25499
56	16631	35006	85900	98275	32388	52390	16815	69298	82732	38480	73817	32523	41961	44437
57	96773	20206	42559	78985	05300	22164	24369	54224	35083	19687	11052	91491	60383	19746
58	38935	64202	14349	82674	66523	44133	00697	35552	35970	19124	63318	29686	03387	59846
59	31624	76384	17403	53363	44167	64486	64758	75366	76554	31601	12614	33072	60332	92325
60	78919	19474	23632	27889	47914	02584	37680	20801	72152	39339	34806	08930	85001	87820
61	03931	33309	57047	74211	63445	17361	62825	39908	05607	91284	68833	25570	38818	46920
62	74426	33278	43972	10119	89641	15665	52872	73823	73144	88662	88970	74492	51805	99378
63	09066	00903	20795	95452	92648	45454	09552	88815	16553	51125	79375	97596	16296	66092
64	42238	12426	87025	14267	20979	04508	64535	31355	86064	29472	47689	05974	52468	16834
65	16153	08002	26504	41744	81959	65642	74240	56302	00033	67107	77510	70625	28725	34191
66	21457	40742	29820	96783	29400	21840	15035	34537	33310	06116	95240	15957	16572	06004
67	21581	57802	02050	89728	17937	37621	47075	42080	97403	48626	68995	43805	33386	21597
68	55612	78095	83197	33732	05810	24813	86902	60397	16489	03264	88525	42786	05269	92532
69	44657	66999	99324	51281	84463	60563	79312	93454	68876	25471	93911	25650	12682	73572
70	91340	84979	46949	81973	37949	61023	43997	15263	80644	43942	89203	71795	99533	50501
71	91227	21199	31935	27022	84067	05462	35216	14486	29891	68607	41867	14951	91696	85065
72	50001	38140	66321	19924	72163	09538	12151	06878	91003	18749	34405	56087	82790	70925
73	65390	05224	72958	28609	81406	39147	25549	48542	42627	45233	57202	94617	23772	07896
74	27504	96131	83944	41575	10573	08619	64482	73923	36152	05184	94142	25299	84387	34925
75	37169	94851	39117	89632	00959	16487	65536	49071	39782	17095	02330	74301	00275	48280

	(1)	(2)	(3)	(4)	(5)	(6)	(7)	(8)	(9)	(10)	(11)	(12)	(13)	(14)
76	11508	70225	51111	38351	19444	66499	71945	05422	13442	78675	84081	66938	93654	59894
77	37449	30362	06694	54690	04052	53115	62757	95348	78662	11163	81651	50245	34971	52924
78	46515	70331	85922	38329	57015	15765	97161	17869	45349	61796	66345	81073	49106	79860
79	30986	81223	42416	58353	21532	30502	32305	86482	05174	07901	54339	58861	74818	46942
80	63798	64995	46583	09765	44160	78128	83991	42865	92520	83531	80377	35909	81250	54238
81	82486	84846	99254	67632	43218	50076	21361	64816	51202	88124	41870	52689	51275	83556
82	21885	32906	92431	09060	64297	51674	64126	62570	26123	05155	59194	52799	28225	85762
83	60336	98782	07408	53458	13564	59089	26445	29789	85205	41001	12535	12133	14645	23541
84	43937	46891	24010	25560	86355	33941	25786	54990	71899	15475	95434	98227	21824	19585
85	97656	63175	89303	16275	07100	92063	21942	18611	47348	20203	18534	03862	78095	50136
86	03299	01221	05418	38982	55758	92237	26759	86367	21216	98442	08303	56613	91511	75928
87	79626	06486	03574	17668	07785	76020	79924	25651	83325	88428	85076	72811	22717	50585
88	85636	68335	47539	03129	65651	11977	02510	26113	99447	68645	34327	15152	55230	93448
89	18039	14367	61337	06177	12143	46609	32989	74014	64708	00533	35398	58408	13261	47908
90	08362	15656	60627	36478	65648	16764	53412	09013	07832	41574	17639	82163	60859	75567
91	79556	29068	04142	16268	15387	12856	66227	38358	22478	73373	88732	09443	82558	05250
92	92608	82674	27072	32534	17075	27698	98204	63863	11951	34648	88022	56148	34925	57031
93	23982	25835	40055	67006	12293	02753	14827	22235	35071	99704	37543	11601	35503	85171
94	09915	96306	05908	97901	28395	14186	00821	80703	70426	75647	76310	88717	37890	40129
95	50937	33300	26695	62247	69927	76123	50842	43834	86654	70959	79725	93872	28117	19233
96	42488	78077	69882	61657	34136	79180	97526	43092	04098	73571	80799	76536	71255	64239
97	46764	86273	63003	93017	31204	36692	40202	35275	57306	55543	53203	18098	47625	88684
98	03237	45430	55417	63282	90816	17349	88298	90183	36600	78406	06216	95787	42579	90730
99	86591	81482	52667	61583	14972	90053	89534	76036	49199	43716	97548	04379	46370	28672
100	38534	01715	94964	87288	65680	43772	39560	12918	86537	62738	19636	51132	25739	56947

Reprinted with permission from *Chemical Handbook of Probability and Statistics*, 2d ed. Cleveland, Ohio: Chemical Rubber Co., 1968.

APPENDIX TABLE 4

Cumulative Binomial Probabilities

$B(i; n, p) = P\{y \le i\}$, y is a binomial random
variable of n trials and success probability p

$B(i; n, p)$ $n = 5$

i \ p	0.10	0.20	0.30	0.40	0.50	0.60	0.70	0.80	0.90
0	.590	.328	.168	.078	.031	.010	.002	.000	.000
1	.919	.737	.528	.337	.188	.087	.031	.007	.000
2	.991	.942	.837	.683	.500	.317	.163	.058	.009
3	1.000	.993	.969	.913	.812	.663	.472	.263	.081
4	1.000	1.000	.998	.990	.969	.922	.832	.672	.410

$B(i; n, p)$ $n = 10$

i \ p	0.10	0.20	0.30	0.40	0.50	0.60	0.70	0.80	0.90
0	.349	.107	.028	.006	.001	.000	.000	.000	.000
1	.736	.376	.149	.046	.011	.002	.000	.000	.000
2	.930	.678	.383	.167	.055	.012	.002	.000	.000
3	.987	.879	.650	.382	.172	.055	.011	.001	.000
4	.998	.967	.850	.633	.377	.166	.047	.006	.000
5	1.000	.994	.953	.834	.623	.367	.150	.033	.002
6	1.000	.999	.989	.945	.828	.618	.350	.121	.013
7	1.000	1.000	.998	.988	.945	.833	.617	.322	.070
8	1.000	1.000	1.000	.998	.989	.954	.851	.624	.264
9	1.000	1.000	1.000	1.000	.999	.994	.972	.893	.651

$B(i; n, p)$ $n = 15$

i \ p	0.10	0.20	0.30	0.40	0.50	0.60	0.70	0.80	0.90
0	.206	.035	.005	.000	.000	.000	.000	.000	.000
1	.549	.167	.035	.000	.000	.000	.000	.000	.000
2	.816	.398	.127	.027	.004	.000	.000	.000	.000
3	.944	.648	.297	.091	.018	.002	.000	.000	.000
4	.987	.836	.515	.217	.059	.009	.001	.000	.000

5	.998	.939	.722	.403	.151	.034	.004	.000	.000
6	1.000	.982	.869	.610	.304	.095	.015	.001	.000
7	1.000	.996	.950	.787	.500	.213	.050	.004	.000
8	1.000	.999	.985	.905	.696	.390	.131	.018	.000
9	1.000	1.000	.996	.966	.849	.597	.278	.061	.002
10	1.000	1.000	.999	.991	.941	.783	.485	.164	.013
11	1.000	1.000	1.000	.998	.982	.909	.703	.352	.056
12	1.000	1.000	1.000	1.000	.996	.973	.873	.602	.184
13	1.000	1.000	1.000	1.000	1.000	.995	.965	.833	.451
14	1.000	1.000	1.000	1.000	1.000	1.000	.995	.965	.794

$B(i; n, p)$ $n = 20$

p \ i	0.10	0.20	0.30	0.40	0.50	0.60	0.70	0.80	0.90
0	.122	.002	.001	.000	.000	.000	.000	.000	.000
1	.392	.069	.008	.001	.000	.000	.000	.000	.000
2	.677	.206	.035	.004	.000	.000	.000	.000	.000
3	.867	.411	.107	.016	.001	.000	.000	.000	.000
4	.957	.630	.238	.051	.006	.000	.000	.000	.000
5	.989	.804	.416	.126	.021	.002	.000	.000	.000
6	.998	.913	.608	.250	.058	.006	.000	.000	.000
7	1.000	.968	.772	.416	.132	.021	.001	.000	.000
8	1.000	.990	.887	.596	.252	.057	.005	.000	.000
9	1.000	.997	.952	.755	.412	.128	.017	.001	.000
10	1.000	.999	.983	.872	.588	.245	.048	.003	.000
11	1.000	1.000	.995	.943	.748	.404	.113	.010	.000
12	1.000	1.000	.999	.979	.868	.584	.228	.032	.000
13	1.000	1.000	1.000	.994	.942	.750	.392	.087	.002
14	1.000	1.000	1.000	.998	.979	.874	.584	.196	.011
15	1.000	1.000	1.000	1.000	.994	.949	.762	.370	.043
16	1.000	1.000	1.000	1.000	.999	.984	.893	.589	.133
17	1.000	1.000	1.000	1.000	1.000	.996	.965	.794	.323
18	1.000	1.000	1.000	1.000	1.000	.999	.992	.931	.608
19	1.000	1.000	1.000	1.000	1.000	1.000	.999	.988	.878

APPENDIX TABLE 4 (Continued)

$$B(i;\ n,\ p) \qquad n = 25$$

i \ p	0.10	0.20	0.30	0.40	0.50	0.60	0.70	0.80	0.90
0	.072	.004	.000	.000	.000	.000	.000	.000	.000
1	.271	.027	.002	.000	.000	.000	.000	.000	.000
2	.537	.092	.009	.000	.000	.000	.000	.000	.000
3	.764	.234	.033	.002	.000	.000	.000	.000	.000
4	.902	.421	.090	.009	.000	.000	.000	.000	.000
5	.967	.617	.193	.029	.002	.000	.000	.000	.000
6	.991	.780	.341	.074	.007	.000	.000	.000	.000
7	.998	.891	.512	.154	.022	.001	.000	.000	.000
8	1.000	.953	.677	.274	.054	.004	.000	.000	.000
9	1.000	.983	.811	.425	.115	.013	.000	.000	.000
10	1.000	.994	.902	.586	.212	.034	.002	.000	.000
11	1.000	.998	.956	.732	.345	.078	.006	.000	.000
12	1.000	1.000	.983	.846	.500	.154	.017	.000	.000
13	1.000	1.000	.994	.922	.655	.268	.044	.002	.000
14	1.000	1.000	.998	.966	.788	.414	.098	.006	.000
15	1.000	1.000	1.000	.987	.885	.575	.189	.017	.000
16	1.000	1.000	1.000	.996	.946	.726	.323	.047	.000
17	1.000	1.000	1.000	.999	.978	.846	.488	.109	.002
18	1.000	1.000	1.000	1.000	.993	.926	.659	.220	.009
19	1.000	1.000	1.000	1.000	.998	.971	.807	.383	.033
20	1.000	1.000	1.000	1.000	1.000	.991	.910	.579	.098
21	1.000	1.000	1.000	1.000	1.000	.998	.967	.766	.236
22	1.000	1.000	1.000	1.000	1.000	1.000	.991	.902	.463
23	1.000	1.000	1.000	1.000	1.000	1.000	.998	.973	.729
24	1.000	1.000	1.000	1.000	1.000	1.000	1.000	.996	.928

APPENDIX TABLE 5

Cumulative Poisson Probabilities

$P(i, \lambda) = P\{y \le i\}$, y is a Poisson random
variable with mean λ

i	λ 1.0	1.5	2.0	2.5	3.0	3.5	4.0	4.5	5.0
0	0.3679	0.2231	0.1353	0.0821	0.0498	0.0302	0.0183	0.0111	0.0067
1	0.7358	0.5578	0.4060	0.2873	0.1991	0.1359	0.0916	0.0611	0.0404
2	0.9197	0.8088	0.6767	0.5438	0.4232	0.3208	0.2381	0.1736	0.1247
3	0.9810	0.9344	0.8571	0.7576	0.6472	0.5366	0.4335	0.3423	0.2650
4	0.9963	0.9814	0.9473	0.8912	0.8153	0.7254	0.6288	0.5321	0.4405
5	0.9994	0.9955	0.9834	0.9580	0.9161	0.8576	0.7851	0.7029	0.6160
6	0.9999	0.9991	0.9955	0.9858	0.9665	0.9347	0.8893	0.8311	0.7622
7	1.0000	0.9998	0.9989	0.9958	0.9881	0.9733	0.9489	0.9134	0.8666
8		1.0000	0.9998	0.9989	0.9962	0.9901	0.9786	0.9597	0.9319
9			1.0000	0.9997	0.9989	0.9967	0.9919	0.9829	0.9682
10				0.9999	0.9997	0.9990	0.9972	0.9933	0.9863
11				1.0000	0.9999	0.9997	0.9991	0.9976	0.9945
12					1.0000	0.9999	0.9997	0.9992	0.9980
13						1.0000	0.9999	0.9997	0.9993
14							1.0000	0.9999	0.9998
15								1.0000	0.9999
16									1.0000

i	λ 5.5	6.0	6.5	7.0	7.5	8.0	8.5	9.0	9.5
0	0.0041	0.0025	0.0015	0.0009	0.0006	0.0003	0.0002	0.0001	0.0001
1	0.0266	0.0174	0.0113	0.0073	0.0047	0.0030	0.0019	0.0012	0.0008
2	0.0884	0.0620	0.0430	0.0296	0.0203	0.0138	0.0093	0.0062	0.0042
3	0.2017	0.1512	0.1118	0.0818	0.0591	0.0424	0.0301	0.0212	0.0149
4	0.3575	0.2851	0.2237	0.1730	0.1321	0.0996	0.0744	0.0550	0.0403
5	0.5289	0.4457	0.3690	0.3007	0.2414	0.1912	0.1496	0.1157	0.0885
6	0.6860	0.6063	0.5265	0.4497	0.3782	0.3134	0.2562	0.2068	0.1649
7	0.8095	0.7440	0.6728	0.5987	0.5246	0.4530	0.3856	0.3239	0.2687
8	0.8944	0.8472	0.7916	0.7291	0.6620	0.5925	0.5231	0.4557	0.3918
9	0.9462	0.9161	0.8774	0.8305	0.7764	0.7166	0.6530	0.5874	0.5218
10	0.9747	0.9574	0.9332	0.9015	0.8622	0.8159	0.7634	0.7060	0.6453
11	0.9890	0.9799	0.9661	0.9466	0.9208	0.8881	0.8487	0.8030	0.7520

APPENDIX TABLE 5 (Continued)

i	5.5	6.0	6.5	7.0	7.5	8.0	8.5	9.0	9.5
					λ				
12	0.9955	0.9912	0.9840	0.9730	0.9573	0.9362	0.9091	0.8758	0.8364
13	0.9983	0.9964	0.9929	0.9872	0.9784	0.9658	0.9486	0.9261	0.8981
14	0.9994	0.9986	0.9970	0.9943	0.9897	0.9827	0.9726	0.9585	0.9400
15	0.9998	0.9995	0.9988	0.9976	0.9954	0.9918	0.9862	0.9780	0.9665
16	0.9999	0.9998	0.9996	0.9990	0.9980	0.9963	0.9934	0.9889	0.9823
17	1.0000	0.9999	0.9998	0.9996	0.9992	0.9984	0.9970	0.9947	0.9911
18		1.0000	0.9999	0.9999	0.9997	0.9994	0.9987	0.9976	0.9957
19			1.0000	1.0000	0.9999	0.9997	0.9995	0.9989	0.9980
20					1.000	0.9999	0.9998	0.9996	0.9991
21						1.0000	0.9999	0.9998	0.9996
22							1.0000	0.9999	0.9999
23								1.0000	0.9999
24									1.0000

Reprinted with permission from E.C. Molina, *Poisson's Exponential Binomial Limit*. Princeton: Van Nostrand, 1942.

APPENDIX TABLE 6

Areas of a Standard Normal Distribution

An entry in the table gives the area or probability $P\{0 \le z \le b\}$ under the curve from 0 to any positive number b.

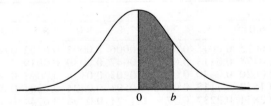

b	.00	.01	.02	.03	.04	.05	.06	.07	.08	.09
0.0	.0000	.0040	.0080	.0120	.0160	.0199	.0239	.0279	.0319	.0359
0.1	.0398	.0438	.0478	.0517	.0557	.0596	.0636	.0675	.0714	.0753
0.2	.0793	.0832	.0871	.0910	.0948	.0987	.1026	.1064	.1103	.1141
0.3	.1179	.1217	.1255	.1293	.1331	.1368	.1406	.1443	.1480	.1517
0.4	.1554	.1591	.1628	.1664	.1700	.1736	.1772	.1808	.1844	.1879

b	.00	.01	.02	.03	.04	.05	.06	.07	.08	.09
0.5	.1915	.1950	.1985	.2019	.2054	.2088	.2123	.2157	.2190	.2224
0.6	.2257	.2291	.2324	.2357	.2389	.2422	.2454	.2486	.2517	.2549
0.7	.2580	.2611	.2642	.2673	.2703	.2734	.2764	.2794	.2823	.2852
0.8	.2881	.2910	.2939	.2967	.2995	.3023	.3051	.3078	.3106	.3133
0.9	.3159	.3186	.3212	.3238	.3264	.3289	.3315	.3340	.3365	.3389
1.0	.3413	.3438	.3461	.3485	.3508	.3531	.3554	.3577	.3599	.3621
1.1	.3643	.3665	.3686	.3708	.3729	.3749	.3770	.3790	.3810	.3830
1.2	.3849	.3869	.3888	.3907	.3925	.3944	.3962	.3980	.3997	.4015
1.3	.4032	.4049	.4066	.4082	.4099	.4115	.4131	.4147	.4162	.4177
1.4	.4192	.4207	.4222	.4236	.4251	.4265	.4279	.4292	.4306	.4319
1.5	.4332	.4345	.4357	.4370	.4382	.4394	.4406	.4418	.4429	.4441
1.6	.4452	.4463	.4474	.4484	.4495	.4505	.4515	.4525	.4535	.4545
1.7	.4554	.4564	.4573	.4582	.4591	.4599	.4608	.4616	.4625	.4633
1.8	.4641	.4649	.4656	.4664	.4671	.4678	.4686	.4693	.4699	.4706
1.9	.4713	.4719	.4726	.4732	.4738	.4744	.4750	.4756	.4761	.4767
2.0	.4772	.4778	.4783	.4788	.4793	.4798	.4803	.4808	.4812	.4817
2.1	.4821	.4826	.4830	.4834	.4838	.4842	.4846	.4850	.4854	.4857
2.2	.4861	.4864	.4868	.4871	.4875	.4878	.4881	.4884	.4887	.4890
2.3	.4893	.4896	.4898	.4901	.4904	.4906	.4909	.4911	.4913	.4916
2.4	.4918	.4920	.4922	.4925	.4927	.4929	.4931	.4932	.4934	.4936
2.5	.4938	.4940	.4941	.4943	.4945	.4946	.4948	.4949	.4951	.4952
2.6	.4953	.4955	.4956	.4957	.4959	.4960	.4961	.4962	.4963	.4964
2.7	.4965	.4966	.4967	.4968	.4969	.4970	.4971	.4972	.4973	.4974
2.8	.4974	.4975	.4976	.4977	.4977	.4978	.4979	.4979	.4980	.4981
2.9	.4981	.4982	.4982	.4983	.4984	.4984	.4985	.4985	.4986	.4986
3.0	.4987	.4987	.4987	.4988	.4988	.4989	.4989	.4989	.4990	.4990

Reprinted with permission from A. Hald, *Statistical Tables and Formulas*. New York: Wiley, 1953.

APPENDIX TABLE 7 Student's *t* Distribution

An entry in the table gives the area or probability $P(t > t_{\alpha, \nu}) = \alpha$, where t has a Student's t distribution with $\nu = $ degrees of freedom.

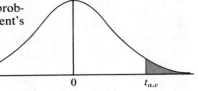

α ν	.10	.05	.025	.01	.005
1	3.078	6.314	12.706	31.821	63.657
2	1.886	2.920	4.303	6.965	9.925
3	1.638	2.353	3.182	4.541	5.841
4	1.533	2.132	2.776	3.747	4.604
5	1.476	2.015	2.571	3.365	4.032
6	1.440	1.943	2.447	3.143	3.707
7	1.415	1.895	2.365	2.998	3.499
8	1.397	1.860	2.306	2.896	3.355
9	1.383	1.833	2.262	2.821	3.250
10	1.372	1.812	2.228	2.764	3.169
11	1.363	1.796	2.201	2.718	3.106
12	1.356	1.782	2.179	2.681	3.055
13	1.350	1.771	2.160	2.650	3.012
14	1.345	1.761	2.145	2.624	2.977
15	1.341	1.753	2.131	2.602	2.947
16	1.337	1.746	2.120	2.583	2.921
17	1.333	1.740	2.110	2.567	2.898
18	1.330	1.734	2.101	2.552	2.878
19	1.328	1.729	2.093	2.539	2.861
20	1.325	1.725	2.086	2.528	2.845
21	1.323	1.721	2.080	2.518	2.831
22	1.321	1.717	2.074	2.508	2.819
23	1.319	1.714	2.069	2.500	2.807
24	1.318	1.711	2.064	2.492	2.797
25	1.316	1.708	2.060	2.485	2.787
26	1.315	1.706	2.056	2.479	2.779
27	1.314	1.703	2.052	2.473	2.771
28	1.313	1.701	2.048	2.467	2.763
29	1.311	1.699	2.045	2.462	2.756
30	1.310	1.697	2.042	2.457	2.750
40	1.303	1.684	2.021	2.423	2.704
60	1.296	1.671	2.000	2.390	2.660
120	1.289	1.658	1.980	2.358	2.617
∞	1.282	1.645	1.960	2.326	2.576

APPENDIX TABLE 8 The χ^2 Distribution

An entry in the table gives the area or probability $P(\chi^2 > \chi^2_{\alpha,\nu}) = \alpha$, where χ^2 has a chi-square distribution with $\nu =$ degrees of freedom.

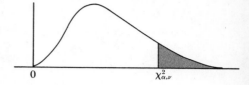

ν \ P	0.995	0.990	0.975	0.950	0.050	0.025	0.010	0.005
1	0.0000393	0.0001571	0.0009821	0.0039321	3.84146	5.02389	6.63490	7.87944
2	0.0100251	0.0201007	0.0506356	0.102587	5.99147	7.37776	9.21034	10.5966
3	0.0717212	0.114832	0.215795	0.351846	7.81473	9.34840	11.3449	12.8381
4	0.206990	0.297110	0.484419	0.710721	9.48773	11.1433	13.2767	14.8602
5	0.411740	0.554300	0.831211	1.145476	11.0705	12.8325	15.0863	16.7496
6	0.675727	0.872085	1.237347	1.63539	12.5916	14.4494	16.8119	18.5476
7	0.989265	1.239043	1.68987	2.16735	14.0671	16.0128	18.4753	20.2777
8	1.344419	1.646482	2.17973	2.73264	15.5073	17.5346	20.0902	21.9550
9	1.734926	2.087912	2.70039	3.32511	16.9190	19.0228	21.6660	23.5893
10	2.15585	2.55821	3.24697	3.94030	18.3070	20.4831	23.2093	25.1882
11	2.60321	3.05347	3.81575	4.57481	19.6751	21.9200	24.7250	26.7569
12	3.07382	3.57056	4.40379	5.22603	21.0261	23.3367	26.2170	28.2995
13	3.56503	4.10691	5.00874	5.89186	22.3621	24.7356	27.6883	29.8194
14	4.07468	4.66043	5.62872	6.57063	23.6848	26.1190	29.1413	31.3193
15	4.60094	5.22935	6.26214	7.26094	24.9958	27.4884	30.5779	32.8013
16	5.14224	5.81221	6.90766	7.96164	26.2962	28.8454	31.9999	34.2672
17	5.69724	6.40776	7.56418	8.67176	27.5871	30.1910	33.4087	35.7185
18	6.26481	7.01491	8.23075	9.39046	28.8693	31.5264	34.8053	37.1564
19	6.84398	7.63273	8.90655	10.1170	30.1435	32.8523	36.1908	38.5822
20	7.43386	8.26040	9.59083	10.8508	31.4104	34.1696	37.5662	39.9968
21	8.03366	8.89720	10.28293	11.5913	32.6705	35.4789	38.9321	41.4010
22	8.64272	9.54249	10.9823	12.3380	33.9244	36.7807	40.2894	42.7956
23	9.26042	10.19567	11.6885	13.0905	35.1725	38.0757	41.6384	44.1813
24	9.88623	10.8564	12.4011	13.8484	36.4151	39.3641	42.9798	45.5585
25	10.5197	11.5240	13.1197	14.6114	37.6525	40.6465	44.3141	46.9278
26	11.1603	12.1981	13.8439	15.3791	38.8852	41.9232	45.6417	48.2899
27	11.8076	12.8786	14.5733	16.1513	40.1133	43.1944	46.9630	49.6449
28	12.4613	13.5648	15.3079	16.9279	41.3372	44.4607	48.2782	50.9933
29	13.1211	14.2565	16.0471	17.7083	42.5569	45.7222	49.5879	52.3356
30	13.7867	14.9535	16.7908	18.4926	43.7729	46.9792	50.8922	53.6720
40	20.7065	22.1643	24.4331	26.5093	55.7585	59.3417	63.6907	66.7659
50	27.9907	29.7067	32.3574	34.7642	67.5048	71.4202	76.1539	79.4900
60	35.5346	37.4848	40.4817	43.1879	79.0819	83.2976	88.3794	91.9517
70	43.2752	45.4418	48.7576	51.7393	90.5312	95.0231	100.425	104.215
80	51.1720	53.5400	57.1532	60.3915	101.879	106.629	112.329	116.321
90	59.1963	61.7541	65.6466	69.1260	113.145	118.136	124.116	128.299
100	67.3276	70.0648	74.2219	77.9295	124.342	129.561	135.807	140.169

APPENDIX TABLE 9   F Distribution

5% (upper entry) and 1% (lower entry) points for the distribution of F

An entry in the table gives the area or probability $P(F > F_{\nu_1, \nu_2, \alpha}) = \alpha$, where F has an F distribution with ν_1 degrees of freedom in the numerator and ν_2 degrees of freedom in the denominator.

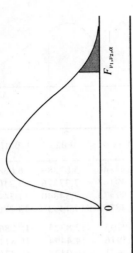

$F_{\nu_1, \nu_2, \alpha}$

Degrees of freedom for numerator (ν_1)

ν_2	entry	1	2	3	4	5	6	7	8	9	10	11	12	14	16	20	24	30	40	50	75	100	200	500	∞
1	5%	161	200	216	225	230	234	237	239	241	242	243	244	245	246	248	249	250	251	252	253	253	254	254	254
	1%	4052	4999	5403	5625	5764	5859	5928	5981	6022	6056	6082	6106	6142	6169	6208	6234	6258	6286	6302	6323	6334	6352	6361	6366
2	5%	18.51	19.00	19.16	19.25	19.30	19.33	19.36	19.37	19.38	19.39	19.40	19.41	19.42	19.43	19.44	19.45	19.46	19.47	19.47	19.48	19.49	19.49	19.50	19.50
	1%	98.49	99.01	99.17	99.25	99.30	99.33	99.34	99.36	99.38	99.40	99.41	99.42	99.43	99.44	99.45	99.46	99.47	99.48	99.48	99.49	99.49	99.49	99.50	99.50
3	5%	10.13	9.55	9.28	9.12	9.01	8.94	8.88	8.84	8.81	8.78	8.76	8.74	8.71	8.69	8.66	8.64	8.62	8.60	8.58	8.57	8.56	8.54	8.54	8.53
	1%	34.12	30.81	29.46	28.71	28.24	27.91	27.67	27.49	27.34	27.23	27.13	27.05	26.92	26.83	26.69	26.60	26.50	26.41	26.30	26.27	26.23	26.18	26.14	26.12
4	5%	7.71	6.94	6.59	6.39	6.26	6.16	6.09	6.04	6.00	5.96	5.93	5.91	5.87	5.84	5.80	5.77	5.74	5.71	5.70	5.68	5.66	5.65	5.64	5.63
	1%	21.20	18.00	16.69	15.98	15.52	15.21	14.98	14.80	14.66	14.54	14.45	14.37	14.24	14.15	14.02	13.93	13.83	13.74	13.69	13.61	13.57	13.52	13.48	13.46
5	5%	6.61	5.79	5.41	5.19	5.05	4.95	4.88	4.82	4.78	4.74	4.70	4.68	4.64	4.60	4.56	4.53	4.50	4.46	4.44	4.42	4.40	4.38	4.37	4.36
	1%	16.26	13.27	12.06	11.39	10.97	10.67	10.45	10.27	10.15	10.05	9.96	9.89	9.77	9.68	9.55	9.47	9.38	9.29	9.24	9.17	9.13	9.07	9.04	9.02
6	5%	5.99	5.14	4.76	4.53	4.39	4.28	4.21	4.15	4.10	4.06	4.03	4.00	3.96	3.92	3.87	3.84	3.81	3.77	3.75	3.72	3.71	3.69	3.68	3.67
	1%	13.74	10.92	9.78	9.15	8.75	8.47	8.26	8.10	7.98	7.87	7.79	7.72	7.60	7.52	7.39	7.31	7.23	7.14	7.09	7.02	6.99	6.94	6.90	6.88
7	5%	5.59	4.74	4.35	4.12	3.97	3.87	3.79	3.73	3.68	3.63	3.60	3.57	3.52	3.49	3.44	3.41	3.38	3.34	3.32	3.29	3.28	3.25	3.24	3.23
	1%	12.25	9.55	8.45	7.85	7.46	7.19	7.00	6.84	6.71	6.62	6.54	6.47	6.35	6.27	6.15	6.07	5.98	5.90	5.85	5.78	5.75	5.70	5.67	5.65
8	5%	5.32	4.46	4.07	3.84	3.69	3.58	3.50	3.44	3.39	3.34	3.31	3.28	3.23	3.20	3.15	3.12	3.08	3.05	3.03	3.00	2.98	2.96	2.94	2.93
	1%	11.26	8.65	7.59	7.01	6.63	6.37	6.19	6.03	5.91	5.82	5.74	5.67	5.56	5.48	5.36	5.28	5.20	5.11	5.06	5.00	4.96	4.91	4.88	4.86
9	5%	5.12	4.26	3.86	3.63	3.48	3.37	3.29	3.23	3.18	3.13	3.10	3.07	3.02	2.98	2.93	2.90	2.86	2.82	2.80	2.77	2.76	2.73	2.72	2.71
	1%	10.56	8.02	6.99	6.42	6.06	5.80	5.62	5.47	5.35	5.26	5.18	5.11	5.00	4.92	4.80	4.73	4.64	4.56	4.51	4.45	4.41	4.36	4.33	4.31

	1	2	3	4	5	6	7	8	9	10	11	12	14	16	20	24	30	40	50	75	100	200	500	∞
10	4.96 10.04	4.10 7.56	3.71 6.55	3.48 5.99	3.33 5.64	3.22 5.39	3.14 5.21	3.07 5.06	3.02 4.95	2.97 4.85	2.94 4.78	2.91 4.71	2.86 4.60	2.82 4.52	2.77 4.41	2.74 4.33	2.70 4.25	2.67 4.17	2.64 4.12	2.61 4.05	2.59 4.01	2.56 3.96	2.55 3.93	2.54 3.91
11	4.84 9.65	3.98 7.20	3.59 6.22	3.36 5.67	3.20 5.32	3.09 5.07	3.01 4.88	2.95 4.74	2.90 4.63	2.86 4.54	2.82 4.46	2.79 4.40	2.74 4.29	2.70 4.21	2.65 4.10	2.61 4.02	2.57 3.94	2.53 3.86	2.50 3.80	2.47 3.74	2.45 3.70	2.42 3.66	2.41 3.62	2.40 3.60
12	4.75 9.33	3.88 6.93	3.49 5.95	3.26 5.41	3.11 5.06	3.00 4.82	2.92 4.65	2.85 4.50	2.80 4.39	2.76 4.30	2.72 4.22	2.69 4.16	2.64 4.05	2.60 3.98	2.54 3.86	2.50 3.78	2.46 3.70	2.42 3.61	2.40 3.56	2.36 3.49	2.35 3.46	2.32 3.41	2.31 3.38	2.30 3.36
13	4.67 9.07	3.80 6.70	3.41 5.74	3.18 5.20	3.02 4.86	2.92 4.62	2.84 4.44	2.77 4.30	2.72 4.19	2.67 4.10	2.63 4.02	2.60 3.96	2.55 3.85	2.51 3.78	2.46 3.67	2.42 3.59	2.38 3.51	2.34 3.42	2.32 3.37	2.28 3.30	2.26 3.27	2.24 3.21	2.22 3.18	2.21 3.16
14	4.60 8.86	3.74 6.51	3.34 5.56	3.11 5.03	2.96 4.69	2.85 4.46	2.77 4.28	2.70 4.14	2.65 4.03	2.60 3.94	2.56 3.86	2.53 3.80	2.48 3.70	2.44 3.62	2.39 3.51	2.35 3.43	2.31 3.34	2.27 3.26	2.24 3.21	2.21 3.14	2.19 3.11	2.16 3.06	2.14 3.02	2.13 3.00
15	4.54 8.68	3.68 6.36	3.29 5.42	3.06 4.89	2.90 4.56	2.79 4.32	2.70 4.14	2.64 4.00	2.59 3.89	2.55 3.80	2.51 3.73	2.48 3.67	2.43 3.56	2.39 3.48	2.33 3.36	2.29 3.29	2.25 3.20	2.21 3.12	2.18 3.07	2.15 3.00	2.12 2.97	2.10 2.92	2.08 2.89	2.07 2.87
16	4.49 8.53	3.63 6.23	3.24 5.29	3.01 4.77	2.85 4.44	2.74 4.20	2.66 4.03	2.59 3.89	2.54 3.78	2.49 3.69	2.45 3.61	2.42 3.55	2.37 3.45	2.33 3.37	2.28 3.25	2.24 3.18	2.20 3.10	2.16 3.01	2.13 2.96	2.09 2.89	2.07 2.86	2.04 2.80	2.02 2.77	2.01 2.75
17	4.45 8.40	3.59 6.11	3.20 5.18	2.96 4.67	2.81 4.34	2.70 4.10	2.62 3.93	2.55 3.79	2.50 3.68	2.45 3.59	2.41 3.52	2.38 3.45	2.33 3.35	2.29 3.27	2.23 3.16	2.19 3.08	2.15 3.00	2.11 2.92	2.08 2.86	2.04 2.79	2.02 2.76	1.99 2.70	1.97 2.67	1.96 2.65
18	4.41 8.28	3.55 6.01	3.16 5.09	2.93 4.58	2.77 4.25	2.66 4.01	2.58 3.85	2.51 3.71	2.46 3.60	2.41 3.51	2.37 3.44	2.34 3.37	2.29 3.27	2.25 3.19	2.19 3.07	2.15 3.00	2.11 2.91	2.07 2.83	2.04 2.78	2.00 2.71	1.98 2.68	1.95 2.62	1.93 2.59	1.92 2.57
19	4.38 8.18	3.52 5.93	3.13 5.01	2.90 4.50	2.74 4.17	2.63 3.94	2.55 3.77	2.48 3.63	2.43 3.52	2.38 3.43	2.34 3.36	2.31 3.30	2.26 3.19	2.21 3.12	2.15 3.00	2.11 2.92	2.07 2.84	2.02 2.76	2.00 2.70	1.96 2.63	1.94 2.60	1.91 2.54	1.90 2.51	1.88 2.49
20	4.35 8.10	3.49 5.85	3.10 4.94	2.87 4.43	2.71 4.10	2.60 3.87	2.52 3.71	2.45 3.56	2.40 3.45	2.35 3.37	2.31 3.30	2.28 3.23	2.23 3.13	2.18 3.05	2.12 2.94	2.08 2.86	2.04 2.77	1.99 2.69	1.96 2.63	1.92 2.56	1.90 2.53	1.87 2.47	1.85 2.44	1.84 2.42
21	4.32 8.02	3.47 5.78	3.07 4.87	2.84 4.37	2.68 4.04	2.57 3.81	2.49 3.65	2.42 3.51	2.37 3.40	2.32 3.31	2.28 3.24	2.25 3.17	2.20 3.07	2.15 2.99	2.09 2.88	2.05 2.80	2.00 2.72	1.96 2.63	1.93 2.58	1.89 2.51	1.87 2.47	1.84 2.42	1.82 2.38	1.81 2.36
22	4.30 7.94	3.44 5.72	3.05 4.82	2.82 4.31	2.66 3.99	2.55 3.76	2.47 3.59	2.40 3.45	2.35 3.35	2.30 3.26	2.26 3.18	2.23 3.12	2.18 3.02	2.13 2.94	2.07 2.83	2.03 2.75	1.98 2.67	1.93 2.58	1.91 2.53	1.87 2.46	1.84 2.42	1.81 2.37	1.80 2.33	1.78 2.31
23	4.28 7.88	3.42 5.66	3.03 4.76	2.80 4.26	2.64 3.94	2.53 3.71	2.45 3.54	2.38 3.41	2.32 3.30	2.28 3.21	2.24 3.14	2.20 3.07	2.14 2.97	2.10 2.89	2.04 2.78	2.00 2.70	1.96 2.62	1.91 2.53	1.88 2.48	1.84 2.41	1.82 2.37	1.79 2.32	1.77 2.28	1.76 2.26
24	4.26 7.82	3.40 5.61	3.01 4.72	2.78 4.22	2.62 3.90	2.51 3.67	2.43 3.50	2.36 3.36	2.30 3.25	2.26 3.17	2.22 3.09	2.18 3.03	2.13 2.93	2.09 2.85	2.02 2.74	1.98 2.66	1.94 2.58	1.89 2.49	1.86 2.44	1.82 2.36	1.80 2.33	1.76 2.27	1.74 2.23	1.73 2.21
25	4.24 7.77	3.38 5.57	2.99 4.68	2.76 4.18	2.60 3.86	2.49 3.63	2.41 3.46	2.34 3.32	2.28 3.21	2.24 3.13	2.20 3.05	2.16 2.99	2.11 2.89	2.06 2.81	2.00 2.70	1.96 2.62	1.92 2.54	1.87 2.45	1.84 2.40	1.80 2.32	1.77 2.29	1.74 2.23	1.72 2.19	1.71 2.17
26	4.22 7.72	3.37 5.53	2.98 4.64	2.74 4.14	2.59 3.82	2.47 3.59	2.39 3.42	2.32 3.29	2.27 3.17	2.22 3.09	2.18 3.02	2.15 2.96	2.10 2.86	2.05 2.77	1.99 2.66	1.95 2.58	1.90 2.50	1.85 2.41	1.82 2.36	1.78 2.28	1.76 2.25	1.72 2.19	1.70 2.15	1.69 2.13
27	4.21 7.68	3.35 5.49	2.96 4.60	2.73 4.11	2.57 3.79	2.46 3.56	2.37 3.39	2.30 3.26	2.25 3.14	2.20 3.06	2.16 2.98	2.13 2.93	2.08 2.83	2.03 2.74	1.97 2.63	1.93 2.55	1.88 2.47	1.84 2.38	1.80 2.33	1.76 2.25	1.74 2.21	1.71 2.16	1.68 2.12	1.67 2.10

TABLE 9 (continued)

Degrees of freedom for numerator (ν_1)

Degrees of freedom for denominator (ν_2)	1	2	3	4	5	6	7	8	9	10	11	12	14	16	20	24	30	40	50	75	100	200	500	∞
28	4.20 / 7.64	3.34 / 5.45	2.95 / 4.57	2.71 / 4.07	2.56 / 3.76	2.44 / 3.53	2.36 / 3.36	2.29 / 3.23	2.24 / 3.11	2.19 / 3.03	2.15 / 2.95	2.12 / 2.90	2.06 / 2.80	2.02 / 2.71	1.96 / 2.60	1.91 / 2.52	1.87 / 2.44	1.81 / 2.35	1.78 / 2.30	1.75 / 2.22	1.72 / 2.18	1.69 / 2.13	1.67 / 2.09	1.65 / 2.06
29	4.18 / 7.60	3.33 / 5.52	2.93 / 4.54	2.70 / 4.04	2.54 / 3.73	2.43 / 3.50	2.35 / 3.33	2.28 / 3.20	2.22 / 3.08	2.18 / 3.00	2.14 / 2.92	2.10 / 2.87	2.05 / 2.77	2.00 / 2.68	1.94 / 2.57	1.90 / 2.49	1.85 / 2.41	1.80 / 2.32	1.77 / 2.27	1.73 / 2.19	1.71 / 2.15	1.68 / 2.10	1.65 / 2.06	1.64 / 2.03
30	4.17 / 7.56	3.32 / 5.39	2.92 / 4.51	2.69 / 4.02	2.53 / 3.70	2.42 / 3.47	2.34 / 3.30	2.27 / 3.17	2.21 / 3.06	2.16 / 2.98	2.12 / 2.90	2.09 / 2.84	2.04 / 2.74	1.99 / 2.66	1.93 / 2.55	1.89 / 2.47	1.84 / 2.38	1.79 / 2.29	1.76 / 2.24	1.72 / 2.16	1.69 / 2.13	1.66 / 2.07	1.64 / 2.03	1.62 / 2.01
32	4.15 / 7.50	3.30 / 5.34	2.90 / 4.46	2.67 / 3.97	2.51 / 3.66	2.40 / 3.42	2.32 / 3.25	2.25 / 3.12	2.19 / 3.01	2.14 / 2.94	2.10 / 2.86	2.07 / 2.80	2.02 / 2.70	1.97 / 2.62	1.91 / 2.51	1.86 / 2.42	1.82 / 2.34	1.76 / 2.25	1.74 / 2.20	1.69 / 2.12	1.67 / 2.08	1.64 / 2.02	1.61 / 1.98	1.59 / 1.96
34	4.13 / 7.44	3.28 / 5.29	2.88 / 4.42	2.65 / 3.93	2.49 / 3.61	2.38 / 3.38	2.30 / 3.21	2.23 / 3.08	2.17 / 2.97	2.12 / 2.89	2.08 / 2.82	2.05 / 2.76	2.00 / 2.66	1.95 / 2.58	1.89 / 2.47	1.84 / 2.38	1.80 / 2.30	1.74 / 2.21	1.71 / 2.15	1.67 / 2.08	1.64 / 2.04	1.61 / 1.98	1.59 / 1.94	1.57 / 1.91
36	4.11 / 7.39	3.26 / 5.25	2.86 / 4.38	2.63 / 3.89	2.48 / 3.58	2.36 / 3.35	2.28 / 3.18	2.21 / 3.04	2.15 / 2.94	2.10 / 2.86	2.06 / 2.78	2.03 / 2.72	1.98 / 2.62	1.93 / 2.54	1.87 / 2.43	1.82 / 2.35	1.78 / 2.26	1.72 / 2.17	1.69 / 2.12	1.65 / 2.04	1.62 / 2.00	1.59 / 1.94	1.56 / 1.90	1.55 / 1.87
38	4.10 / 7.35	3.25 / 5.21	2.85 / 4.34	2.62 / 3.86	2.46 / 3.54	2.35 / 3.32	2.26 / 3.15	2.19 / 3.02	2.14 / 2.91	2.09 / 2.82	2.05 / 2.75	2.02 / 2.69	1.96 / 2.59	1.92 / 2.51	1.85 / 2.40	1.80 / 2.32	1.76 / 2.22	1.71 / 2.14	1.67 / 2.08	1.63 / 2.00	1.60 / 1.97	1.57 / 1.90	1.54 / 1.86	1.53 / 1.84
40	4.08 / 7.31	3.23 / 5.18	2.84 / 4.31	2.61 / 3.83	2.45 / 3.51	2.34 / 3.29	2.25 / 3.12	2.18 / 2.99	2.12 / 2.88	2.07 / 2.80	2.04 / 2.73	2.00 / 2.66	1.95 / 2.56	1.90 / 2.49	1.84 / 2.37	1.79 / 2.29	1.74 / 2.20	1.69 / 2.11	1.66 / 2.05	1.61 / 1.97	1.59 / 1.94	1.55 / 1.88	1.53 / 1.84	1.51 / 1.81
42	4.07 / 7.27	3.22 / 5.15	2.83 / 4.29	2.59 / 3.80	2.44 / 3.49	2.32 / 3.26	2.24 / 3.10	2.17 / 2.96	2.11 / 2.86	2.06 / 2.77	2.02 / 2.70	1.99 / 2.64	1.94 / 2.54	1.89 / 2.46	1.82 / 2.35	1.78 / 2.26	1.73 / 2.17	1.68 / 2.08	1.64 / 2.02	1.60 / 1.94	1.57 / 1.91	1.54 / 1.85	1.51 / 1.80	1.49 / 1.78
44	4.06 / 7.24	3.21 / 5.12	2.82 / 4.26	2.58 / 3.78	2.43 / 3.46	2.31 / 3.24	2.23 / 3.07	2.16 / 2.94	2.10 / 2.84	2.05 / 2.75	2.01 / 2.68	1.98 / 2.62	1.92 / 2.52	1.88 / 2.44	1.81 / 2.32	1.76 / 2.24	1.72 / 2.15	1.66 / 2.06	1.63 / 2.00	1.58 / 1.92	1.56 / 1.88	1.52 / 1.82	1.50 / 1.78	1.48 / 1.75
46	4.05 / 7.21	3.20 / 5.10	2.81 / 4.24	2.57 / 3.76	2.42 / 3.44	2.30 / 3.22	2.22 / 3.05	2.14 / 2.92	2.09 / 2.82	2.04 / 2.73	2.00 / 2.66	1.97 / 2.60	1.91 / 2.50	1.87 / 2.42	1.80 / 2.30	1.75 / 2.22	1.71 / 2.13	1.65 / 2.04	1.62 / 1.98	1.57 / 1.90	1.54 / 1.86	1.51 / 1.80	1.48 / 1.76	1.46 / 1.72
48	4.04 / 7.19	3.19 / 5.08	2.80 / 4.22	2.56 / 3.74	2.41 / 3.42	2.30 / 3.20	2.21 / 3.04	2.14 / 2.90	2.08 / 2.80	2.03 / 2.71	1.99 / 2.64	1.96 / 2.58	1.90 / 2.48	1.86 / 2.40	1.79 / 2.28	1.74 / 2.20	1.70 / 2.11	1.64 / 2.02	1.61 / 1.96	1.56 / 1.88	1.53 / 1.84	1.50 / 1.78	1.47 / 1.73	1.45 / 1.70
50	4.03 / 7.17	3.18 / 5.06	2.79 / 4.20	2.56 / 3.72	2.40 / 3.41	2.29 / 3.18	2.20 / 3.02	2.13 / 2.88	2.07 / 2.78	2.02 / 2.70	1.98 / 2.62	1.95 / 2.56	1.90 / 2.46	1.85 / 2.39	1.78 / 2.26	1.74 / 2.18	1.69 / 2.10	1.63 / 2.00	1.60 / 1.94	1.55 / 1.86	1.52 / 1.82	1.48 / 1.76	1.46 / 1.71	1.44 / 1.68
55	4.02 / 7.12	3.17 / 5.01	2.78 / 4.16	2.54 / 3.68	2.38 / 3.37	2.27 / 3.15	2.18 / 2.98	2.11 / 2.85	2.05 / 2.75	2.00 / 2.66	1.97 / 2.59	1.93 / 2.53	1.88 / 2.43	1.83 / 2.35	1.76 / 2.23	1.72 / 2.15	1.67 / 2.06	1.61 / 1.96	1.58 / 1.90	1.52 / 1.82	1.50 / 1.78	1.46 / 1.71	1.43 / 1.66	1.41 / 1.64
60	4.00 / 7.08	3.15 / 4.98	2.76 / 4.13	2.52 / 3.65	2.37 / 3.34	2.25 / 3.12	2.17 / 2.95	2.10 / 2.82	2.04 / 2.72	1.99 / 2.63	1.95 / 2.56	1.92 / 2.50	1.86 / 2.40	1.81 / 2.32	1.75 / 2.20	1.70 / 2.12	1.65 / 2.03	1.59 / 1.93	1.56 / 1.87	1.50 / 1.79	1.48 / 1.74	1.44 / 1.68	1.41 / 1.63	1.39 / 1.60

	1	2	3	4	5	6	7	8	9	10	11	12	14	16	20	24	30	40	50	75	100	200	500	∞
65	3.99 / 7.04	3.14 / 4.95	2.75 / 4.10	2.51 / 3.62	2.36 / 3.31	2.24 / 3.09	2.15 / 2.93	2.08 / 2.79	2.02 / 2.70	1.98 / 2.61	1.94 / 2.54	1.90 / 2.47	1.85 / 2.37	1.80 / 2.30	1.73 / 2.18	1.68 / 2.09	1.63 / 2.00	1.57 / 1.90	1.54 / 1.84	1.49 / 1.76	1.46 / 1.71	1.42 / 1.64	1.39 / 1.60	1.37 / 1.56
70	3.98 / 7.01	3.13 / 4.92	2.74 / 4.08	2.50 / 3.60	2.35 / 3.29	2.32 / 3.07	2.14 / 2.91	2.07 / 2.77	2.01 / 2.67	1.97 / 2.59	1.93 / 2.51	1.89 / 2.45	1.84 / 2.35	1.79 / 2.28	1.72 / 2.15	1.67 / 2.07	1.62 / 1.98	1.56 / 1.88	1.53 / 1.82	1.47 / 1.74	1.45 / 1.69	1.40 / 1.63	1.37 / 1.56	1.35 / 1.53
80	3.96 / 6.96	3.11 / 4.88	2.72 / 4.04	2.48 / 3.56	2.33 / 3.25	2.21 / 3.04	2.12 / 2.87	2.05 / 2.74	1.99 / 2.64	1.95 / 2.55	1.91 / 2.48	1.88 / 2.41	1.82 / 2.32	1.77 / 2.24	1.70 / 2.11	1.65 / 2.03	1.60 / 1.94	1.54 / 1.84	1.51 / 1.78	1.45 / 1.70	1.42 / 1.65	1.38 / 1.57	1.35 / 1.52	1.32 / 1.49
100	3.94 / 6.90	3.09 / 4.82	2.70 / 3.98	2.46 / 3.51	2.30 / 3.20	2.19 / 2.99	2.10 / 2.82	2.03 / 2.69	1.97 / 2.59	1.92 / 2.51	1.88 / 2.43	1.85 / 2.36	1.79 / 2.26	1.75 / 2.19	1.68 / 2.06	1.63 / 1.98	1.57 / 1.89	1.51 / 1.79	1.48 / 1.73	1.42 / 1.64	1.39 / 1.59	1.34 / 1.51	1.30 / 1.46	1.28 / 1.43
125	3.92 / 6.84	3.07 / 4.78	2.68 / 3.94	2.44 / 3.47	2.29 / 3.17	2.17 / 2.95	2.08 / 2.79	2.01 / 2.65	1.95 / 2.56	1.90 / 2.47	1.86 / 2.40	1.83 / 2.33	1.77 / 2.23	1.72 / 2.15	1.65 / 2.03	1.60 / 1.94	1.55 / 1.85	1.49 / 1.75	1.45 / 1.68	1.39 / 1.59	1.36 / 1.54	1.31 / 1.46	1.27 / 1.40	1.25 / 1.37
150	3.91 / 6.81	3.06 / 4.75	2.67 / 3.91	2.43 / 3.44	2.27 / 3.13	2.16 / 2.92	2.07 / 2.76	2.00 / 2.62	1.94 / 2.53	1.89 / 2.44	1.85 / 2.37	1.82 / 2.30	1.76 / 2.20	1.71 / 2.12	1.64 / 2.00	1.59 / 1.91	1.54 / 1.83	1.47 / 1.72	1.44 / 1.66	1.37 / 1.56	1.34 / 1.51	1.29 / 1.43	1.25 / 1.37	1.22 / 1.33
200	3.89 / 6.76	3.04 / 4.71	2.65 / 3.88	2.41 / 3.41	2.26 / 3.11	2.14 / 2.90	2.05 / 2.73	1.98 / 2.60	1.92 / 2.50	1.87 / 2.41	1.83 / 2.34	1.80 / 2.28	1.74 / 2.17	1.69 / 2.09	1.62 / 1.97	1.57 / 1.88	1.52 / 1.79	1.45 / 1.69	1.42 / 1.62	1.35 / 1.53	1.32 / 1.48	1.26 / 1.39	1.22 / 1.33	1.19 / 1.28
400	3.86 / 6.70	3.02 / 4.66	2.62 / 3.83	2.39 / 3.36	2.23 / 3.06	2.12 / 2.85	2.03 / 2.69	1.96 / 2.55	1.90 / 2.46	1.85 / 2.37	1.81 / 2.29	1.78 / 2.23	1.72 / 2.12	1.67 / 2.04	1.60 / 1.92	1.54 / 1.84	1.49 / 1.74	1.42 / 1.64	1.38 / 1.57	1.32 / 1.47	1.28 / 1.42	1.22 / 1.32	1.16 / 1.24	1.13 / 1.19
1000	3.85 / 6.66	3.00 / 4.62	2.61 / 3.80	2.38 / 3.34	2.22 / 3.04	2.10 / 2.82	2.02 / 2.66	1.95 / 2.53	1.89 / 2.43	1.84 / 2.34	1.80 / 2.26	1.76 / 2.20	1.70 / 2.09	1.65 / 2.01	1.58 / 1.89	1.53 / 1.81	1.47 / 1.71	1.41 / 1.61	1.36 / 1.54	1.30 / 1.44	1.26 / 1.38	1.19 / 1.28	1.13 / 1.19	1.08 / 1.11
∞	3.84 / 6.64	2.99 / 4.60	2.60 / 3.78	2.37 / 3.32	2.21 / 3.02	2.09 / 2.80	2.01 / 2.64	1.94 / 2.51	1.88 / 2.41	1.83 / 2.32	1.79 / 2.24	1.75 / 2.18	1.69 / 2.07	1.64 / 1.99	1.57 / 1.87	1.52 / 1.79	1.46 / 1.69	1.40 / 1.59	1.35 / 1.52	1.28 / 1.41	1.24 / 1.36	1.17 / 1.25	1.11 / 1.15	1.00 / 1.00

APPENDIX TABLE 10

Studentized Range Distribution

An entry in the table gives the area or probability $P(Q > Q_{v_1, v_2, \alpha}) = \alpha$, where Q has a studentized range distribution with v_1 degrees of freedom in the numerator and v_2 degrees of freedom in the denominator.

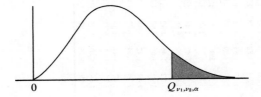

0 $Q_{v_1, v_2, \alpha}$

UPPER 1 PERCENT POINTS OF THE STUDENTIZED RANGE ($\alpha = .01$)

v_1 / v_2	2	3	4	5	6	7	8	9	10
1	90.03	135.0	164.3	185.6	202.2	215.8	227.2	237.0	245.6
2	14.04	19.02	22.29	24.72	26.63	28.20	29.53	30.68	31.69
3	8.26	10.62	12.17	13.33	14.24	15.00	15.64	16.20	16.69
4	6.51	8.12	9.17	9.96	10.58	11.10	11.55	11.93	12.27
5	5.70	6.98	7.80	8.42	8.91	9.32	9.67	9.97	10.24
6	5.24	6.33	7.03	7.56	7.97	8.32	8.61	8.87	9.10
7	4.95	5.92	6.54	7.01	7.37	7.68	7.94	8.17	8.37
8	4.75	5.64	6.20	6.62	6.96	7.24	7.47	7.68	7.86
9	4.60	5.43	5.96	6.35	6.66	6.91	7.13	7.33	7.49
10	4.48	5.27	5.77	6.14	6.43	6.67	6.87	7.05	7.21
11	4.39	5.15	5.62	5.97	6.25	6.48	6.67	6.84	6.99
12	4.32	5.05	5.50	5.84	6.10	6.32	6.51	6.67	6.81
13	4.26	4.96	5.40	5.73	5.98	6.19	6.37	6.53	6.67
14	4.21	4.89	5.32	5.63	5.88	6.08	6.26	6.41	6.54
15	4.17	4.84	5.25	5.56	5.80	5.99	6.16	6.31	6.44
16	4.13	4.79	5.19	5.49	5.72	5.92	6.08	6.22	6.35
17	4.10	4.74	5.14	5.43	5.66	5.85	6.01	6.15	6.27
18	4.07	4.70	5.09	5.38	5.60	5.79	5.94	6.08	6.20
19	4.05	4.67	5.05	5.33	5.55	5.73	5.89	6.02	6.14
20	4.02	4.64	5.02	5.29	5.51	5.69	5.84	5.97	6.09
24	3.96	4.55	4.91	5.17	5.37	5.54	5.69	5.81	5.92
30	3.89	4.45	4.80	5.05	5.24	5.40	5.54	5.65	5.76
40	3.82	4.37	4.70	4.93	5.11	5.26	5.39	5.50	5.60
60	3.76	4.28	4.59	4.82	4.99	5.13	5.25	5.36	5.45
120	3.70	4.20	4.50	4.71	4.87	5.01	5.12	5.21	5.30
∞	3.64	4.12	4.40	4.60	4.76	4.88	4.99	5.08	5.16

ν_1 ν_2	11	12	13	14	15	16	17	18	19	20
1	253.2	260.0	266.2	271.8	277.0	281.8	286.3	290.4	294.3	298.0
2	32.59	33.40	34.13	34.81	35.43	36.00	36.53	37.03	37.50	37.95
3	17.13	17.53	17.89	18.22	18.52	18.81	19.07	19.32	19.55	19.77
4	12.57	12.84	13.09	13.32	13.53	13.73	13.91	14.08	14.24	14.40
5	10.48	10.70	10.89	11.08	11.24	11.40	11.55	11.68	11.81	11.93
6	9.30	9.48	9.65	9.81	9.95	10.08	10.21	10.32	10.43	10.54
7	8.55	8.71	8.86	9.00	9.12	9.24	9.35	9.46	9.55	9.65
8	8.03	8.18	8.31	8.44	8.55	8.66	8.76	8.85	8.94	9.03
9	7.65	7.78	7.91	8.03	8.13	8.23	8.33	8.41	8.49	8.57
10	7.36	7.49	7.60	7.71	7.81	7.91	7.99	8.08	8.15	8.23
11	7.13	7.25	7.36	7.46	7.56	7.65	7.73	7.81	7.88	7.95
12	6.94	7.06	7.17	7.26	7.36	7.44	7.52	7.59	7.66	7.73
13	6.79	6.90	7.01	7.10	7.19	7.27	7.35	7.42	7.48	7.55
14	6.66	6.77	6.87	6.96	7.05	7.13	7.20	7.27	7.33	7.39
15	6.55	6.66	6.76	6.84	6.93	7.00	7.07	7.14	7.20	7.26
16	6.46	6.56	6.66	6.74	6.82	6.90	6.97	7.03	7.09	7.15
17	6.38	6.48	6.57	6.66	6.73	6.81	6.87	6.94	7.00	7.05
18	6.31	6.41	6.50	6.58	6.65	6.73	6.79	6.85	6.91	6.97
19	6.25	6.34	6.43	6.51	6.58	6.65	6.72	6.78	6.84	6.89
20	6.19	6.28	6.37	6.45	6.52	6.59	6.65	6.71	6.77	6.82
24	6.02	6.11	6.19	6.26	6.33	6.39	6.45	6.51	6.56	6.61
30	5.85	5.93	6.01	6.08	6.14	6.20	6.26	6.31	6.36	6.41
40	5.69	5.76	5.83	5.90	5.96	6.02	6.07	6.12	6.16	6.21
60	5.53	5.60	5.67	5.73	5.78	5.84	5.89	5.93	5.97	6.01
120	5.37	5.44	5.50	5.56	5.61	5.66	5.71	5.75	5.79	5.83
∞	5.23	5.29	5.35	5.40	5.45	5.49	5.54	5.57	5.61	5.65

(*Appendix table 10 continues on the following page.*)

APPENDIX TABLE 10 (continued)

UPPER 5 PERCENT POINTS OF THE STUDENTIZED RANGE ($\alpha = .05$)

$\nu_2 \backslash \nu_1$	2	3	4	5	6	7	8	9	10
1	17.97	26.98	32.82	37.08	40.41	43.12	45.40	47.36	49.07
2	6.08	8.33	9.80	10.88	11.74	12.44	13.03	13.54	13.99
3	4.50	5.91	6.82	7.50	8.04	8.48	8.85	9.18	9.46
4	3.93	5.04	5.76	6.29	6.71	7.05	7.35	7.60	7.83
5	3.64	4.60	5.22	5.67	6.03	6.33	6.58	6.80	6.99
6	3.46	4.34	4.90	5.30	5.63	5.90	6.12	6.32	6.49
7	3.34	4.16	4.68	5.06	5.36	5.61	5.82	6.00	6.16
8	3.26	4.04	4.53	4.89	5.17	5.40	5.60	5.77	5.92
9	3.20	3.95	4.41	4.76	5.02	5.24	5.43	5.59	5.74
10	3.15	3.88	4.33	4.65	4.91	5.12	5.30	5.46	5.60
11	3.11	3.82	4.26	4.57	4.82	5.03	5.20	5.35	5.49
12	3.08	3.77	4.20	4.51	4.75	4.95	5.12	5.27	5.39
13	3.06	3.73	4.15	4.45	4.69	4.88	5.05	5.19	5.32
14	3.03	3.70	4.11	4.41	4.64	4.83	4.99	5.13	5.25
15	3.01	3.67	4.08	4.37	4.59	4.78	4.94	5.08	5.20
16	3.00	3.65	4.05	4.33	4.56	4.74	4.90	5.03	5.15
17	2.98	3.63	4.02	4.30	4.52	4.70	4.86	4.99	5.11
18	2.97	3.61	4.00	4.28	4.49	4.67	4.82	4.96	5.07
19	2.96	3.59	3.98	4.25	4.47	4.65	4.79	4.92	5.04
20	2.95	3.58	3.96	4.23	4.45	4.62	4.77	4.90	5.01
24	2.92	3.53	3.90	4.17	4.37	4.54	4.68	4.81	4.92
30	2.89	3.49	3.85	4.10	4.30	4.46	4.60	4.72	4.82
40	2.86	3.44	3.79	4.04	4.23	4.39	4.52	4.63	4.73
60	2.83	3.40	3.74	3.98	4.16	4.31	4.44	4.55	4.65
120	2.80	3.36	3.68	3.92	4.10	4.24	4.36	4.47	4.56
∞	2.77	3.31	3.63	3.86	4.03	4.17	4.29	4.39	4.47

ν_1 ν_2	11	12	13	14	15	16	17	18	19	20
1	50.59	51.96	53.20	54.33	55.36	56.32	57.22	58.04	58.83	59.56
2	14.39	14.75	15.08	15.38	15.65	15.91	16.14	16.37	16.57	16.77
3	9.72	9.95	10.15	10.35	10.53	10.69	10.84	10.98	11.11	11.24
4	8.03	8.21	8.37	8.52	8.66	8.79	8.91	9.03	9.13	9.23
5	7.17	7.32	7.47	7.60	7.72	7.83	7.93	8.03	8.12	8.21
6	6.65	6.79	6.92	7.03	7.14	7.24	7.34	7.43	7.51	7.59
7	6.30	6.43	6.55	6.66	6.76	6.85	6.94	7.02	7.10	7.17
8	6.05	6.18	6.29	6.39	6.48	6.57	6.65	6.73	6.80	6.87
9	5.87	5.98	6.09	6.19	6.28	6.36	6.44	6.51	6.58	6.64
10	5.72	5.83	5.93	6.03	6.11	6.19	6.27	6.34	6.40	6.47
11	5.61	5.71	5.81	5.90	5.98	6.06	6.13	6.20	6.27	6.33
12	5.51	5.61	5.71	5.80	5.88	5.95	6.02	6.09	6.15	6.21
13	5.43	5.53	5.63	5.71	5.79	5.86	5.93	5.99	6.05	6.11
14	5.36	5.46	5.55	5.64	5.71	5.79	5.85	5.91	5.97	6.03
15	5.31	5.40	5.49	5.57	5.65	5.72	5.78	5.85	5.90	5.96
16	5.26	5.35	5.44	5.52	5.59	5.66	5.73	5.79	5.84	5.90
17	5.21	5.31	5.39	5.47	5.54	5.61	5.67	5.73	5.79	5.84
18	5.17	5.27	5.35	5.43	5.50	5.57	5.63	5.69	5.74	5.79
19	5.14	5.23	5.31	5.39	5.46	5.53	5.59	5.65	5.70	5.75
20	5.11	5.20	5.28	5.36	5.43	5.49	5.55	5.61	5.66	5.71
24	5.01	5.10	5.18	5.25	5.32	5.38	5.44	5.49	5.55	5.59
30	4.92	5.00	5.08	5.15	5.21	5.27	5.33	5.38	5.43	5.47
40	4.82	4.90	4.98	5.04	5.11	5.16	5.22	5.27	5.31	5.36
60	4.73	4.81	4.88	4.94	5.00	5.06	5.11	5.15	5.20	5.24
120	4.64	4.71	4.78	4.84	4.90	4.95	5.00	5.04	5.09	5.13
∞	4.55	4.62	4.68	4.74	4.80	4.85	4.89	4.93	4.97	5.01

Reprinted with permission from *Chemical Handbook of Probability and Statistics*, 2d ed. Cleveland, Ohio: Chemical Rubber Co., 1968.

APPENDIX TABLE 11

Cumulative Probabilities for the Wilcoxon Signed Rank Statistic

$P(T^+ \leq c)$, $T^+ =$ Wilcoxon signed rank statistic

n = 5

c	$P(T^+ \leq c)$
0	.0313
1	.0625
2	.0938
3	.1563

n = 6

c	$P(T^+ \leq c)$
0	.0156
1	.0313
2	.0469
3	.0781
4	.1094

n = 7

c	$P(T^+ \leq c)$
0	.0078
1	.0156
2	.0234
3	.0391
4	.0547
5	.0781
6	.1094

n = 8

c	$P(T^+ \leq c)$
0	.0039
1	.0078
2	.0117
3	.0195
4	.0273
5	.0391
6	.0547
7	.0742
8	.0977
9	.1250

n = 9

c	$P(T^+ \leq c)$
1	.0039
2	.0059
3	.0098
4	.0137
5	.0195
6	.0273
7	.0371
8	.0488
9	.0645
10	.0820
11	.1016

n = 10

c	$P(T^+ \leq c)$
3	.0049
4	.0068
5	.0098
6	.0137
7	.0186
8	.0244
9	.0322
10	.0420
11	.0527
12	.0654
13	.0801
14	.0967
15	.1162

n = 11

c	$P(T^+ \leq c)$
5	.0049
6	.0068
7	.0093
8	.0122
9	.0161
10	.0210
11	.0269
12	.0337
13	.0415
14	.0508
15	.0615
16	.0737
17	.0874
18	.1030

n = 12

c	$P(T^+ \leq c)$
7	.0046
8	.0061
9	.0081
10	.0105
11	.0134
12	.0171
13	.0212
14	.0261
15	.0320
16	.0386
17	.0461
18	.0549
19	.0647
20	.0757
21	.0881
22	.1018

n = 13

c	$P(T^+ \leq c)$
9	.0040
10	.0052
11	.0067
12	.0085
13	.0107
14	.0133
15	.0164
16	.0199
17	.0239
18	.0287
19	.0341
20	.0402
21	.0471
22	.0549
23	.0636
24	.0732
25	.0839
26	.0955
27	.1082

n = 14

c	$P(T^+ \leq c)$
12	.0043
13	.0054
14	.0067
15	.0083
16	.0101
17	.0123
18	.0148
19	.0176
20	.0209
21	.0247
22	.0290
23	.0338
24	.0392
25	.0453
26	.0520
27	.0594
28	.0676
29	.0765
30	.0863
31	.0969
32	.1083

n = 15

c	$P(T^+ \leq c)$
15	.0042
16	.0051
17	.0062
18	.0075
19	.0090
20	.0108
21	.0128
22	.0151
23	.0177
24	.0206
25	.0240
26	.0277
27	.0319
28	.0365
29	.0416
30	.0473
31	.0535
32	.0603
33	.0677
34	.0757
35	.0844
36	.0938
37	.1039

n = 16

c	$P(T^+ \leq c)$
19	.0046
20	.0055
21	.0065
22	.0078
23	.0091
24	.0107
25	.0125
26	.0145
27	.0168
28	.0193
29	.0222
30	.0253
31	.0288
32	.0327
33	.0370
34	.0416
35	.0467
36	.0523
37	.0583
38	.0649
39	.0719
40	.0795
41	.0877
42	.0964
43	.1057

n = 17

c	$P(T^+ \leq c)$
23	.0047
24	.0055
25	.0064
26	.0075
27	.0087
28	.0101
29	.0116
30	.0133
31	.0153
32	.0174
33	.0198
34	.0224
35	.0253
36	.0284
37	.0319
38	.0357
39	.0398
40	.0443
41	.0492

n = 17		n = 18		n = 19		n = 20	
c	$P(T^+ \le c)$	c	$P(T^+ \le c)$	c	$P(T^+ \le c)$	c	$P(T^+ \le c)$
42	.0544	44	.0368	44	.0201	43	.0096
43	.0601	45	.0407	45	.0223	44	.0107
44	.0662	46	.0449	46	.0247	45	.0120
45	.0727	47	.0494	47	.0273	46	.0133
46	.0797	48	.0542	48	.0301	47	.0148
47	.0871	49	.0594	49	.0331	48	.0164
48	.0950	50	.0649	50	.0364	49	.0181
49	.1034	51	.0708	51	.0399	50	.0200
		52	.0770	52	.0437	51	.0220
n = 18		53	.0837	53	.0478	52	.0242
		54	.0907	54	.0521	53	.0266
27	.0045	55	.0982	55	.0567	54	.0291
28	.0052	56	.1061	56	.0616	55	.0319
29	.0060			57	.0668	56	.0348
30	.0069			58	.0723	57	.0379
31	.0080	**n = 19**		59	.0782	58	.0413
32	.0091	32	.0047	60	.0844	59	.0448
33	.0104	33	.0054	61	.0909	60	.0487
34	.0118	34	.0062	62	.0978	61	.0527
35	.0134	35	.0070	63	.1051	62	.0570
36	.0152	36	.0080			63	.0615
37	.0171	37	.0090	**n = 20**		64	.0664
38	.0192	38	.0102	37	.0047	65	.0715
39	.0216	39	.0115	38	.0053	66	.0768
40	.0241	40	.0129	39	.0060	67	.0825
41	.0269	41	.0145	40	.0068	68	.0884
42	.0300	42	.0162	41	.0077	69	.0947
43	.0333	43	.0180	42	.0086	70	.1012

Extracted with permission from *Selected Tables in Mathematical Statistics*, vol. I (sponsored by the Institute of Mathematical Statistics and edited by H. L. Harter and D. B. Owen), Markham Publishing Company, Chicago, 1970.

APPENDIX TABLE 12

Critical Values and Probability Levels for the Wilcoxon Rank Sum Test

A table entry gives three numbers (c_1, c_2, p) such that $P(T_x \leq c_1)$ $= P(T_x \geq c_2) = p$, where T_x is the Wilcoxon rank sum statistic.

$\alpha = .01$, one-sided $\alpha = .02$, two-sided

n	$m = 6$	$m = 7$	$m = 8$	$m = 9$	$m = 10$
6	24, 54 .0076 25, 53 .0130				
7	25, 59 .0070 26, 58 .0111	34, 71 .0087 35, 70 .0131			
8	27, 63 .0100 28, 62 .0147	35, 77 .0070 36, 76 .0103	45, 91 .0074 46, 90 .0103		
9	28, 68 .0088 29, 67 .0128	37, 82 .0082 38, 81 .0115	47, 97 .0076 48, 96 .0103	59, 112 .0094 60, 111 .0122	
10	29, 73 .0080 30, 72 .0112	39, 87 .0093 40, 86 .0125	49, 103 .0078 50, 102 .0103	61, 119 .0086 62, 118 .0110	74, 136 .0093 75, 135 .0116
11	30, 78 .0073 31, 77 .0101	40, 93 .0077 41, 92 .0102	51, 109 .0079 52, 108 .0102	63, 126 .0079 64, 125 .0100	77, 143 .0098 78, 142 .0121
12	32, 82 .0091 33, 81 .0122	42, 98 .0085 43, 97 .0111	53, 115 .0079 54, 114 .0101	66, 132 .0092 67, 131 .0114	79, 151 .0084 80, 150 .0103
13	33, 87 .0084 34, 86 .0110	44, 103 .0093 45, 102 .0118	56, 120 .0099 57, 119 .0123	68, 139 .0085 69, 138 .0104	82, 158 .0089 83, 157 .0107
14	34, 92 .0077 35, 91 .0100	45, 109 .0079 46, 108 .0100	58, 126 .0098 59, 125 .0120	71, 145 .0096 72, 144 .0115	85, 165 .0093 86, 164 .0110
15	36, 96 .0092 37, 95 .0117	47, 114 .0086 48, 113 .0106	60, 132 .0097 61, 131 .0117	73, 152 .0089 74, 151 .0106	88, 172 .0096 89, 171 .0113
16	37, 101 .0085 38, 100 .0107	49, 119 .0092 50, 118 .0112	62, 138 .0096 63, 137 .0115	76, 158 .0098 77, 157 .0116	91, 179 .0099 92, 178 .0115
17	39, 105 .0099 40, 104 .0122	51, 124 .0097 52, 123 .0118	64, 144 .0095 65, 143 .0113	78, 165 .0091 79, 164 .0107	93, 187 .0088 94, 186 .0102
18	40, 110 .0091 41, 109 .0112	52, 130 .0085 53, 129 .0103	66, 150 .0094 67, 149 .0110	81, 171 .0100 82, 170 .0116	96, 194 .0090 97, 193 .0104
19	41, 115 .0085 42, 114 .0104	54, 135 .0090 55, 134 .0108	68, 156 .0093 69, 155 .0108	83, 178 .0093 84, 177 .0108	99, 201 .0093 100, 200 .0106

APPENDIX TABLE 12 (continued)

$\alpha = .05$, one-sided $\alpha = .10$, two-sided

n	m = 6	m = 7	m = 8	m = 9	m = 10
6	28, 50 .0465 29, 49 .0660				
7	29, 55 .0367 30, 54 .0507	39, 66 .0487 40, 65 .0641			
8	31, 59 .0406 32, 58 .0539	41, 71 .0469 42, 70 .0603	51, 85 .0415 52, 84 .0524		
9	33, 63 .0440 34, 62 .0567	43, 76 .0454 44, 75 .0571	54, 90 .0464 55, 89 .0570	66, 105 .0470 67, 104 .0567	
10	35, 67 .0467 36, 66 .0589	45, 81 .0439 46, 80 .0544	56, 96 .0416 57, 95 .0506	69, 111 .0474 70, 110 .0564	82, 128 .0446 83, 127 .0526
11	37, 71 .0491 38, 70 .0608	47, 86 .0427 48, 85 .0521	59, 101 .0454 60, 100 .0543	72, 117 .0476 73, 116 .0560	86, 134 .0493 87, 133 .0572
12	38, 76 .0415 39, 75 .0512	49, 91 .0416 50, 90 .0501	62, 106 .0489 63, 105 .0576	75, 123 .0477 76, 122 .0555	89, 141 .0465 90, 140 .0536
13	40, 80 .0437 41, 79 .0530	52, 95 .0484 53, 94 .0573	64, 112 .0445 65, 111 .0521	78, 129 .0478 79, 128 .0551	92; 148 .0441 93, 147 .0505
14	42, 84 .0457 43, 83 .0547	54, 100 .0469 55, 99 .0550	67, 117 .0475 68, 116 .0550	81, 135 .0478 82, 134 .0547	96, 154 .0478 97, 153 .0542
15	44, 88 .0474 45, 87 .0561	56, 105 .0455 57, 104 .0531	69, 123 .0437 70, 122 .0503	84, 141 .0478 85, 140 .0542	99, 161 .0455 100, 160 .0513
16	46, 92 .0490 47, 91 .0574	58, 110 .0443 59, 109 .0513	72, 128 .0463 73, 127 .0528	87, 147 .0477 88, 146 .0538	103, 167 .0487 104, 166 .0545
17	47, 97 .0433 48, 96 .0505	61, 114 .0497 62, 113 .0569	75, 133 .0487 76, 132 .0552	90, 153 .0476 91, 152 .0534	106, 174 .0465 107, 173 .0517
18	49, 101 .0448 50, 100 .0518	63, 119 .0484 64, 118 .0550	77, 139 .0452 78, 138 .0510	93, 159 .0475 94, 158 .0531	110, 180 .0493 111, 179 .0546
19	51, 105 .0462 52, 104 .0530	65, 124 .0471 66, 123 .0533	80, 144 .0475 81, 143 .0532	96, 165 .0474 97, 164 .0527	113, 187 .0472 114, 186 .0521

Extracted with permission from *Selected Tables in Mathematical Statistics*, vol. I (sponsored by the Institute of Mathematical Statistics and edited by H. L. Harter and D. B. Owen), Markham Publishing Company, Chicago, 1970.

APPENDIX TABLE 13

Critical Values for Spearman's Rank Correlation

A table entry is that value, r_α, which for a given value of n satisfies $P(R \geq r_\alpha) = \alpha$, where R is Spearman's rank correlation statistic.

n	$\alpha = .10$	.05	.025	.01	.005	.001
4	.8000	.8000				
5	.7000	.8000	.9000	.9000		
6	.6000	.7714	.8286	.8857	.9429	
7	.5357	.6786	.7450	.8571	.8929	.9643
8	.5000	.6190	.7143	.8095	.8571	.9286
9	.4667	.5833	.6833	.7667	.8167	.9000
10	.4424	.5515	.6364	.7333	.7818	.8667
11	.4182	.5273	.6091	.7000	.7455	.8364
12	.3986	.4965	.5804	.6713	.7273	.8182
13	.3791	.4780	.5549	.6429	.6978	.7912
14	.3626	.4593	.5341	.6220	.6747	.7670
15	.3500	.4429	.5179	.6000	.6536	.7464
16	.3382	.4265	.5000	.5824	.6324	.7265
17	.3260	.4118	.4853	.5637	.6152	.7083
18	.3148	.3994	.4716	.5480	.5975	.6904
19	.3070	.3895	.4579	.5333	.5825	.6737
20	.2977	.3789	.4451	.5203	.5684	.6586
21	.2909	.3688	.4351	.5078	.5545	.6455
22	.2829	.3597	.4241	.4963	.5426	.6318
23	.2767	.3518	.4150	.4852	.5306	.6186
24	.2704	.3435	.4061	.4748	.5200	.6070
25	.2646	.3362	.3977	.4654	.5100	.5962
26	.2588	.3299	.3894	.4564	.5002	.5856
27	.2540	.3236	.3822	.4481	.4915	.5757
28	.2490	.3175	.3749	.4401	.4828	.5660
29	.2443	.3113	.3685	.4320	.4744	.5567
30	.2400	.3059	.3620	.4251	.4665	.5479

Reprinted with permission from W.J. Conover, *Practical Nonparametric Statistics.* New York: Wiley, 1971.

Answers to Odd-Numbered Problems

PROBLEMS 1.2

1. a. 3.07; 2.40; 2.31; 2.16; 3.12 **b.** 28.10 **c.** 19.97 **d.** 2.81 **e.** 84.3
f. 78.1 **g.** 8.728
3. a. (23, 19); (47, 35); (29, 32) **b.** 196; 189 **c.** 385 **d.** 22, 887
e. 5803
7. a. 2.74; 2.47; 2.33; 3.28 **b.** 2.78; 2.83; 2.58; 2.86 **c.** 2.734

PROBLEMS 2.1

1. $\{H, T\}$
3. $\{0, 1, 2, \ldots\}$
5. $\{1, 2, 3, \ldots\}$
7. $\{2, 3, 4, 5, 6, 7, 8, 9, 10, J, Q, K, A\}$
9. $\{YYYYYY, YYYYYN, YYYYNY, \ldots, NNNNYN, NNNNNY, NNNNNN\}$ (Y = Yes, N = No, $2^6 = 64$ outcomes)
11. 2; 52; $2^6 = 64$; No
13. 2; $2^2 = 4$; $2^3 = 8$; $2^4 = 16$; 2^n
15. $A = \{HHH, TTT\}$; $B = \{HHH, HHT, HTH, THH, HTT, THT, TTH\}$
17. $A = \{0\}$; $B = \{0, 1, 2, 3, 4, 5, 6, 7, 8, 9, 10\}$; $C = \{5, 6, 7, \ldots\}$
19. $A = \{J, Q, K\}$; $B = \{1, 2, 3, 4, 5, 6, 7\}$; $C = \{2, 4, 6, 8, 10, J, Q, K\}$
21. $A = \{4, 5, 6\}$; $B = \{0, 1, 2\}$; $I = \{0, 1, 2, 3, 4, 5, 6\}$
23. $I = \{2, 3, 4, 5, 6, 7, 8\}$; $A = \{2, 4, 6, 8\}$; $B = \{5, 6, 7, 8\}$; C cannot be described

PROBLEMS 2.2

1. a. one or more head appears = $\{HHH, HHT, HTH, THH, HTT, THT, TTH\}$ **b.** all heads = $\{HHH\}$ **c.** all tails = $\{TTT\}$ **d.** an even number of heads = $\{HHT, HTH, THH, TTT\}$ **e.** at least one tail = $\{THH, HTH, HHT, TTH, THT, HTT, TTT\}$ **f.** total sample space = I **g.** the impossible event = ϕ **h.** one or two heads = $\{HTT, THT, TTH, HHT, HTH, THH\}$
3. a. C' = card is not a club **b.** card is the jack, queen, or king of clubs **c.** card is not a diamond **d.** ϕ, the impossible event **e.** card is a club = C **f.** card is black = B **g.** card is face card or club **h.** card is the jack, queen, or king of hearts
5. a. $\{21 < x \leq 65\}$ **b.** $\{x \geq 0\}$ **c.** $\{x < 50\}$ **d.** $\{x > 65\}$ **e.** $\{x \geq 0\}$
f. $\{50 \leq x \leq 65\}$ **g.** $\{13 \leq x \leq 21\}$ **h.** $\{0 \leq x < 13$ or $18 < x \leq 65\}$
7. (number recorded is number of girls born) **a.** $\{1, 3, 5\}$ **b.** $\{0, 1, 2, 5\}$
c. ϕ **d.** $\{1, 3\}$ **e.** $\{0, 2, 4\}$ **f.** $\{1\}$ **g.** $\{1, 3, 4, 5\}$ **h.** ϕ **i.** $\{0, 2\}$
j. $\{0, 2, 4\}$
9. a. $\{RIn, InR, DR, RD, RR\}$ **b.** $\{DD, InIn\}$ **c.** $\{DD, RR, InIn, DR, RD, DIn, InD\}$ **d.** $\{DD, RR, InIn, RIn, InR, DIn, InD\}$ **e.** $\{DR, RD, InIn\}$ **f.** $\{DIn, InD\}$

PROBLEMS 2.3

1. .36; .20; .16; .28
3. 1/3, .5, 2/3, 1/6
5. 4/5, 2/5
9. .36, .64, .56, .72
11. a. .43   **b.** .94   **c.** .57
13. a. 1/8   **b.** 1/8   **c.** 1/4

PROBLEMS 2.4

1. $I = F, S, J, A$; $P(F) = .36$; $P(S) = .20$; $P(J) = .16$; $P(A) = .28, .56, .64$
3. 16 outcomes;

$$I' = \begin{matrix} (1, 1) & (1, 2) & (1, 3) & (1, 4) \\ (2, 1) & (2, 2) & (2, 3) & (2, 4) \\ (3, 1) & (3, 2) & (3, 3) & (3, 4) \\ (4, 1) & (4, 2) & (4, 3) & (4, 4) \end{matrix}$$

α_i	α_2	α_3	α_4	α_5	α_6	α_7	α_8
p_i	$\dfrac{1}{16}$	$\dfrac{2}{16}$	$\dfrac{3}{16}$	$\dfrac{4}{16}$	$\dfrac{3}{16}$	$\dfrac{2}{16}$	$\dfrac{1}{16}$

$P(A) = \dfrac{1}{2}$; $P(B) = \dfrac{5}{8}$

5. $\dfrac{11}{12}$

7. $P(U \text{ or } M) = \dfrac{17}{24}$; $P(M') = 5/8$; $P(M \text{ or } M') = 7/8$.

9. a. .7   **b.** .9

PROBLEMS 2.5

1. $\dfrac{5}{14} = .357$; .5
3. $P(A) = 1/6$; $P(A/B) = 1/3$
5. .5; .125

7.

Event	B	B'	Total
A	.30	.05	.35
A'	.30	.35	.65
Total	.60	.40	1.00

$P(A|B) = .5$; $P(A'|B) = .5$; $P(A|B') = .125$; $P(A'|B') = .875$; $P(B|A) = \dfrac{6}{7} = .857$; $P(B|A') = \dfrac{6}{13} = .462$

9. 700; 500;

A_i	A_1	A_2	A_3	A_4
$P_1(A_i|M)$	.071	.286	.429	.214
$P(A_i|F)$	.080	.280	.400	.240

PROBLEMS 2.6

1. .04

3. a. $\frac{19}{30} = .633$ **b.** $\frac{1}{30} = .033$

5. a. $\frac{1}{13} = .077$ **b.** $\frac{4}{13} = .308$

PROBLEMS 2.7

1. a. independent   **b.** independent   **c.** not independent

3. a. $\frac{1}{16} = .0625$ **b.** $\frac{1}{4} = .25$; Yes

PROBLEMS 2.8

1. $P(A_0) = P(A_2) = \frac{1}{4}$, $P(A_1) = \frac{1}{2}$

3. $P(B) = .49$; $P(A_1|B) = .184$; $P(A_2|B) = .459$; $P(A_3|B) = .357$

5. a. $\frac{96}{447} = .215$; $\frac{105}{447} = .235$; $\frac{116}{447} = .260$; $\frac{130}{447} = .291$ **b.** $\frac{117}{254} = .461$;

$\frac{62}{254} = .244$; $\frac{43}{254} = .169$; $\frac{32}{254} = .126$

7. a. $\frac{10}{11} = .909$ **b.** $\frac{1}{11} = .091$

PROBLEMS 2.9

1. $P(5 \text{ heads in 5 tosses}) = \frac{1}{32} = .031$; $P(10 \text{ heads in 10 tosses}) =$

$\frac{1}{1024} = .001$

3. .333

PROBLEMS 3.1

1. a. discrete: $x = 2, 3, 4, \ldots, 12$ **b.** continuous: $\{0 \le x \le 4\}$
   c. continuous: $\{-\infty < x < +\infty\}$ **d.** discrete: $x = 0, 1, \ldots, 1000$
   e. discrete: $x = 0, 1, \ldots, 1500$

3. $x = 0, 1, 2, \ldots, 40$; discrete

5. C = cold; N = no cold

$$a_1 = NNNN, a_2 = CNNN, a_3 = NCNN, a_4 = NNCN, a_5 = NNNC,$$
$$I = \quad a_6 = NNCC, a_7 = NCNC, a_8 = CNNC, a_9 = NCCN, a_{10} = CNCN,$$
$$a_{11} = CCNN, a_{12} = NCCC, a_{13} = CNCC, a_{14} = CCNC, a_{15} = CCCN,$$
$$a_{16} = CCCC$$

$x(a_1) = 0, x(a_i) = 1, i = 2, 3, 4, 5; x(a_i) = 2, i = 6, 7, 8, 9, 10, 11;$
$x(a_i) = 3, i = 12, 13, 14, 15; x(a_{16}) = 4$

$\{x = 0\} = \{a_1\}$; $\{x = 1\} = \{a_2, a_3, a_4, a_5\}$; $\{x = 2\} = \{a_6, a_7, a_8, a_9,$
$a_{10}, a_{11}\}$; $\{x = 3\} = \{a_{12}, a_{13}, a_{14}, a_{15}\}$; $\{x = 4\} = \{a_{16}\}$

PROBLEMS 3.2

1. x:

Prob.	$\frac{1}{2}$	$\frac{1}{2}$
Value	0	1

3. x:

Prob.	.6	.2	.2
Value	1	2	3

5. x:

Prob.	.12	.20	.26	.24	.14	.04
Value	14	15	16	17	18	19

7. x:

Prob.	.36	.24	.28	.08	.04
Value	2	3	4	5	6

9. a. $\frac{1}{6}$ **b.** $\frac{3}{8}$ **c.** .6

PROBLEMS 3.3

1. .5
3. 1.6
5. 16.2
7. 3.2; 11.6

PROBLEMS 3.4

1. $\frac{1}{4}$; $\frac{1}{2}$
3. .64; .8
5. 1.8; 1.34
7. 1.28; 1.13
9. a. 0; 1.414 **b.** 0; 1.643 **c.** 0; 1.095
11. 33; 12
13. a. 10; 16; 4 **b.** 25; 144; 12 **c.** 7; 4; 2 **d.** 4; 0; 0 **e.** -3; 4; 2
    f. $5b - 1$; $4b^2$; $2b$

PROBLEMS 3.5

1. a. $\frac{1}{4}$ **b.** $\frac{1}{9}$

3.

problem part	a.	b.	c.	d.
direct computation	.50	.20	.06	.02
bound	1.00	.44	.25	.16

PROBLEMS 3.6

1. Yes; $\frac{16}{81} = .198$
3. a. .02 **b.** .125 **c.** .207
5. a. .333, .6, .6 (without replacement); .36, .6, .6 (with replacement)
    b. .133, .4, .4 (without replacement); .16, .4, .4 (with replacement)

PROBLEMS 3.7

1. **a.** binomial   **b.** not a binomial, 2 fails to hold   **c.** binomial   **d.** not a binomial, 1, 2, and 4 fail to hold

3. y:

Prob.	.3277	.4096	.2048	.0512	.0064	.0003
Value	0	1	2	3	4	5

$$\mu_y = 1,\ \sigma^2_y = .8$$

5. **a.** .010   **b.** .078   **c.** .922   **d.** .230
7. **a.** .804   **b.** .000   **c.** .370   **d.** .205
9. .000

11. $n = 2$, y:

Prob.	$\frac{1}{4}$	$\frac{1}{2}$	$\frac{1}{4}$
Value	0	1	2

$\mu y = 1,\ \sigma^2 y = .5$

$n = 3$, y:

Prob.	$\frac{1}{8}$	$\frac{3}{8}$	$\frac{3}{8}$	$\frac{1}{8}$
Value	0	1	2	3

$\mu y = 1.5,\ \sigma^2_y = .75$

$n = 4$, y:

Prob.	$\frac{1}{16}$	$\frac{4}{16}$	$\frac{6}{16}$	$\frac{4}{16}$	$\frac{1}{16}$
Value	0	1	2	3	4

$\mu_y = 2,\ \sigma^2_y = 1$

$n = 5$, y:

Prob.	$\frac{1}{32}$	$\frac{5}{32}$	$\frac{10}{32}$	$\frac{10}{32}$	$\frac{5}{32}$	$\frac{1}{32}$
Value	0	1	2	3	4	5

$\mu_y = 2.5,\ \sigma^2_y = 1.25$

PROBLEMS 3.8

1.

n	10	20	100	500
$\mu_{\hat{p}}$	.5	.5	.5	.5
$\sigma^2_{\hat{p}}$	.025	.0125	.0025	.0005
bound	2.5	1.25	.25	.05

$$P(|\hat{p} - .5| \geq .1) = \begin{array}{l} .754 \text{ for } n = 10 \\ .497 \text{ for } n = 20 \end{array}$$

3. **a.** $\dfrac{277.78}{n}$ for $\epsilon = .03$; $\dfrac{2500}{n}$ for $\epsilon = .01$ **b.** $n = 5556$ for $\epsilon = .03$; $n = 50{,}000$ for $\epsilon = .01$

PROBLEMS 3.9

1. y:

Prob.	$\frac{5}{30}$	$\frac{15}{30}$	$\frac{9}{30}$	$\frac{1}{30}$
Value	0	1	2	3

3. **a.** $\dfrac{2}{17} = .118$ **b.** $\dfrac{11}{1105} = .01$

5. $\mu_y = \dfrac{6}{5}$; $\sigma^2_y = \dfrac{14}{25} = .56$

PROBLEMS 3.10

1. a. .1954   b. .1953   c. .9817   d. .0511
3. 4; 4
5. a. .2052   b. .9179   c. .0001

PROBLEMS 4.1

1. $y/20$; .85
3. .8; .008; .8441; .9900
5. $\hat{p} = y/n$

n	10	25	100	400	1600
$\mu_{\hat{p}}$	.4	.4	.4	.4	.4
$\sigma^2_{\hat{p}}$	.024	.0098	.0024	.0006	.00015

Yes; No; .36

7. $P(|\hat{p} - p| \geq .1) \leq 16/n$;

n	10	25	100	400	1600
bound	1.6	.64	.16	.04	.01

PROBLEMS 4.2

1. .95
3. (.505, .555)
5. (.199, .241)

PROBLEMS 4.3

1. a. $a = 14$, $\alpha = .058$ b. $a = 16$, $\alpha = .006$
3. a. .750 for $p = .6$; .392 for $p = .7$ b. .949 for $p = .6$; .762 for $p = .7$
5. Reject H_0: $\begin{cases} \text{if } y \geq 217, \alpha = .05 \\ \text{if } y \geq 224, \alpha = .01 \end{cases}$
7. a. Reject H_0 if $y \geq 9$ with $\alpha = .045$ for $n = 10$; reject H_0 if $y \geq 16$ with $\alpha = .051$ for $n = 20$.   b. Reject H_0 if $y \geq 69$ for $n = 100$; reject H_0 if $y \geq 259$ for $n = 400$.

PROBLEMS 4.4

1. H_0: $p = .5$ vs H_1: $p \neq .5$ (p = prob. of female birth); two-sided
3. H_0: $p = .1$ vs H_1: $p \neq .1$ (p = prob. the customer had an accident within last 12 months); two-sided
5. Reject H_0 if $y \leq 2$ or $y \geq 8$ for $n = 10$; reject H_0 if $y \leq 6$ or $y \geq 14$ for $n = 20$
7. $P_{\hat{p}}(\text{reject } H_0)$:

p	0	.1	.2	.3	.4	.5	.6	.7	.8	.9	1
$n = 10$	1	.930	.678	.385	.179	.110	.179	.385	.678	.930	1
$n = 20$	1	.998	.913	.608	.256	.116	.256	.608	.913	.998	1

9. Reject H_0 if $y \leq 183$ or $y \geq 217$; conclude that H_1 is true and say $p > .5$ if $y = 220$; type I.
11. Reject H_0 if $y \leq 415$ or $y \geq 485$; decide that H_1 is true and say $p > .5$ if $y = 503$; type I.

PROBLEMS 4.5

1. Reject H_0 if $y \leq 1$ or $y \geq 9$, where $y =$ number of pairs and where after-before temperature is > 0; conclude H_1 is true and say the after temperature is more likely to be higher than the before temperature, since $y = 1$ for these data.
3. Reject H_0 if $y \leq 12$ or $y \geq 24$, where $y =$ number pairs for which the 60 mph gal. consumption is larger than the 50 mph gal. consumption. Since for these data, $y = 26$, reject H_0 and say the 60 mph speed is the more likely to result in higher gas consumption.

PROBLEMS 4.7

1. Reject H_0 if $y_1 \leq 2$; since $y_1 = 2$, accept H_1.
3. (Let $p_1 =$ probability of recurrence within one year for treatment T_i, $i = 1, 2$.) $H_0 : p_2 \geq p_1$ vs $H_1 : p_2 < p_1$; reject H_0 if $y_2 \leq 1$, where $y_2 =$ number of recurrences for T_2 treatment; level is $\alpha = .094$ and conclusion is T_2 is better than T_1; that is, H_1 is true.

PROBLEMS 5.1

3. 10.3; 109.57; 10.47
5. 125; 154.84; 12.44

PROBLEMS 5.2

1. **a.** 2; 2   **b.** y:

Prob.	1/9	2/9	3/9	2/9	1/9
Value	2	3	4	5	6

   c. Yes   **d.** y:

Prob.	1/9	2/9	2/9	1/9	2/9	1/9
Value	1	2	3	4	5	6

   e. Yes; Yes; $\mu_y = 4$
3. **a.** 0   **b.** 33.33
5. **a.** 30; 60   **b.** 12; 8   **c.** 3; .5
7. **a.** 230; 4; 2   **b.** 230; .4; .633   **c.** 230; .1; .316
9. 50, 25, 5 for $n = 100$; 200, 100, 10 for $n = 400$; 450, 225, 15 for $n = 900$
11. **a.** 1; .667   **b.** $\bar{x}$:

Prob.	1/27	3/27	6/27	7/27	6/27	3/27	1/27
Value	0	1/3	2/3	1	4/3	5/3	2

   c. 1   **d.** s^2:

Prob.	3/27	12/27	6/27	6/27
Value	0	1/3	1	4/3

   e. .667

13. **a.**

n	10	100	1000
upper bound	.5	.05	.005

   b. As n becomes larger, $\sigma^2/(n\epsilon^2)$ approaches zero implying by (14) that $P\{|\bar{x} - \mu| \geq \epsilon\}$ approaches zero. This says the statistic $\bar{x}$ is a consistent estimator of μ.

PROBLEMS 5.3

3. 74; 4.01; 2.003

5. a.

N	200	400	1000	5000
mean	120	120	120	120
variance	.402	.602	.721	.784

b. As N becomes larger, the mean stays at 120 and the variance approaches $.8 = \sigma^2/n$.

PROBLEMS 5.4

1. a. .3413 b. .4772 c. .4332 d. .3413 e. .4772 f. .4332
3. a. .6826 b. .9544 c. .9974 d. .8400 e. .9270 f. .8890
5. a. .7551 b. .9015 c. .1336 d. .0456 e. .2818 f. .1218
7. a. .5000 b. .5000 c. .7745 d. .1186 e. .7073 f. .9544
9. a. .6104 b. .0367 c. .5279 d. .9148
11. a. .78 b. 1.16 c. 1.5 d. 1.96 e. 2.33 f. .74
13. a. 125.2 b. 61.6 c. 20.1

PROBLEMS 5.5

1. a. .9182 b. .0045 c. .1922
3. a. .0087 b. manufacturer's claim is too low
5. a. .0272 b. .0032
7. a. .7814 b. .9515 c. .0143
9. a. .207, exact; .2123, approximation b. .147, exact; .1585, approximation c. .823, exact; .8253, approximation d. .485, exact; .5, approximation
11. a. .9642 b. .001 c. .0796
13. a. .0162 b. .9676
15. $y_0 = 221$; if $y = 233$, he should conclude that 20% is no longer correct and that his percentage is now higher.
17. a. .5438 b. .9890 c. 0

PROBLEMS 6.1

1. a. true b. true c. false d. false e. true
3. (69.32, 71.28)
5. (205.68, 218.32)

PROBLEMS 6.2

1. (.28, .34)

PROBLEMS 6.3

1. 2401
3. 3393

PROBLEMS 6.4

1. $-35, 93.4, 9.66$
3. a. 1.00 **b.** $.9198$
5. a. $(4.44, 11.56)$ **b.** $(4.45, 11.55)$
7. $(4.51, 11.49)$
9. a. $(376.06, 1179.94)$ **b.** $(380.43, 1175.57)$

PROBLEMS 6.5

1. $(-.004, .084)$

PROBLEMS 6.6

1. a. Reject H_0 if $\bar{x} < 10.88$.   **b.** Reject H_0 if $\bar{x} < 10.86$.   **c.** (a) Reject H_0; (b) Reject H_0.   **d.** type II in both cases
3. a. $.8708$ **b.** $.0294$
5. a. $H_0 ; p \geq .05$ versus $H_1 : p < .05$ **b.** Reject H_0 if $\hat{p} < .044$.   **c.** Yes

PROBLEMS 6.7

1. a. $H_0 : \mu \geq 118$ versus $H_1 : \mu > 118$ **b.** Reject H_0 if $\bar{x} > 120.83$.   **c.** No
3. a. $H_0 : \mu = 3.30$ versus $H_1 : \mu \neq 3.30$ **b.** Reject H_0 if $\dfrac{\bar{x} - 3.30}{s/10} > 1.96$
or < -1.96.   **c.** Do not reject H_0.   **d.** type II if we accept H_0
5. a. $H_0 : p = .5$ versus $H_1 : p \neq .5$ **b.** Reject H_0 if $\hat{p} > .64$ or $\hat{p} < .36$.
c. Reject H_0 and say $p > .5$.
7. a. $.8159$ **b.** $.842$ **c.** $.4325$
9. a. Reject H_0 if $y \leq 18$ or $y \geq 32$.

p	.2	.3	.4	.5	.6	.7	.8
power	.999	.860	.334	.066	.334	.860	.999

b. Reject H_0 if $y \leq 40$ or $y \geq 60$

p	.2	.3	.4	.5	.6	.7	.8
power	1.000	.989	.540	.058	.540	.989	1.000

c. Reject H_0 if $y \leq 180$ or $y \geq 220$.

p	.2	.3	.4	.5	.6	.7	.8
power	1.000	1.000	.982	.051	.982	1.000	1.000

d. Power curve increases with n for all values $p \neq .05$.

PROBLEMS 6.8

1. a. $H_0 : \mu_1 = \mu_2$ versus $H_1 : \mu_1 \neq \mu_2$
b. Reject H_0 if $\bar{x}_1 - \bar{x}_2 > 1.96C$ or $< -1.96C$,

$$C = \sqrt{\frac{79 s_1^2 + 49 s_2^2}{128}} \sqrt{\frac{1}{80} + \frac{1}{50}}$$

c. Reject H_0 and say $\mu_1 > \mu_2$, $C = .86$.

d. Reject H_0 and say $\mu_1 > \mu_2$, $C = \sqrt{\dfrac{s_1^2}{80} + \dfrac{s_2^2}{50}} = .87$.

3. (b) Reject H_0 if $\bar{x}_1 - \bar{x}_2 > 1.96C$ or $< -1.96C$, C as in part b of problem 1; (c) do not reject H_0, $C = .923$; (d) reject H_0 and say

$$\mu_1 > \mu_2, \ C = \sqrt{\frac{s_1^2}{n_1} + \frac{s_2^2}{n_2}} = .842; \text{ do not assume } \sigma_1 = \sigma_2.$$

PROBLEMS 6.9

1. a. $H_0 : p_1 = p_2$ versus $H_1 : p_1 \neq p_2$ **b.** Reject H_0 if $\hat{p}_1 - \hat{p}_2 > 1.96C$ or $< -1.96C$, where $C = .0707$. **c.** Reject H_0 and say $p_1 < p_2$.

PROBLEMS 7.1

1. a. 1.00 **b.** .954

PROBLEMS 7.2

1. a. 11.0705 **b.** .025 **c.** 7.01491 **d.** .945
3. a. .0126 **b.** Machine is out of alignment and $\sigma > .01$

PROBLEMS 7.3

1. a. 1.86 **b.** .05 **c.** 2.101 **d.** 2.681
3. a. (i) .02; (ii) .80 **b.** (i) .7687; (ii) .9653

PROBLEMS 7.4

1. (8516.9, 9937.1)
3. (213.6, 250)
5. a. $H_0 : \mu \leq 78.4$ versus $H_1 : \mu > 78.4$ **b.** Reject H_0 if $t = \dfrac{\bar{x} - 78.4}{s/5} >$ 1.711. **c.** Reject H_0 and say $\mu > 78.4$ since $t = 1.95$.
7. a. $H_0 : \mu \leq 58$ versus $H_1 : \mu > 58$ **b.** Reject H_0 if $t = \dfrac{\bar{x} - 58}{s/\sqrt{10}} > 1.833$.
c. Reject H_0 and say $\mu > 58$ since $t = 2.12$.

PROBLEMS 7.5

1. $(-1.03, 5.03)$
3. (1575.3, 3486.7)
5. a. $H_0 : \mu_1 \leq \mu_2$ versus $H_1 : \mu_1 > \mu_2$ where $\mu_1 =$ mean for men and $\mu_2 =$ mean for women **b.** Reject H_0 if $t > 1.701$. **c.** Reject H_0 and say $\mu_1 > \mu_2$ since $t = 5.42$.
7. a. $H_0 : \mu_1 = \mu_2$ versus $H_1 : \mu_1 \neq \mu_2$ **b.** Reject H_0 if $t > 2.552$ or < -2.552. **c.** Do not reject H_0 since $t = -1.35$.
9. a. $H_0 : \mu_1 = \mu_2$ versus $H_1 : \mu_1 \neq \mu_2$ **b.** Reject H_0 if $t > 2.074$.
c. Reject H_0 and say $\mu_1 > \mu_2$ (make 1 mean > make 2 mean) since $t = 2.76$.

PROBLEMS 7.6

1. a. $H_0 : \mu_1 \le \mu_2$ versus $H_1 : \mu_1 > \mu_2$ **b.** Reject H_0 if $t = \dfrac{d}{s/\sqrt{10}} >$
1.833. **c.** Do not reject H_0 since $t = .807$ and say no evidence of loss
of sleep.
3. (3.21, 6.19)
5. (.21, .95)

PROBLEMS 7.7

1. (11.437, 58.19)
3. $H_0 : \sigma^2 \le .25$ versus $H_1 : \sigma^2 > .25$; the rejection region is reject H_0 if
$s^2 > .367$; conclusion is reject H_0 and say $\sigma^2 > .25$.

PROBLEMS 7.8

1. (a) 10.27; (b) 4.82; (c) .271
3. (a) 8.81; (b) .51; (c) 8.81
5. $H_0 : \sigma_1^2 = \sigma_2^2$ versus $H_1 : \sigma_1^2 \neq \sigma_2^2$; rejection region is reject H_0 if
$F > 2.65$ or $< .33$; conclusion is do not reject H_0 since $F = .78$.
7. a. F has an F distribution with $n_1 - 1$ degrees of freedom in the
numerator and $n_2 - 1$ degrees of freedom in the denominator. **b.** (i)
$a = 1/F_{n_2 - 1, n_1 - 1, .01}$; (ii) $b = F_{n_1 - 1, n_2 - 1, .01}$
9. problem 5 (.258, 2.06); problem 6 (1.54, 7.02)

PROBLEMS 8.1

1. a.

brand	1	2	3
mean	35.8	40.2	30.6
variance	15.7	22.7	18.3

b.

Source of variation	Degrees of freedom	Sum of squares	Mean square	F ratio
brands	2	230.98	115.47	6.11
error	12	226.8	18.9	

c. Reject hypothesis of equality of means at level $\alpha = .05$ since
$F = 6.11 > 3.88$.

3. a.

state	Wisconsin	Michigan	Minnesota
mean	181	152	262
variance	2122	2721.33	3378

b.

Source of variation	Degrees of freedom	Sum of squares	Mean square	F ratio
state	2	40640	20320	7.69
error	20	52858	2642.9	

c. Reject hypothesis of equality of means at level $\alpha = .05$ since
$F = 7.69 > 5.85$.

PROBLEMS 8.2

1. $m.v. (MS_T) = 144.67$; $m.v. (MS_F) = 18$; ratio $= 8.04$; Yes

PROBLEMS 8.3

1.

Unknown population mean difference	Lower confidence limit	Upper confidence limit
$\mu_1 - \mu_2$	-11.73	2.93
$\mu_1 - \mu_3$	-2.13	12.53
$\mu_3 - \mu_2$	-16.93	-2.27

$\mu_3 > \mu_2$ at level $\alpha = .05$

3. t statistic interval $(-16.2, -3.0)$; simultaneous interval $(-16.93, -2.27)$

PROBLEMS 8.4

1.

Factor A \ Factor B	B_1	B_2	A means
A_1	-2	-2	-2
A_2	0	0	0
A_3	2	2	2
B means	0	0	0 = grand mean

$$SS = 60,\ SS_A = 48,\ SS_B = 0,\ SS_{AB} = 0,\ SS_E = 12$$

3.

Factor A \ Factor B	B_1	B_2	B_3	A means
A_1	-2	0	2	0
A_2	0	0	0	0
A_3	2	0	-2	0
B means	0	0	0	0 = grand mean

$$SS = 66,\ SS_A = 0,\ SS_B = 0,\ SS_{AB} = 48,\ SS_E = 18$$

PROBLEMS 8.5

1. a.

Sex	Diet I	Diet II	Means for sex
men	10.7	15.33	13.02
women	11.05	11.98	11.52
means for diet	10.88	13.66	12.27 = grand mean

b.

Source of variation	Degrees of freedom	Sum of squares	Mean square	F ratio
sex	1	13.50	13.50	1.38
diet	1	46.48	46.48	4.74
interaction	1	20.53	20.53	2.14
error	20	195.98	9.8	

c. Diet effect since $F = 4.74 > 4.35$; no sex or interaction effects

3. a.

Type of noise \ Noise level	Very loud	Loud	Soft	Type mean
predictable	61.7	65.1	71.1	65.97
unpredictable	52.2	58.3	68.1	59.53
level means	56.95	61.70	69.60	62.75

b.

Source of variation	Degrees of freedom	Sum of squares	Mean square	F ratio
type of noise	1	620.82	620.82	6.05
noise level	2	1633.30	816.65	7.96
interaction	2	106.63	53.32	.52
error	54	5538.50	102.56	

c. There is a type effect since $6.05 > 4.02$; there is a level effect since $7.96 > 3.17$; no interaction effect.

PROBLEMS 8.6

1. a.

Temp. \ Detergent	120°	140°	160°	180°	Detergent means
D_1	59.5	51.5	61.5	62.5	58.75
D_2	44.0	57.5	73.0	80.5	63.75
temperature means	51.75	54.5	67.25	71.5	61.25

b.

Source of variation	Degrees of freedom	Sum of squares	Mean square	F ratio
detergent	1	200	200	2.03
temperature	3	2215	738.33	7.49
interaction	3	1265	421.67	4.28
error	24	2366	98.58	

c. Temperature effect since $7.49 > 3.01$; interaction effect since $4.28 > 3.01$; no detergent effect.

PROBLEMS 8.7

1. a.

varieties	V_1	V_2	V_3
means	60.3	50.9	64.3

block	1	2	3	4	5	6
means	55.3	60.2	62.2	59.6	58.7	55

b.

Source of variation	Degrees of freedom	Sum of squares	Mean square	F ratio
variety	2	567.84	283.92	5.28
block	5	120.96	24.19	.45
error	10	537.68	53.77	

c. Variety effect since $5.28 > 4.10$; no block effect.

PROBLEMS 9.1

3. a. 2, 5, 8   **b.** $-4.5, -4, -3.5$ **c.** 9, 7, 5   **d.** $-4, -5, -6$

PROBLEMS 9.2

1. a. Yes   **b.** $\bar{x} = 1960$, $S_x^2 = 250$, $\bar{y} = 2.83$, $S_y^2 = .1994$, $S_{xy} = 6.65$
   c. $y = -49.306 + (.0266)x$; Yes
3. a. Yes   **b.** $\bar{x} = 1930$, $S_x^2 = 6000$, $\bar{y} = 1.733$, $S_y^2 = 7.48$, $S_{xy} = 208.79$
   c. $y = -65.431 + (.0348)x$; Yes

5. a. No **b.** $\bar{x} = 1300$, $S_x^2 = 5,720,000$, $\bar{y} = 26.492$, $S_y^2 = 54.6492$, $S_{xy} = 5544.8$ **c.** $y = 25.232 + (.000969)x$; No

PROBLEMS 9.3

1. $r = .94$; $\dfrac{y - 2.83}{.447} = .94\left(\dfrac{x - 1960}{15.811}\right)$; $SS_E = .0225$

3. $r = .986$; $\dfrac{y - 1.733}{2.735} = .986\left(\dfrac{x - 1930}{77.48}\right)$; $SS_E = .214$

PROBLEMS 9.4

1. $SS_R = .1769$; $r^2 = .887$
3. $SS_R = 7.266$; $r^2 = .971$

PROBLEMS 9.5

1. No; Yes

PROBLEMS 9.6

1. a. $\hat{\alpha} = -49.306$, $\hat{\beta} = .0266$ **b.** .0075 **c.** 115.25, .00003 **d.** Chi-squared with 3 d.f., t with 3 d.f., t with 3 d.f.
3. a. $\hat{\alpha} = -65.43$, $\hat{\beta} = .0348$ **b.** .1527 **c.** 94.816, .0000255 **d.** Chi-squared with 7 d.f., t with 7 d.f., t with 7 d.f.

PROBLEMS 9.7

1. $(-83.465, -15.147)$, $(.0092, .044)$
3. $(-88.46, -42.40)$, $(.0229, .0467)$

PROBLEMS 9.8

1. Reject H_0 if $t_2 > 4.541$; since $t_2 = 4.85$, conclude $\beta > 0$.
3. Reject H_0 if $t_2 > 3.499$ or < -3.499; since $t_2 = 6.89$, conclude $\beta \neq 0$ and say $\beta > 0$.

PROBLEMS 9.9

1. $(2.650, 2.904)$ for 1958; $(2.857, 3.229)$ for 1968

PROBLEMS 9.10

1. $(2.896, 3.456)$ for 1973; $(2.934, 3.524)$ for 1975
3. $(32.2, 99.0)$ for 60; $(38.6, 106.0)$ for 70; $(49.1, 122.3)$ for 90

PROBLEMS 10.1

1. $H_0 : p_1 = p_2$ versus $H_1 : p_1 \neq p_2$ (p_1 = proportion of freshmen believing Yes, p_2 = proportion of seniors believing Yes); critical region is reject H_0 if $Y > 6.6349$; conclusion is H_1 is true since $Y = 6.876$.

3. $H_0 : A$ and B independent versus $H_1 : A$ and B not independent ($A =$ age 30 or under, $B =$ vote for Democratic candidate); critical region is reject H_0 if $Y > 3.84146$; conclusion is not independent since $Y = 4.4956$.

PROBLEMS 10.2

1. .0154
3. .0279
5.

Response	Yes	No	Undecided
Expected freq.	752	640	208

$H_0 : p_1 = .47, p_2 = .40, p_3 = .13$ versus $H_1 : H_0$ is not true, where p_1, p_2, p_3 are, respectively, the proportion of voters this year who answered Yes, No, and undecided. Critical region is reject H_0 if $Y = \sum_{i=1}^{3} (O_i - E_i)^2 / E_i > 5.99147$; conclusion is H_0 is not true since $Y = 7.6385$

7. $H_0 : p_1 = .229, p_2 = .605, p_3 = .126, p_4 = .04$ versus $H_1 : H_0$ is not true, where p_1, p_2, p_3, p_4 are, respectively, the proportion of Illinois women single, married, widowed, and divorced in 1974.

Marital status	Single	Married	Widowed	Divorced
Expected frequencies	1145	3025	630	200

Critical region is reject H_0 if $Y = \sum_{i=1}^{3} (o_i - E_i)^2 / E_i > 7.81473$; conclusion is H_0 is not true and there has been a change in marital status from 1970 to 1974 since $Y = 9.6109$.

9.

Group	G_1	G_2	G_3	G_4
Expected freq.	14	59	86	41

$\hat{\theta} = .41$

Reject H_0 if $Y > 5.99147$; data fits model since $Y = .4987$.

PROBLEMS 10.3

1. Expected frequency table

Cause of death Smoking habit	Respiratory disease	Heart disease	Other
heavy smoker	81	135	234
moderate smoker	288	480	832
nonsmoker	531	885	1534

$H_0 :$ smoking habit independent of cause of death versus $H_1 :$ not independent; critical region is reject H_0 if $Y = \sum_{i,j} (0_{ij} - E_{ij})^2 / E_{ij} > 13.2767$; conclusion is H_0 is not true since $Y = 45.3766$.

3. $H_0 :$ homogeneity between drugs D_1 and D_2 versus $H_1 : H_0$ is not true.

Expected frequency table

No. of Episodes Drug	0	1	2	3 or more
D_1	17	8	12	17
D_2	17	8	12	17

Critical region is reject H_o if $Y = \sum_{i,j} (0_{ij} - E_{ij})^2/E_{ij} > 7.81473$;

conclusion is H_0 is false since $Y = 9.67647$ (drugs have different effect, with D_1 looking better).

PROBLEMS 11.1

1. a. 7.2 **b.** 7.9 **c.** Yes

3. a.

i	1	2	3	4	5	6	7	8
$x_{(i)}$	3381	3365	3812	3910	4129	4340	4521	4628

i	9	10	11	12	13	14	15	16
$x_{(i)}$	5021	5047	5298	5798	6107	6147	6247	7018

i	17	18	19	20	21	22	23	24
$x_{(i)}$	7147	7264	7621	8742	9047	9605	10,647	12,620

b. 5952.5 **c.** No

PROBLEMS 11.2

1. (4274, 72,097); $\alpha = .978$
3. a. (6.2, 14.1); $\alpha = .978$ **b.** (6.3, 8.7); $\alpha = .890$

PROBLEMS 11.3

1. (130, 175)
3. a. (4340, 7621) **b.** (4628, 7147)

PROBLEMS 11.4

1. a. H_1: $\tau_d \neq 0$, where τ_d is the median of the difference d = cost on Jan. 4, 1974 minus cost on April 5, 1974). **b.** Reject H_0 if $T^+ \leq 8$ or $T^+ \geq 47$. **c.** Reject H_1 and say $\tau_d < 0$, since $T^+ = 6.5$, that is, there has been an increase in market basket price.
3. a. $H_0 : \tau_d = 0$ versus $H_1 : \tau_d \neq 0$, where d is difference between verbal and quantitative scores. **b.** Reject if $T^+ > 219.99$ or $T^+ < 80.01$. **c.** Do not reject H_0 since $T^+ = 137.5$.
5. a. $H_0 : \tau_d \leq 0$ versus $H_1 : \tau_d > 0$, where $d =$ hours of sleep (before) minus hours of sleep (after). **b.** Reject H_0 if $T^+ \geq 44$. **c.** Since $T_+ = 43.5$ there is not enough evidence to reject H_0 at (exact) level $\alpha = .0527$; there is enough evidence at (exact) level $\alpha = .0654$.

PROBLEMS 11.5

1. a. $H_0: \mu_x = \mu_y$ versus $H_1: \mu_x \neq \mu_y$, where μ_x and μ_y are, respectively, the mean calorie content per gallon for brand 1 and brand 2.   **b.** Reject H_0: if $T_x \leq 82$ or $T_x \geq 128$ with $\alpha = .0892$, if $T_x \leq 83$ or $T_x \geq 127$ with $\alpha = .1052$ **c.** Since $T_x = 129.5$, reject H_0 and say brand 1 mean $>$ brand 2 mean.

3. a. $H_0: \mu_x = \mu_y$ versus $H_1: \mu_x \neq \mu_y$, where μ_x are, respectively, the mean weight gains on the standard and experimental diets.   **b.** Reject H_0 if $T_x \leq 74$ or $T_x \geq 136$ with $\alpha = .0186$, $T_x \leq 75$ or $T_x \geq 135$ with $\alpha = .0232$.   **c.** Since $T_x = 87.5$, do not reject H_0.

5. a. $H_0: \mu_x = \mu_y$ versus $H_1: \mu_x \neq \mu_y$, where μ_x and μ_y are, respectively; the mean traveling times before and after the change.   **b.** Reject H_0 if $T_x \geq 545.8$ or $T_x \leq 416.2$.   **c.** Since $T_x = 560.5$, reject H_0 and say $\mu_x > \mu_y$.

PROBLEMS 11.6

1. a. $R = .6107$ **b.** Reject hypothesis of independence if $R \geq .5179$ or $R \leq -.5179$; since $R = .6107$, we reject H_0 and assert that the rankings in the two semesters are dependent.

3. a. $R = .9266$ **b.** Reject H_0 if $R > .6713$; since $R = .9266$, assert that $\mu_R > 0$.   **c.** to be expected

5. a. $R = .874$ **b.** Reject H_0 if $R\sqrt{n-1} > 2.33$; since $R\sqrt{n-1} = 4.95$, we reject H_0.

Index

Index

Introduction to Statistics was set in Times Roman body type and Peignot Demi-Bold display type by Black Dot. The book was printed and bound by Kingsport Press. Beth Slye designed the book and cover. Carol Schwartzback prepared the technical illustrations. Paul Kelly was the sponsoring editor, and Sara Boyd the project editor.

5678/4321